Mineral Engineering Conference (MEC 2019)

AA007089

IOP Conference Series: Materials Science and Engineering
Volume 641

Kocierz, Poland
16 - 19 September 2019

ISBN: 978-1-7138-0906-7
ISSN: 1757-8981

Printed from e-media with permission by:

Curran Associates, Inc.
57 Morehouse Lane
Red Hook, NY 12571

CURRAN ASSOCIATES INC.
proceedings
.com

Some format issues inherent in the e-media version may also appear in this print version.

Institute of Physics
Dirac House, Temple Back
Bristol BS1 6BE UK

Phone: 44 1 17 929 7481
Fax: 44 1 17 920 0979

techtracking@iop.org

Additional copies of this publication are available from:

Curran Associates, Inc.
57 Morehouse Lane
Red Hook, NY 12571 USA
Phone: 845-758-0400
Fax: 845-758-2633
Email: curran@proceedings.com
Web: www.proceedings.com

TABLE OF CONTENTS

IOP Conf. Series: Materials Science and Engineering **641** (2019) 011001 doi:10.1088/1757-899X/641/1/011001

The Minerals Engineering Conference 2019 was held in Kocierz, between 16-19 of September 2019. The total number of participants was 78, included representatives from science and industry. The total number of 38 presentations were done, among which 35 were submitted to be published in *IOP Conference Series: Materials Science and Engineering*.

All papers published in this volume of *IOP Conference Series: Materials Science and Engineering* have been peer reviewed through processes administered by the Editors. Reviews were conducted by expert referees to the professional and scientific standards expected of a proceedings journal published by IOP Publishing.

Assoc. Prof. Tomasz Niedoba

Chairman of MEC 2019

IOP Conf. Series: Materials Science and Engineering **641** (2019) 011002 doi:10.1088/1757-899X/641/1/011002

Peer review statement

All papers published in this volume of *IOP Conference Series: Materials Science and Engineering* have been peer reviewed through processes administered by the proceedings Editors. Reviews were conducted by expert referees to the professional and scientific standards expected of a proceedings journal published by IOP Publishing.

The trial of immobilization amphoteric metals cations in clay-cement hydroisolation barierrs

Agata Stempkowska

Faculty of Mining and Geoengineering, AGH University of Science and Technology, Al. Mickiewicza 30, PL-30059 Cracow, Poland

Corresponding author: stemp@agh.edu.pl

Abstract. One of the main problem of degraded post-industrial areas, preventing their introduction into the secondary economic cycle, is pollution of soil and the impact of these pollution on groundwaters. With the new European Union directives, managers are encouraged to find sound solution for these problems. The process of interaction of contaminated areas is complicated, and the transport of pollutants from the danger place to the usable underground aquifers levels passes through a series of stages of varied mileages.The article presents the possibilities of using ground binders to reduce the emission of ions from soil. The tests have shown that in the case of amphoteric metals, it is possible to accumulate almost 100% of the contamination using clay-cement suspensions.

1. Introduction

The post-industrial ground materials are considered as a waste according to the Polish decree of 27 April 2001 [1]. These sediments can contain a variable amount of inorganic pollutants (heavy, transitions and amphoteric metals) and organic ones [2-6]. In general, this materials have insufficient mechanical properties for Civil Engineering applications, such as hydroisolation barriers [7,8]. The treatment of sediments using hydraulic binders and granular corrector could improve the mechanical and physical characteristics [9-12].

Many experimental works have shown the feasibility of waste materials in civil engineering and have been explored by several authors in many different fields such as for sub-base course and road construction, [13] for manufacture of aggregates for concrete mixtures and also for cement, [14] for brick, [15] and glass or glass–ceramic materials [16,17], and hydroisolation barriers production [18].

The environmental compatibility is an important issue and the waste reuse can contribute to the pollutant release in the environment, especially when concrete is demolished or comes in contact with water [19, 20].

Some of the harmful elements have the amphoteric properties, which mean that they can behave as both the acid and base. Transition metals produce the inorganic compounds that show the strongest amphoteric properties. This property is very common for the hydroxides of the metals with a medium electronegativity. The amphoteric property of the compound is related to the ability of each element to create the anions and cations in the aqueous solution. As an example, the chromium Ion, Cr^{3+} in the strong acidic solution forms the salt, $CrCl_3$ (in the presence of abundance of chloride ions forms a complex ion). In the weak acidic and neutral solution chromium ion precipitates as little soluble hydroxide $Cr(OH)_3$. In that form chromium hydroxide in the alkalic solution dissolve to create chromium ions $[Cr(OH)_4]^-$ and has a tendency to migrate to the environment [21-23].

The researches show that clay-cement hydroisolation barriers have a very good immobilization properties for the metal cations. Despite the successful inhibition there is the risk that amphoteric metals in the strong basic solution can form compounds easily dissolved in water. This publication explains the relation between very strong basic clay-cement hydrobarriers and possibility to release the harmful metal cations to the environment. The article also considers the possibility of the forming the silicate compounds in the reaction with sodium silicate (commonly known as a waterglass), that is addend to the clay-cement hydrobarriers to control the hydratation process [24-26].

2. Sample preparation

The various samples of clay-cement binders were prepared using as a base two different types of the mineral compounds, the first one was Koniecpol clay and the second one was Bełchatów clay, and the third type of samples the waste ashes were used. In this preparation as a filler the medium mesh size sand was imputed. Samples contain also 1% wt of sodium silicate (waterglass) type R145 with Mk=2,5.

The standards for hydroisolation slurry preparation indicate the quantity of sodium silicate should not exceed 1% of composition because the higher values of that has a negative impact on the rheological properties. However for academic purposes and comparison study, the samples with high concentration of sodium silicate and the samples without it were tested.

Amount and type of the compounds in the samples are presented in the Table 1, as well as the pH values for that type of mixtures.

Table 1. Composition of clay-cement mixtures.

Sample	Weight [g]	Sodium silicate [g]	Cement [g]	Soil [g]	pH
P25.50.0	106,3	0	53,2	53,2	13,03
P25.50.1	109,2	1,09	54,6	54,6	13,29
P25.50.2	105,6	2,11	52,8	52,8	13,44
P25.60.0	106,5	0	63,9	42,6	13,27
P25.60.1	102,8	1,03	61,7	41,1	13,48
P25.60.2	108,1	2,16	64,9	43,2	13,48
P25.70.0	105,6	0	73,9	31,7	13,37
P25.70.1	100,3	2,01	70,2	30,1	13,54
P25.70.2	109,2	2,18	76,4	32,8	13,25
K.50.0	107,0	0	53,5	53,5	13,25
K.50.1	103,1	1,03	51,5	51,5	13,34
K.50.2	105,4	2,11	52,7	52,7	13,34
K.60.0	108,5	0	65,1	43,4	13,15
K.60.1	109,2	1,09	65,5	43,7	13,58
K.60.2	106,7	2,13	64,0	42,7	13,43
K.70.0	108.0	0	75,6	32,4	13,48
K.70.1	106,1	1,06	74,3	31,8	13,37
K.70.2	101,8	2,04	71,3	30,5	13,54
B.50.0	107,6	0	53,8	53,8	13,43
B.50.1	102,3	1,02	51,2	51,2	13,25
B.50.2	105,1	2,10	52,6	52,5	13,34
B.60.0	104,3	0	62,6	41,7	13,15
B.60.1	108,2	1,08	64,9	43,3	13,23
B.60.2	105,6	2,11	63,4	42,2	13,58
B.70.0	107,5	0	75,3	32,2	13,25
B.70.1	106,3	1,06	74,4	31,9	13,15
B.70.2	102,8	2,06	71,9	30,8	13,23

The slurry mixes were spiker with various amphoteric hydroxides of metals that are considered as a harmful after Minister of Environment act „Standards for soil and earth quality" published in 2001. For the purposes of ths research, there elements were chosen: Lead II Zinc (II) and Chromium (III). The standards for the those elements contents are show in Table 2.

The hydroxides of those elements were added to the slurry mixes in the quantity exceed twice the standards for its concentration in the soil, with the parameters as follows:

- Lead – 2000 mg/kg
- Zinc – 40 mg/kg
- Chromium – 1600 mg/kg

On account of slurry high pH factor, the hydroxides started dissolve and created aqua soluble complex ions such as: $[Cr(OH)_4]^-$, $[Zn(OH)_4]^{2-}$, $[Pb(OH)_4]^{2-}$. In this state investigated compouds should be sucesfully inhibited in clay-cement slurry.

Table 2. The standards fort he contents of metals in the different type of soils.

No.	Pollution	Grupa A	Grupa B					Grupa C		
			Depth [m]							
			0-0,03	0,3-15,0		>15		0-2	2-15	
			Water infiltration [m/s]							
				up to	below	up to	below		up to	below
				$1x10^{-7}$		$1x10^{-7}$			$1x10^{-7}$	
1	2	3	4	5	6	7	8	9	10	11
Metals [mg/kg]										
1	**Chromium**	50	150	150	190	150	380	500	150	800
2	**Zinc**	1	4	5	6	4	10	15	6	20
3	**Lead**	50	100	100	200	100	200	600	200	1000

The samples were saturated with distilled water and extraction was allowed to occur for 48h. In the next step, the samples were filtered under the pressure of 1atm to obtain 100ml of extract. The filtration system has been shown on Figure 1.

Figure 1. Filtration set.

3. Results

The physical and chemical characteristics of effluents are presented in Table 3 and 4 and concentration of metals cations are show the Figures 1-3. The trace amounts of the metal ions were observed in the samples. The percentage of the leaching of this ions to the soil is very low, therefore it is not significant for the study of cement-clay slurry as the hydroisolation barriers.

Table 3. The concentration of the selected metal cations in the effluents, determined by ASA method.

Sample	Pb^{2+} [mg/l]	Zn^{2+} [mg/l]	Cr^{3+} [mg/l]
P25.50.0	0,083	0,0033	0,433
P25.50.1	0,071	0,0027	0,333
P25.50.2	0,071	0,0076	0,322
P25.60.0	0,073	0,0029	0,286
P25.60.1	0,068	0,0012	0,296
P25.60.2	0,067	0,0087	0,222
P25.70.0	0,047	0,0031	0,271
P25.70.1	0,038	0,0045	0,231
P25.70.2	0,053	0,0012	0,246
K.50.0	0,135	0,0045	0,377
K.50.1	0,081	0,0023	0,361
K.50.2	0,083	0,0031	0,343
K.60.0	0,085	0,0022	0,327
K.60.1	0,056	0,0056	0,276
K.60.2	0,066	0,0037	0,273
K.70.0	0,082	0,0045	0,254

K.70.1	0,077	0,0023	0,241
K.70.2	0,079	0,0029	0,268
B.50.0	0,048	0,0031	0,453
B.50.1	0,045	0,0045	0,439
B.50.2	0,068	0,0012	0,376
B.60.0	0,057	0,0026	0,365
B.60.1	0,051	0,0045	0,329
B.60.2	0,031	0,0070	0,366
B.70.0	0,042	0,0045	0,361
B.70.1	0,015	0,0023	0,275
B.70.2	0,063	0,0026	0,243

Figures below (2-4) show the relationship between cation charge and concentrations of elements in effluent after washing. The higher concentration value of chromium ions be caused by different ions migration mechanism.

The maximum concentration is 0,45 mg/L which is considered as trace quality.

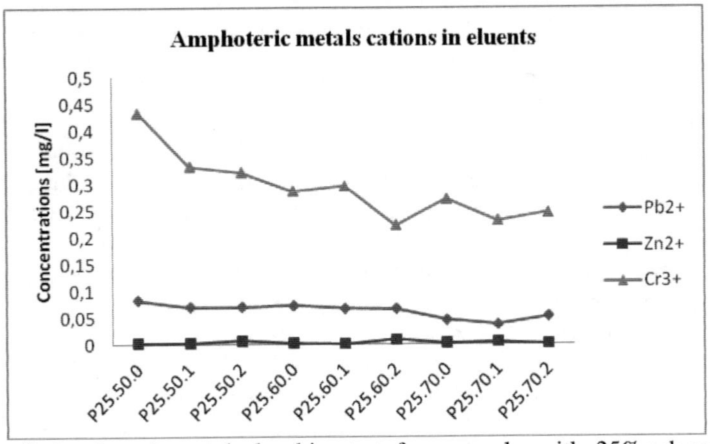

Figure 2. Amphoteric metals leaching test, from samples with 25% ash content.

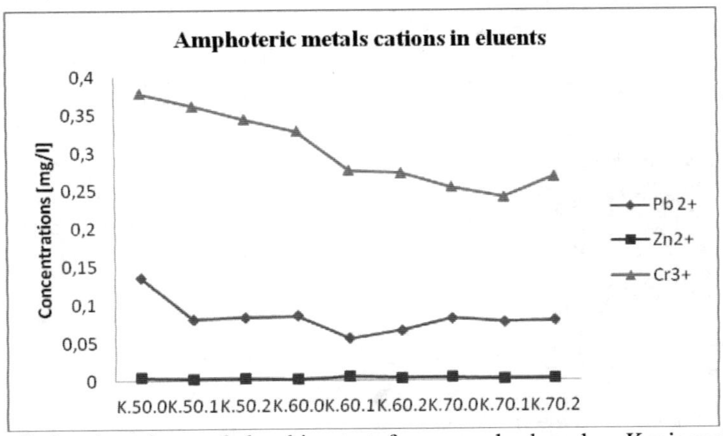

Figure 3. Amphoteric metals leaching test, from samples based on Koniecpol clay.

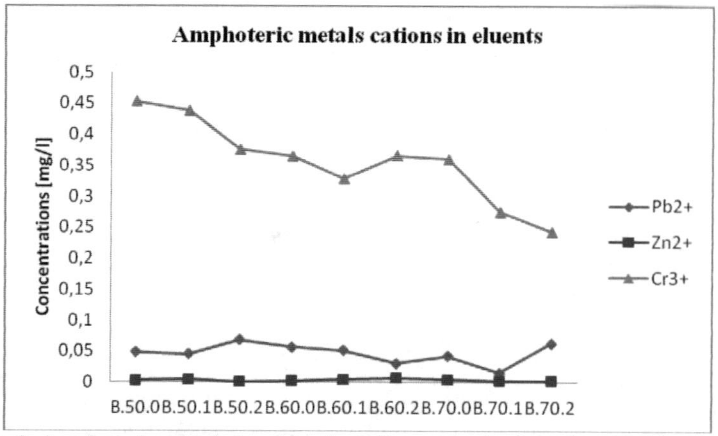

Figure 4. Amphoteric metals leaching test, from samples based on Bełchatów clay.

The results show negative dependence between cations leaching and the compositions of slurry mixtures samples. The data show no relation between ions migrations and the percentage of sodium silicate in the composition of binder. The observation was made that the type of materials (like clays or ashes) used in binder's composition should not affect the accumulation of harmful elements.

3.1. Quality precipitation of silicates of the selected amphoteric metal cations.

The experiment was carried to confirm the prediction about the possibility that certain amphoteric metal cations may precipitate as insoluble and stable salts in strong alkaline solution. To each solution of soluble salts of the selected metal cations, the sodium silicate was addend, to observe if the precipitate will form. The experiment ws conducted in the following conditions:

- the concentration of 20% of the following salts $PbNO_3$, $ZnCl_2$ and $CrCl_3$
- the sodium silicate Mk = 2,5
- reagents in the proportion 1:1

To accelerate the rate of re action the samples were put in the laboratory drier at 80 degree Celsius. All samples formed the insoluble precipitant as follows:

- monohydrate lead II silicate $PbO{\cdot}SiO_2{\cdot}H_2O$ (white crystals)
- monohydrate zinc II silicate $ZnO{\cdot}SiO_2{\cdot}H_2O$ (blue opalescent gelatinous precipitate)
- monohydrate chromium III silicate $Cr_2O_3\ {\cdot}SiO_2{\cdot}H_2O$ (pale green crystals)

Additional validation of creating unsoluble chemical bounds were obtained by SEM images with EDS analysis (figure 5-7). The EDS analysis shows that transition metals content is significantly increased, while the contents of impurity elements (Zn,Cr, Pb). These metals are immobilized in cement phases (long tiny crystals).

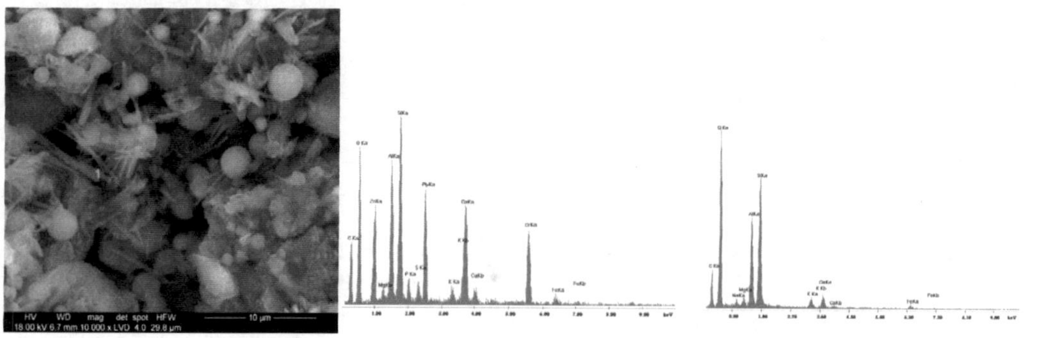

Figure 5. SEM and EDS analysis of sample with 25% ash content.

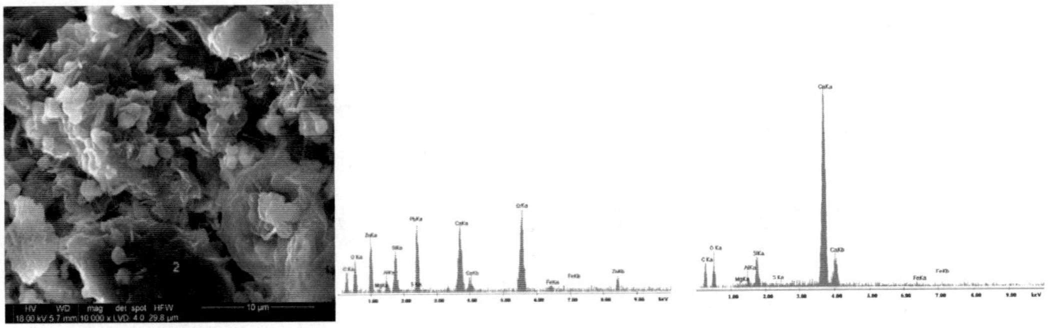

Figure 6. SEM and EDS analysis of sample based on Koniecpol clay.

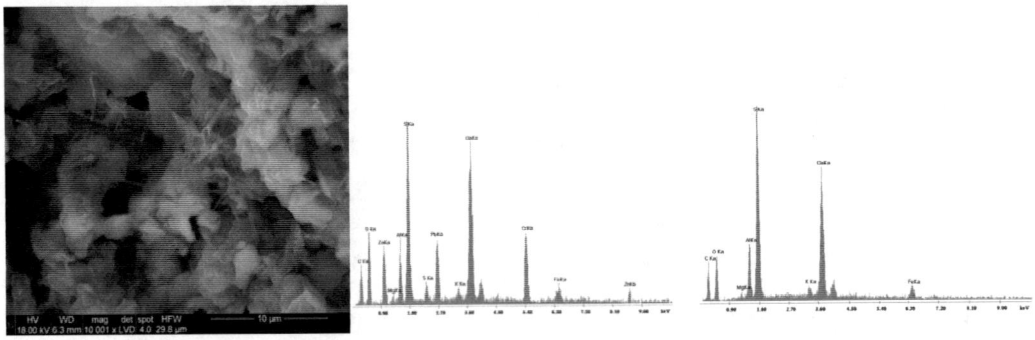

Figure 7. SEM and EDS analysis of sample based on Bełchatów clay.

4. Conclucions

1. The cement-clay barriers have very good properties to retain the metal cations, as well as amphoteric metal cations, in their structure. The amphoteric metals in the strong alkalic solution undergo complex reactions and may create soluble compounds.
2. The trace amount of the metal cations were observed in the effluents, which can suggest that they do not dissociate from cement-clay binders, especially in the case of zinc.
3. The use if the sodium silicate as the additive in the cement-clay binders, improves retention of the harmful metal cations. The silicates form with lead, chromium and zinc.
4. The higher quantities of sodium silicate added to the cement-clay binders will probably retain the migration of metal cations, however the quantity of sodium silicate use as an additive to the cement-clay binders is restricted by decay the reological properties of those binders.

References

[1] Prawo ochrony środowiska (Dz.U. Nr 62, poz. 627) http://prawo.sejm.gov.pl/isap.nsf/DocDetails.xsp?id=WDU20010620627
[2] Andersen S, Ødegård S and Seip H M 1994 *Ecol. Eng.* **3** pp 245-253
[3] Malviya R andChaudhary R J 2006 *J. Mater. Cycles Waste* **8** pp78-87
[4] Seip H M, Pawałowski L and Sulliven T 1994 *Ecol. Eng.* **3** pp 205-206
[5] Wuana R A, Okieimen F E.2011, *ISRN Ecol.* Article ID 402647, http://dx.doi.org/10.5402/2011/402647
[6] Chibuike G U, Obiora S C 2014 *Applied and Environmental Soil Science* Article ID 752708, http://dx.doi.org/10.1155/2014/752708

[7] Wang L K, Hung Y-T, Shammas N K 2010 *Handbook of Advanced Industrial and Hazardous Wastes Treatment*, CRC Press
[8] Spence W P, Kultermann E 2017 *Construction Materials, Methods and Techniques*, CENGAGE Learning
[9] Wójcik Ł, Izak P, Mastalska-Popławska J, Gajek M, 2015 *J.Phys. Conference Series*, **790**, , pp 1–7
[10] Stempkowska A, Wójcik Ł, Izak P, 2011, *Materiały Ceramiczne = Ceramic Materials / Polskie Towarzystwo Ceramiczne, Kraków*, **6**, pp. 278–282
[11] Wójcik Ł, Izak P, Kuś R, 2009, *Materiały Ceramiczne = Ceramic Materials / Polskie Towarzystwo Ceramiczne, Kraków*, **61**, pp 27-30
[12] Izak P, Wójcik Ł, Słowikowski D, 2015 *Materiały Ceramiczne = Ceramic Materials / Polskie Towarzystwo Ceramiczne, Kraków,* **67,** pp 158-163
[13] Kasmi A, Abriak N E, Benzerzour M et al. 2017, *J. Mater. Cycles Waste Manag.* **19,** https://doi.org/10.1007/s10163-016-0529-5
[14] Dalton J L, Gardner K H, Seager T P, Weimer M I, Spear J C M, Magee B J 2004 *Resour. Conserv. Recycl.* **41** pp 227–241
[15] Collivignarelli M C, Abbà A, Sorlini S. et al. 2017 *J. Mater. Cycles Waste Manag.* **19** p 1374 https://doi.org/10.1007/s10163-016-0523
[16] Andreola F, Barbieri L, Corradi A, Lancellotti I, Manfredini T, 2001, *J. Mater. Sci.* **36** pp 4869–4873
[17] Monteiro R C C, Figueiredo C F, Alendouro M S, Ferro M C, Davim E J R, Fernandes M H V 2008 *Waste Manag.* **28** pp 1119–1125 doi: 10.1016/j.wasman.2007.05.004
[18] Stempkowska A, Wójcik Ł, Izak P, Staszewska M, Mastalska-Popławska J 2018 IOP Conf. Ser.: Mater. Sci. Eng. **427** p 1
[19] Tang P, Florea M V A, Spiesz P, Brouwers H J H 2015 *Construct Build Mater.* **83** pp 77–94. doi: 10.1016/j.conbuildmat.2015.02.033
[20] Boghetich G, Liberti L, Notarnicola M, Palma M, Petruzzelli D 2005 Waste Manag. Res. **23** pp 57–61 doi: 10.1177/0734242X05051017
[21] Stempkowska A, Izak P, Mastalska-Popławska J 2017 *Gospodarka Surowcami Mineralnymi = Mineral Resources Management* **33** pp 139–149
[22] Lafhaj Z, Samara M, Agostini F, Boucard L, Skoczylas F, Depelsenaire G 2007 Constr. Build Mater. **148** pp 606–612
[23] Varshney S, Jain P, Srivastava S J 2017 *Mater. Cycles Waste Manag.* https://doi.org/10.1007/s10163-016-0539-3
[24] Zhang H, He P J, Shao L M. et al. 2008 *J. Mater. Cycles Waste Manag.* https://doi.org/10.1007/s10163-007-0191
[25] Wang D, Liu D, Tao L et al. 2017 *J. Mater. Cycles Waste Manag.* https://doi.org/10.1007/s10163-016-0508-x
[26] Bashir M J K, Aziz H A, Yusoff M S, 2011 *J. Hazard. Mater.* **186** pp 92–102

IOP Conf. Series: Materials Science and Engineering **641** (2019) 012002 doi:10.1088/1757-899X/641/1/012002

Evaluation of the impact of the CO/C reducer on the CO_2 formation in the process of pyrometallurgical recovery of Fe from converter slag

D Kalisz[1], A Młynarczykowska[2] and A Chyczyński[1]

[1]Faculty of Foundry Engineering,
[2]Faculty of Mining and Geoengineering
AGH University of Science and Technology, Al. Mickiewicza 30, PL-30059 Cracow, Poland

E-mail: dak@agh.edu.pl

Abstract. The results of simulations of Fe recovery from steel slag containing iron oxides with C reducer dissolved in liquid slag and gaseous CO were presented in the paper. The simulations were performed with the use of a commercial program FactSage, and the calculations followed the procedure of dosing the reducer to slag in portions, each time reaching the state of thermodynamic equilibrium. The calculation procedure was realized sequentially, and the equilibrium composition of gaseous phase, nonmetallic phase and separated Fe was established at each calculation step. Gaseous products of CO and CO_2 reduction were removed from the system with each successive calculation step. The simulation revealed that reaching comparable results of reduction requires using a considerable amount of CO. Moreover, the CO_2 content in the gaseous phase and amount of separated Fe depend on the type of reducer. It was observed that the main mechanism was the reduction of iron with C. In this case the composition of gaseous products was mainly dominated by CO-CO_2.

1. Introduction

The steel production technology generates industrial waste containing high quantities of metal-containing by-products, which can be recycled in iron-recovery processes [1-6]. The waste re-use operation lies in its reintroduction to the sinter mix as a furnace charge supplement, or the iron fraction is removed from the slag with a magnetic method. The main by-product of steel production is slag consisting mainly of: CaO, SiO_2, Al_2O_3, FeO, MgO and MnO [7, 8]. Slag from the furnace processes contains under 1.5 % FeO, therefore no Fe-oriented recycling is realized. A similar situation is observed for high phosphorus converter slags. Here the applicability is limited in the steel production processes as in the complete reduction conditions it returns to liquid metal. Neither slag after steel refining processes can be used for iron production and this is connected with the high aluminum oxide content. Attempts were made to manage this slag in a ladle furnace as part of calcium and fluorite substitute, though its applicability was limited because of the use of refractory materials and other problems with its processing [1]. The basic component of steel slag is FeO (7-30%), the content of which depends on the applied technology. The chemical composition also depends on the assortment of the produced steel; in the case of special steels, slag may contain MnO, Cr_2O_3, V_2O_5 and TiO_2 [7, 8].

In the integrated steel plant, about 130-200 kg of slag is produced with the basic oxygen furnace (BOF) per ton of produced raw steel. The conventional way of managing slag as a blast furnace additive gives some side effects, i.e. higher coke consumption during slag processing, as well as higher CO and CO_2 content. This does not comply with the present trend to reduce CO_2 emissions.

IOP Conf. Series: Materials Science and Engineering **641** (2019) 012002 doi:10.1088/1757-899X/641/1/012002

The sustained development strategy is aimed at limiting waste production and unfavorable effects connected with their recycling. Accordingly, alternative methods are searched for to recover metals (Fe) and also to limit gas emissions. The basic technology of Fe recovery from slag is the pyrometallurgical reduction with carbonaceous materials [9].

2. Mineralogical composition and build of slag:

In the converter process, slag is produced with the main components FeO, CaO and SiO_2. Iron in slag may assume the form of Fe_2O_3 – hematite, which has a romboid shape, and Fe_3O_4 – magnetite having a crystalline structure of spinelle. There may be also present the maghemite (gamma) phase of Fe_2O_3 – an allotropic form having an isomorphic spinelle form (like magnetite) and ferromagnetic properties and chemical composition (like hematite). There is also present FeO phase –wustite with paramagnetic properties [10].

Each of the oxides has different chemical composition and build, which may consequently affect the course of processes in the presence of the reducer in liquid phase. When the SiO_2 content is increased in slag, pure wustite FeO in equilibrium with Fe contains about 10% Fe_2O_3, whereas after adding CaO to wustite, being in equilibrium with Fe, the Fe_2O_3 may reach 20%. Slag may also contain complex forms being a result of chemical processes taking place in the system. In the case of a system composed of FeO, CaO, SiO_2 presented on Figure 1 the possible presence of the following chemical compounds should be taken into account: Ca_2SiO_4, $CaSiO_3$, $FeSiO_3$, Fe_2SiO_4, $Ca_2Si_2O_6$ and $Ca_4Si_2O_8$ [10].

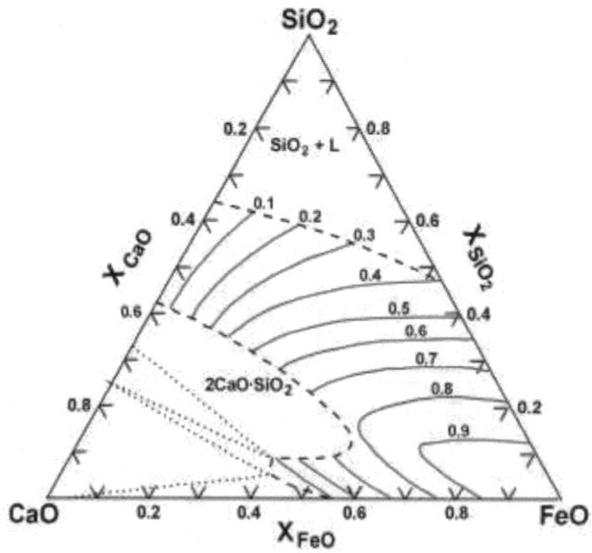

Figure 1. Activity of FeO in liquid solution of FeO-CaO-SiO_2 at temp. 1550^{0}C in equilibrium with liquid Fe.

The chemical and mineral composition of slag in solid state was considerably well analyzed, but in the case of liquid systems we can infer on its build. In the analysis of the structure of liquid slag and its physicochemical structure, slag is treated as an ionic liquid, where one of the main components is silica appearing in a tetrahedral form built of big oxygen ions centrally surrounding the silicon ion (figure 2)

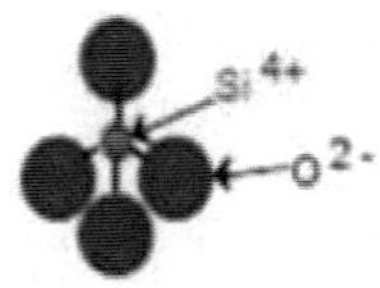

Figure 2. Build of Si-O tetrahedron.

3. Iron recovery from iron with the participation of C and CO reducers

The pyrometallurgical reduction of iron oxides in liquid slag takes place as a result of reactions taking place on the interface [10]:

a) slag/coal (hard coal, coke, lignite or other)

$$FeO_{(l)} + C_{(s)} = Fe_{(s/l)} + CO \quad (1)$$

$$Fe_{(s/l)} + C_{(s)} = Fe\text{-}C_{(l)} \quad (2)$$

c) slag/gas

$$FeO_{(l)} + CO = Fe_{(s/l)} + CO_2 \quad (3)$$

d) coal/gas

$$CO_2 + C = 2\,CO \quad (4)$$

Reaction (1) takes place in the initial stage of high temperature reduction; the formation of gaseous CO product initiates reaction (3). Consequently, a mixture of gaseous products of reactions (1) and (3) is generated in the form of a CO-CO_2 mixture on the surface of solid carbon reducer in the form of a gaseous bubble The activity of FeO will affect the reaction parameters and equilibrium between phases.

$$\frac{p_{CO_2}}{p_{CO}} = K \cdot a_{FeO} \quad (5)$$

Authors performed calculations relating to the formation of CO and CO_2 phase during reduction of liquid converter slag with the use of C and CO_2 with the use of FACTSage software.

4. Simulation Calculations

Simulations were performed at temperature 1700K for the reduction process with the use of CO and C. The reduction was realized for slags having chemical composition as in table 1. Simulated slags contained four basic components; CaO, SiO_2, Al_2O_3 and FeO. In all analyzed cases the FeO content was about 10%, and the basic differences were observed for SiO_2 content (22.56 – 40.13%)

Table 1. Chemical composition of slags used in calculations (wt%).

Slag	% CaO	% SiO_2	% Al_2O_3	% FeO
S1	41.67	**40.13**	7.60	10.60
S2	40.38	34.60	**14.68**	10.34
S3	**58.98**	22.56	7.66	**10.80**

The first stage of calculations concentrated on the simulation of slags reduction with carbon portions (5 g) of solid reducer were introduced. In each calculation step, new phases were formed after the state of thermodynamic equilibrium was reached, i.e. liquid Fe and gaseous solution CO-CO_2. The cycle was repeated till the moment minimum FeO content in slag was obtained. The same procedure was applied for the reduction process making use of CO. In this case the reduction took place on the phase contact, i.e. on the liquid slag/gas interface, where gas appears in the form of CO bubbles, and the CO-CO_2 mixture is the product of the reaction. The calculations were performed at a temperature of 1700 K. It was observed that only FeO was reduced. The results of calculations of chemical composition of particular phases are presented in figures 3-6. The change of Fe content after the reaction of slags 1-3 with C and CO is presented in figure 3 and figure 4.

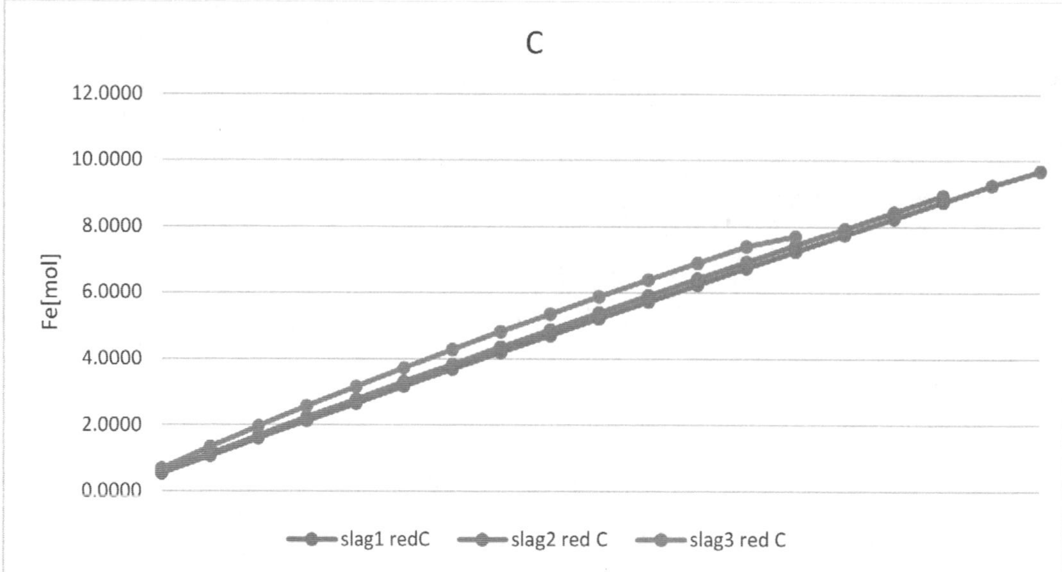

Figure 3. Change of Fe content after reduction with C (T=1700 K).

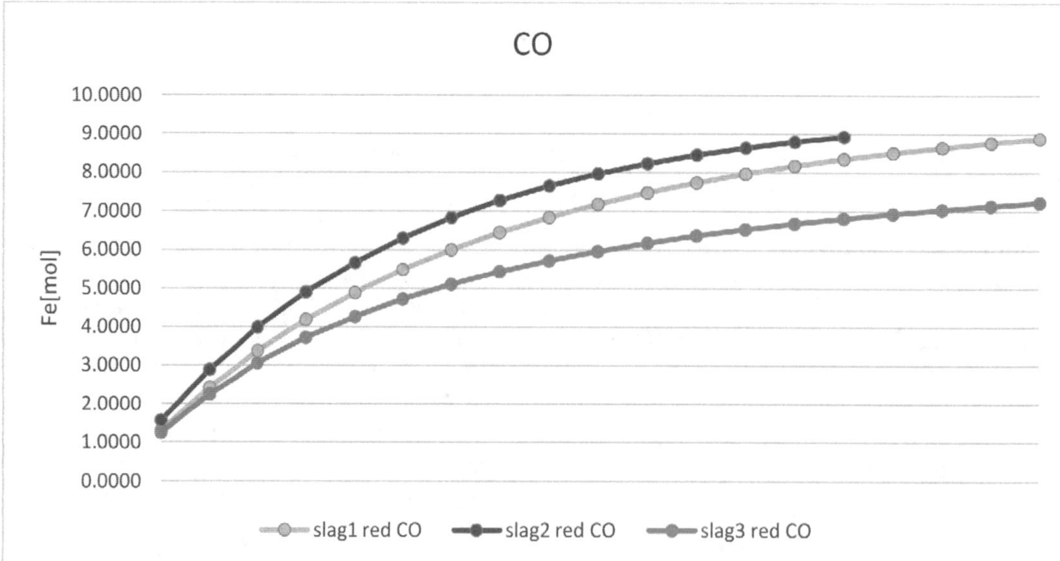

Figure 4. Change of Fe content after reduction with CO (T=1700 K).

The comparison of figures 3 and 4 reveals that the reduction with carbon is much more efficient than in the case of only gaseous CO. In this case the participation of gaseous reducer should be excessive. Moreover, at the final stages of reduction with the use of CO the reaction was observed to stop. At this stage the equilibrium concentration of CO_2 in gaseous phase was very low because of the low FeO content, which results in considerable lowering of the reaction. The amount of produced Fe increased nearly linearly with the increase of added reducer. In the case of reduction realized with CO the amount of Fe obtained in each successive calculation step was lower.

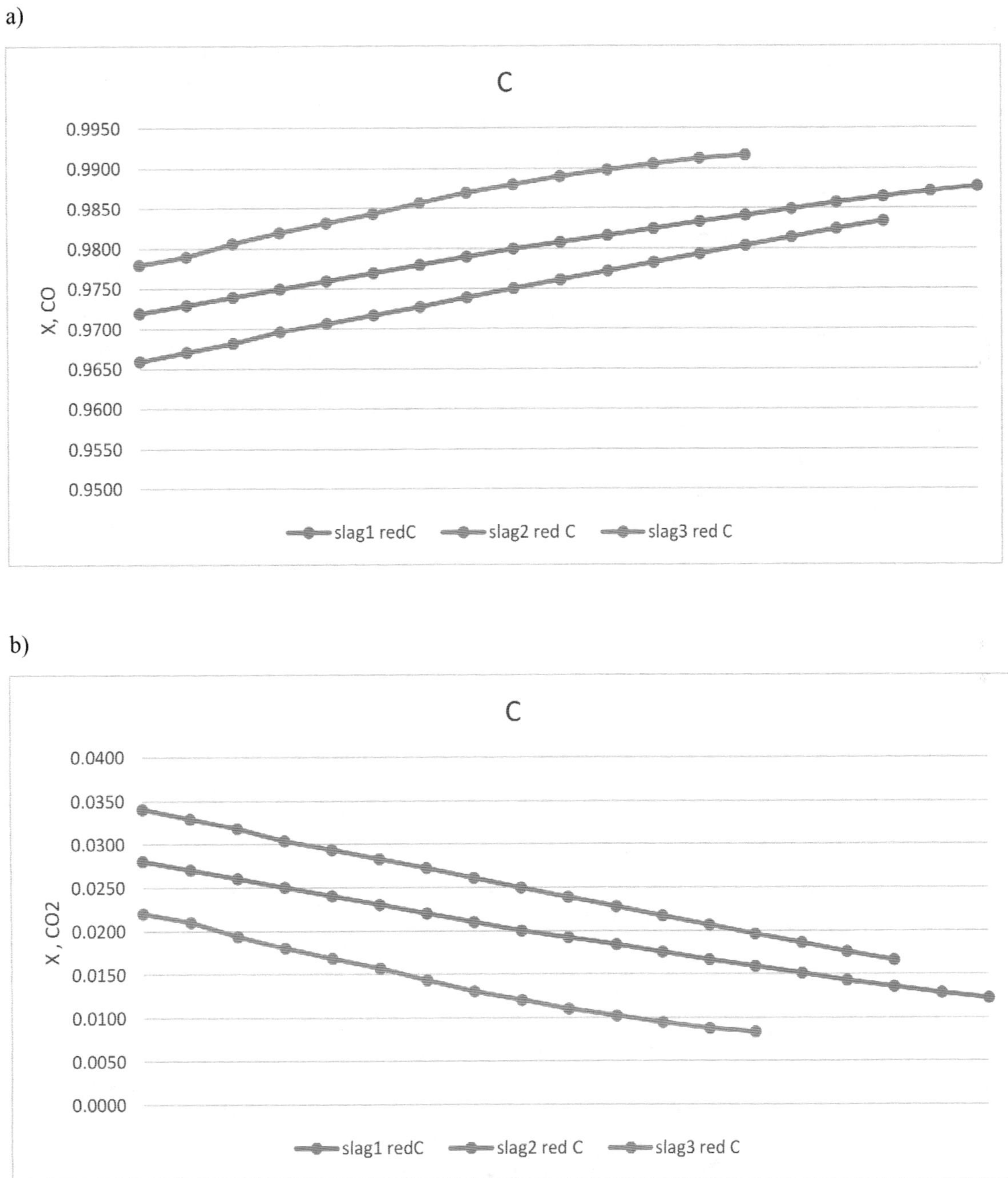

Figures 5 a, b. Change of composition of gaseous phase for slags 1, 2, 3 for reduction with carbon.

a)

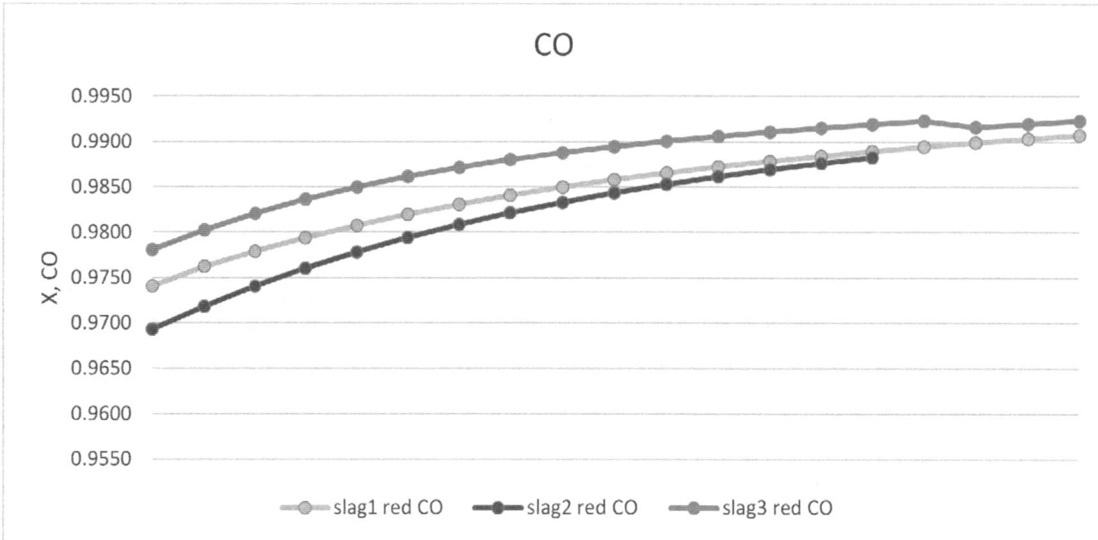

b)

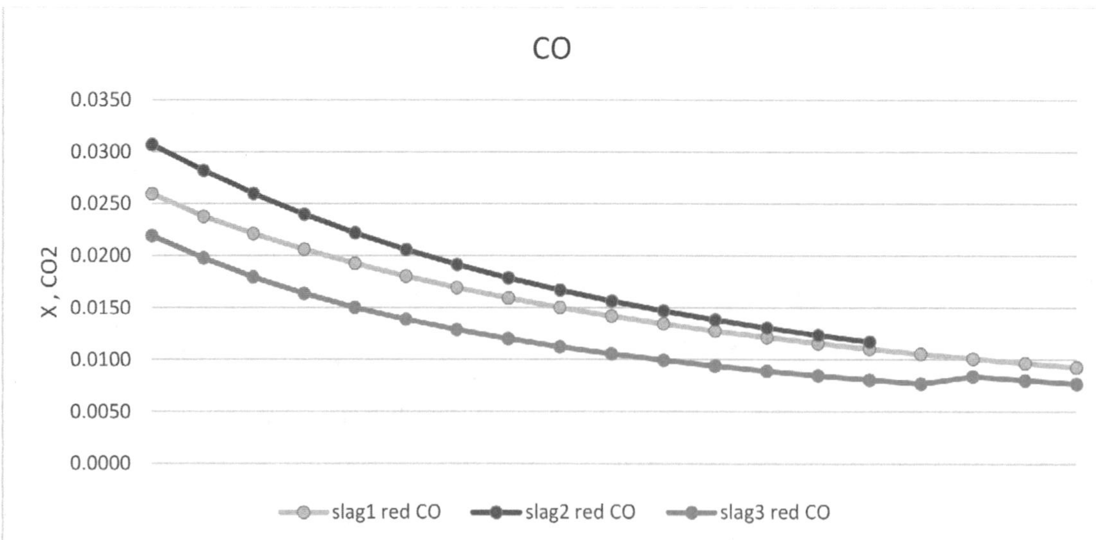

Figures 6 a, b. Change of composition of gaseous phase for slags 1, 2, 3 for reduction with CO.

The CO_2 concentration in the gaseous phase is considerably diversified and depends on the applied reducer. In the case of reduction with carbon In the case of coal reduction, it does not exceed the value of X = 0.035 (X = 0.0341 for the slag1) and decreases to the value of X = 0.0084 for the slag 3. In the case of reduction with CO the amount of produced CO_2 is highest in the initial stages of reduction and considerably higher than in reduction with carbon.

5. Conclusions

The presented simulation of reduction in the condition of thermodynamic equilibrium illustrates the course of elementary reactions of Fe phase formation and evolution of gaseous phase during these processes. The applied calculation procedure is considerably simplified as in each calculation step the produced solid Fe and gaseous phase are removed from the analyzed system. The comparison of the effect of use of two types of reducers suggests that the reduction with carbon is more efficient. The validity of the simulation has been verified experimentally and will constitute a separate study.

6. References

[1] Podorska D, Wypartowicz J. Termodynamiczna analiza elementarnych procesów redukcji ciekłego żużla tlenkowego *Hutnik – Wiadomości Hutnicze*, 2009, 77 (4): 139-146.
[2] Wei P, Sano M, Hirasawa M, Mori K. Kinetics of carbon oxidation reaction between molten iron of high carbon Concentration and Iron Oxide Slag, *ISIJ Int*. 1991, 31: 358.
[3] Pribulova, A, Futas P, Baricova, D, Eperjesi, S. Cupola furnace slag - Its origin, properties and utilization, 73rd World Foundry Congress & quot; Creative Foundry & quot;, WFC 2018 - Proceedings .
[4] Guo J, Bao Y, Wang M. Steel slag in Chibna: Treatment, recycling, and management, *Waste Management* 2018, 78: 318-330.
[5] Podorska D, Wypartowicz J. Thermodynamic analysis of elementary processes in molten oxide slag reduction, *Archives of Metallurgy and Materials*. 2008, 53(2): 595-600.
[6] Sinelnikov V O, Kalisz D, Kuzemko R D, Study of the Phase and Mineralogical Properties of Converter Slag During Splashing to Improve Lining Resistance *Refractories and Industrial Ceramics* 2018, 59 (4:) 403-409.
[7] Niesler M, Blacha L, Łabaj J, Matuła T. A study on the process of fine-grained plumbiferous material agglomeration *Metalurgija* 2013, 52(4): 521-524.
[8] Chyczyński A, Kuglin K, Kalisz D. Applicability of solid gaseous reducer for Pb and Cu recuperation from metallurgical slag *Rudy i Metale Nieżelazne Recykling* 2019, 64:213-18.
[9] Matuła T, Siwiec G. Reduction of lead oxide by fine-grained carbonaceous materials *Archives of Metallurgy and Materials* 2019, 64 (2): 647-652.
[10] Kuglin K, Sinelnikov V O, Kalisz D Computer simulation of iron converter slag with reduction method *Rudy i Metale Nieżelazne Recykling* 2019, 64(2): 8-12.

IOP Conf. Series: Materials Science and Engineering **641** (2019) 012003 doi:10.1088/1757-899X/641/1/012003

Hydrocyclone classification control

A Wieniewski, B Skorupska, K Szczepaniak and W Tomaka

Sieć Badawcza Łukasiewicz-Instytut Metali Nieżelaznych, ul. Sowińskiego 5, 44-100 Gliwice, Poland

E-mail: bozenas@imn.gliwice.pl

Abstract. An overview of the classification systems in hydrocyclones in the copper ore enrichment departments at KGHM Polska Miedź SA was presented. In recent years, IMN has been conducting an investment - replacing hydrocyclones with modern HC hydrocyclone solutions - manufactured by ZAM Kęty and IMN. The results of implementing modern hydrocyclones are presented. The important issue is to define relation between values of pressure and/or hydrocyclone feed density and cut point achieved in these conditions for chosen classification node By disposing this relation, implemented to classification monitoring system is possible to maintain cut point value within the range ± 5 % of assumed value by preserving acceptable feed variation in industrial conditions: - change of suspension density ± 20 % in ratio to assumed value, - change of feed particle size d80 ± 15 % in ratio to assumed value.

1. Introduction

Hydrocyclone classification requires a feed to be properly prepared and the process to be conducted under strictly controlled conditions with properly selected structural parameters. Classification is conducted at various stages in the enriching process. Hydrocyclones can be used in the classification of a number of mineral raw materials (e.g. ores of copper, zinc, lead, coal, sulphur, quartz, graphite), circulating water reclamation (clarification), and sewage treatment.

The development research, which was carried out, concerned a new technology for hydrocyclone classification process stabilisation using system for measuring grain size distributions of feed and classification products and also assessment of its capability for use in the copper ore enrichment process.

2. The aim of the investigations

Tested solution with the use of a three-product particle size analyzer consisted in the construction of a pilot installation based on the following basic components: HC 500/12° ZAM-IMN hydrocyclone cluster, three-product particle size analyzer system and "IMNCLASS" recording and computing system.

Technology of ore preparation to beneficiation is main stage of mineral processing. It decides about efficiency of useful minerals recovery as a result of proper liberation level of beneficiated minerals from gangue [1]. It also influences significantly on costs of concentrates production. Currently, processes of ore preparation to flotation contain crushing, screening, grinding in rod and ball mills, additional grinding of semi-products in pebble mills and hydraulic classification in spiral classifiers and hydrocyclones. The crucial influence on proper preparation of flotation feed has properly conducted process of classification of ore suspension in hydrocyclones. In purpose of ensuring proper work of hydrocyclones the following parameters should be monitored: density of feed and classification products, feed pressure, hydrocyclone capacity, products particle size distribution.

Dependably on size of classified particles in Flotation Departments KGHM PM S.A. the hydrocyclones of cylindrical diameter being equal to 500 mm (for coarse particles) and 350 mm (for fine particles) are being applied, of various convergence angles of cone parts. To ensure appropriate capacity of systems, single hydrocyclones are grouped in batteries.

Because of different lithologic composition of products of Comminution Departments, in Flotation Departments of KGHM PM S.A. O/ZWR various technological schemes are adapted to beneficiate material reach in sandstone fraction and of increased contents of carbonate fraction (Figure 1).

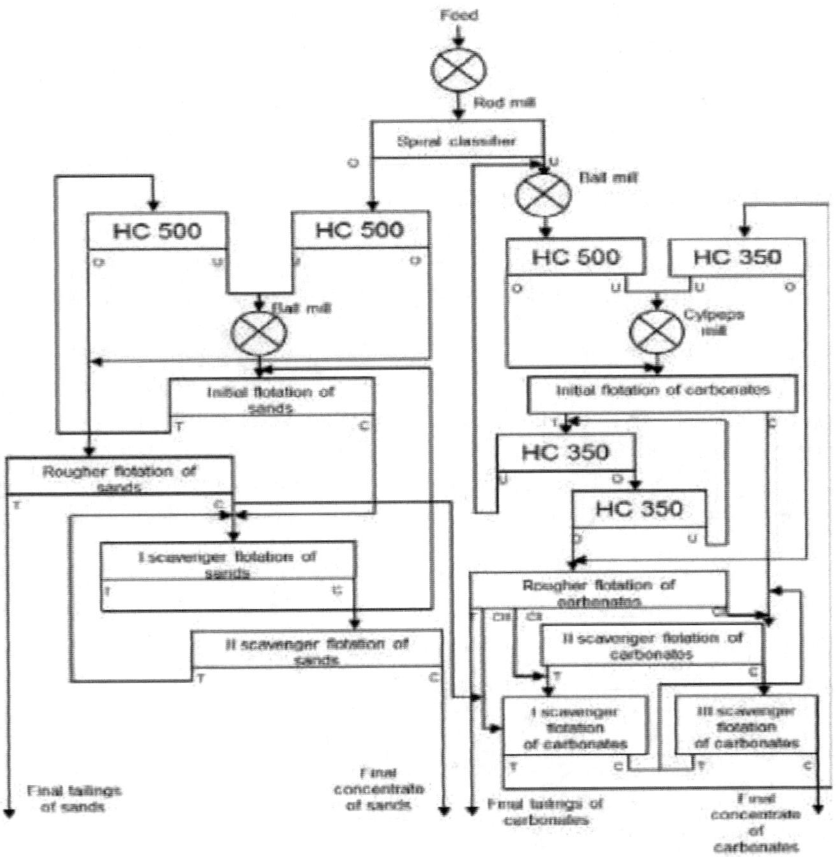

Figure 1. Scheme of beneficiation of material reach in sandstone and carbonate fractions in KGHM PM S.A. O/ZWR Region Rudna.

Currently for sandstone fraction, overflows of spiral classifiers are directed to first stage of classification in hydrocyclones ø 500 mm, from which overflows are feed for main flotation of sands and underflows after additional grinding in mills are feed for initial flotation of sands. Waste from initial flotation of sands is directed to second stage of classification of sands in hydrocyclones ø 500 mm. Overflows from these hydrocyclones are directed to main flotation of sands and underflows to additional grinding.

For carbonate ore wastes from initial flotation are directed to first stage of classification in hydrocyclones ø 500 mm, which overflows are classified in second stage of classification in hydrocyclones ø 350 mm and underflows are additionally ground in ball mills. Overflows of hydrocyclones of second stage of classification are directed to main flotation while underflows are being re-directed to first stage of classification of carbonates. Tailings from flotation I of carbonate cleaning are classified on third stage of classification in hydrocyclones ø 350 mm, from which overflows are directed to main flotation while underflows are additionally ground in pebble mill.

In KGHM PM S.A., because of lack of previous modernization, hydrocyclones classification systems characterize with relatively low sharpness of products separation. It influences on creation of big returns in grinding and additional grinding systems what causes shortening of grinding time and growth of energy consumption of production process. Classification sharpness influences significantly on quality of preparation of flotation feed. Growth of classification sharpness causes elongation of flotation time because of decreasing amount of material returns. It causes growth of copper recovery. Currently, classification sharpness in hydrocyclones is equal to about 82% and is upper value possible to achieve in industrial conditions. Even this value is hard to maintain because of various characteristics of feed parameters connected with previously conducted comminution and beneficiation processes and changes of characteristics of material treated by mineral processing.

Polish copper ores are mixtures of three lithological types: sandstones, carbonates and shales, which contents are changeable in ore dependably on exploitive fields.

The purpose of the task are identifying investigations of individual classification systems in range of determination of work characteristics concerning evaluation of their work efficiency in conditions of beneficiation of sandstone and carbonate copper ores in KGHM PM S.A. Efficiency of classification in hydrocyclones will be determined on the basis of obtained parameters of classification sharpness and cut point size in industrial conditions of changeable feed. The purpose of conducted researches is construction of database allowing elaboration of algorithms monitoring individual classification systems. The important aspect of the task is also finding possibility of simplifying classification process in hydrocyclones. The replacement of I and II° of carbonate ores classification in hydrocyclones by only one level of classification will cause growth of technological and economic parameters of beneficiation process.

The main parameters being stabilized in hydrocyclones batteries are: feed pressure, feed density in sumps and levels in sumps [2]. Additionally, in monitoring systems the measurement of feed flow is available as well the evaluation of products particle size distribution. Stabilization of individual parameters occurs from the level of programming drivers PLC, by implementation of appropriate algorithms in regulation systems. The task of systems of pressure regulation in case of batteries equipped with knife gate valves is based on maintaining pressure in optimal, assumed range by means of monitoring of knife gate valves. The efficiency of battery work depends on capacity of the automatics system to maintain pressure within certain range as well on selection of this range. This range can be assumed manually as well it can be found by means of pressure optimization dependably on particle size distribution. In case of elaboration of monitoring algorithms the certain value of pressure can be searched which is optimal for battery work for which gate valves pressure monitoring system will select range and will maintain the calculated value within it. Similarly, the optimal values of feed density can be searched and its optimized value can be implemented to density regulation system which will stabilize it by means of monitoring water flow to sumps [3].

The important issue is to define relation between values of pressure and/or hydrocyclone feed density and cut point achieved in these conditions for chosen classification node. By disposing this relation, implemented to classification monitoring system is possible to maintain cut point value within the range ± 5 % of assumed value by preserving acceptable feed variation in industrial conditions:

- change of suspension density ± 20 % in ratio to assumed value,
- change of feed particle size d80 ± 15 % in ratio to assumed value.

After implementation of classification monitoring system on the basis of previously elaborated models the stage of industrial investigations will begin. It will verify the accepted models of sandstone and carbonate ores classification in hydrocyclones. The stabilization of hydrocyclone classification parameters and growth of separation sharpness to maximum value possible to achieve in certain classification system will influence on growth of efficiency of beneficiation of sandstone and carbonate ores in KGHM PM S.A. Also, it is considered to elaborate assumptions with purpose of simplifying classification of carbonate ores in hydrocyclones by replacing two-stage classification system to only one level.

3. Introduction of the Hydrocyclones - ZAM IMN in copper processing plant

The innovative classification system consisting of new type HC 500/12° hydrocyclone batteries is equipped with parameter stabilization system that makes possible to control its proper operation, limit any disturbances and reach optimum technological indicators of the classification process [4]. Currently HC 500/12° hydrocyclone battery is operating in O/ZWR Lubin with high efficiency level of 90 - 95 % at required in O/ZWR regions effectiveness level of 85 %. Hydrocyclone HC 500/12° thickening and classifying hydrocyclone was designed in order to ensure increase of efficiency of grain classes separation in the products and stronger grain diversification in the hydrocyclone of such size. The diameter of the cylindrical part of 500mm is the basic hydrocyclone parameter. This size enables wide range grain and efficiency classification. The height of cylindrical part is equal to the diameter of the hydrocyclone. The hydrocyclone convergence angle has a significant impact both on efficiency and also on technological results of the equipment work. For hydrocyclone of diameter 500 mm the convergence angle is 12°. HC 500/12° hydrocyclone is equipped with composite anti-abrasive linings based on silicon carbide ensuring significant elongation of the equipment lifetime. Basing on the new hydrocyclone an innovative classification system consisting of Hc 500/12°hydrocyclones was built [4]. The system is equipped with parameter stabilization system that makes possible to control its proper operation and reach optimum technological indicators of the enrichment process. Parameter stabilization system makes possible to control the following parameters: pressure, density and quantity of the feed that is put in the hydrocyclone. Hc 500/12° hydrocyclone is adapted for classification of material characterized by diversified grain and density. HC 500/12° thickening and classifying hydrocyclone can be applied in the mineral resources enrichment and hydraulic classification in national and foreign plants dealing with mineral resources processing, circulating waters regeneration and waste water treatment.

Advantages of the solution:

- increase of classification effectiveness,
- increase of equipment efficiency,
- longer hydrocyclone lifetime.

4. Results of sample of the classification system in hydrocyclones in copper ore enrichment plants

Under the OPTICLASS project, a review of the classification systems at KGHM copper enrichment plants. An example of the results of testing the classification system - Rudna region is presented in Table 1.

ZWR Rudna area (A side - technological line)
Classification stage: I ° classification of sandstone ores (classification of the overflow classifier)
Hydrocyclone type: HC500 / 20 °

Table 1. Results of testing carried out to determine the classification parameters in hydrocyclones, broken down into sandstone and carbonate ore classification at KGHM PM S.A.(selected example).

No	Grain class mm from	Grain class mm to	Grain average mm	Sieve analysis j Feed %	Sieve analysis j Underflow %	Sieve analysis j Overflow %	Yield Feed %	Yield Underflow %	Yield Overflow %	distribution %
1	1,00	0,50	0,750	0,10	0,10	0,00	0,07	0,12	0,00	100,00
2	0,50	0,32	0,408	0,60	1,50	0,10	0,85	1,35	0,01	99,64
3	0,32	0,20	0,258	8,60	17,30	1,40	10,40	16,19	0,73	97,36
4	0,20	0,16	0,180	11,20	21,30	3,10	13,35	19,97	2,30	93,54
5	0,16	0,10	0,130	29,90	36,90	8,50	27,53	38,40	9,40	87,20
6	0,10	0,071	0,086	9,60	10,80	5,10	8,99	11,18	5,33	77,78
7	0,07	0,045	0,058	7,10	5,00	6,20	6,02	5,67	6,61	58,89
8	0,05	0	0,023	32,90	7,10	75,60	32,80	7,13	75,62	13,59
Suma :				100,00	100,00	100,00	100,00	100,00	100,00	

Yield :

overflow **37,48 %**

underflow **62,52 %**

Correlation coefficient **R = 0,9832**

d(50) = **0.059 mm**

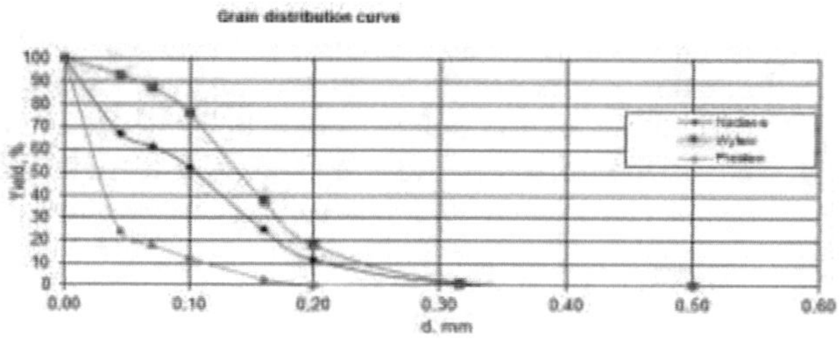

Table 2. Classification parameters in ZWR KGHM - sampling results, Battery HC-111B.

Ore type	Plant name	Hydrocyclones classification stage	Feed (**N**) (**P**-Overflow, **W** - Underflow)	d80 [mm]	Ec (d80) [%]
Ruda piaskowcowa	Lubin	Classification in milling circuit	**N**: underflow MD	0,17	60,4
			P: rougher flotation		
			W: additional milling		
		I° classification (initial flotation waste)	**N**: initial flotation waste	0,165	68,9
			P: rougher flotation		
			W: additional milling		
		classification (Main flotation waste)	**N**: waste rougher flotation	0,135	65,3
			P: final waste		
			W: additional milling		
	Rud na	I° classifcation (classifier overflow)	**N**: spiral classifier overflow	0,14	78,1

			P: rougher flotation **W**: additional milling		
		II° classification (classification in the milling circuit)	**N**: initial flotation waste **P**: rougher flotation **W**: additional milling	0,16 – 0,18	55,2 – 67,9
Ruda węglanowa	Lubin	I° classification (waste from preliminary flotation)	**N**: initial flotation waste **P**: classification in milling circuit **W**: additional milling	0,21	68,3
		Flotation semi-product classification	**N**: flotation semi - products **P**: rougher flotation **W**: additional milling	0,05 – 0,055	76,2 – 77,9
		Milling circuit classification	**N**: underflow MD (additional mill) **P**: rougher flotation **W**: additional milling	0,08 – 0,20	60,8 – 84,2
		Milling circuit classification (Underflow of ball mill classification)	**N**: underflow MK (ball mill) **P**: flash flotation **W**: additional milling	0,22	68,6
		II° classification (flash flotation waste classification)	**N**: flash flotation waste **P**: rougher flotation **W**: additional milling	0,15	60,8
		III° classification (semi-product of initial flotation and waste from I scavenger flotation)	**N**: semiproduct of rougher flotation + waste I scavenger flotation **P**: rougher flotation **W**: additional milling	0,10	73,8
		Classification (waste of milling circiut flotation)	**N**: waste from flotation in milling circuit **P**: rougher flotation **W**: additional milling	0,18	49,4
	Rudna	Classification in milling circuit (classification of underflow from ball mill)	**N**: underflow MK **P**: initial flotation **W**: additional milling	0,23	52,0
		I° Classification	**N**: initial flotation waste + underflow of I° classification **P**: II° classification **W**: additional milling	0,08 – 0,17	63,5 – 76,2
		II° Classification	**N**: overflow HC I° classification	0,10 – 0,14	69,9 – 78,0

IOP Conf. Series: Materials Science and Engineering **641** (2019) 012003 doi:10.1088/1757-899X/641/1/012003

			P: rougher flotation **W**: I° classification HC		
		III° Classification	**N**: waste. I scavenger flot. **P**: rougher flotation **W**: additional milling	0,05 – 0,09	64,5 – 67,6
	Polkowice	I° Classification (classifier overflow)	**N**: spiral classifier overflow **P**: rougher flotation **W**: additional milling	0,12 – 0,145	81,5 – 83,9
	Polkowice	II° classification (waste of initial flotation)	**N**: waste initial flotation **P**: rougher flotation **W**: additional milling	0,065 – 0,085	76,7 – 82,2
	Polkowice	III° classification (I scavenger flotation)	**N**: waste scavenger flot. I **P**: rougher flotation **W**: additional milling	0,04	69,5 - 72,4

5. Pilot installation

The pilot installation comprising a hydrocyclone cluster is equipped with a three-product particle size analyzer which enables the feed and classification products particle size distribution to be measured and data to be sent to the IMNCLASS system [5, 6], thus allowing classification process control.
Characteristics of the HC hydrocyclone cluster in the pilot installation (Table 3).

- feed – overflow of spiral classifier;
- overflow – feed for flotation;
- underflow – regrinding in regrinding mill.
- 4-channel cluster 4 x HC500/12°ZAM-IMN;
- operating pressure 0.1 - 0.15 MPa;
- inlet d_O = 100 and 125 mm;
- vortex finder d_p = 200 mm;
- apex d_w = 50 mm.

Table 3. Parameters of pilot hydrocyclone.

	Capacity of HC cluster [m^3/h]	Feed density [g/dm^3]	Required overflow density [g/dm^3]	Required underflow density [g/dm^3]
Range of values	400 – 750	1150 – 1300	1050 – 1120	1600 – 1800
Mean value	575	1225	1085	1700

Figure 2 shows the hydrocyclone cluster location in the flowsheet of ore preparation for flotation.

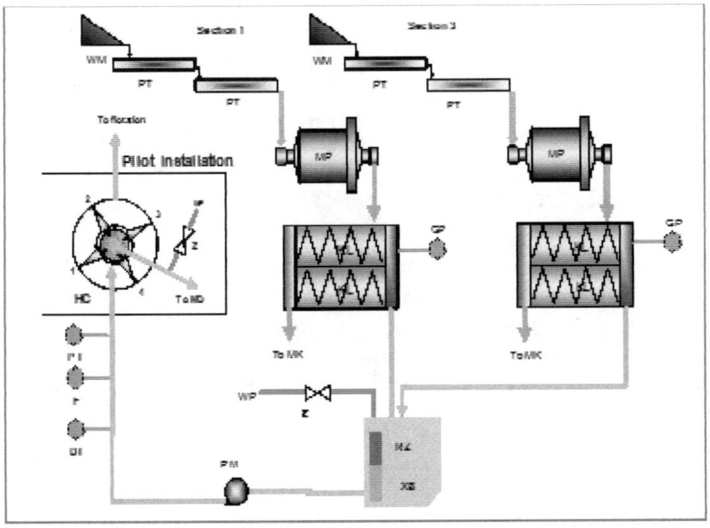

WM	Drawer feeder
PT	Belt conveyor
MP	Rod mill
KL	Spiral classifier
MK	Ball mill
RZ	Sump
PM	Feed pump
HC	Hydrocyclone cluster
Z	Valve
WP	Industrial water
GP	Piezometric densimeter
XB	Sump level
DT	Densimeter
F	Flowmeter
PT	Pressure sensor

Figure 2. Location of the pilot installation, classification assessment and control system.

Figure 3 presents photographs of hydrocyclones installed in KGHM Polska Miedź SA.

Figure 3. Hydrocyclone in pilot installation.

The system is designed to keep the fixed setpoint of (Table 3)

- P80 grain size of hydrocyclone overflow;
- d_{50} cut size of classification;
- total classification efficiency coefficient Ec for P80 grain size of hydrocyclone overflow.

Dependence of technological indicators of the separation process in the hydrocyclone on its design parameters and properties of the feed is shown in Table 4.

Table 4. Denotations of the preset essential operating parameters for the IMNCLASS system.

d_{50}	Regulator of cut size	
	Preset d_{50} Insensibility SP step	Preset d_{50} cut size [mm] Regulator insensibility zone, preset [mm] SP change value of pressure regulator, preset [kPa]
P80	Regulator of P80 grain size of hydrocyclone overflow	
	Preset P80 Insensibility SP step	Preset P80 grain size [mm] Regulator insensibility zone, preset [mm] SP change value of pressure regulator, preset [kPa]
Ec	Regulator of total classification efficiency Ec for P80 grain size	
	Preset Ec Insensibility SP step	Preset value of Ec [%] Regulator insensibility zone, preset [%] SP change value of pressure regulator, preset [kPa]

Table 5. Dependence of technological indicators of the separation process in the hydrocyclone on its design parameters and properties of the feed.

Indicator / Parameter	V_{zn}	V_{zw}	V_{zp}	d_{50}	γ_w	γ_p	α_w	α_p	E_p
D↑	↑	↑	↑	↑	-	-	-	-	-
d_o↑	↑	↑	↑	(↑)	(↓)	(↑)	-	-	-
d_p↑	(↑)	↓	↑	↑	↓	↑	↑	↑	↓
h_p↑	-	-	-	↑	↓	↑	↑	↑	↓↑
d_w↑	-	↑	↓	↓	↑	↓	↓	↓	↓↑

d_w/d_p ↑	-	↑	↓	↓	↑	↓	↓	↓	↓↑
φ ↑	↓	↓	↓	↑	↓	↑	↑	↑	-
p ↑ (V_{zn}=const)	-	-	-	↓	↑	↓	-	-	↓
V_{zn} ↑	-	↑	↑	↑	↓	↑	↑	↑	↑
α_n ↑	-	-	-	↑	↓	↑	↑	↑	↑

where:
d_o [mm]- variable diameter of the overflow nozzle
P [bar];- pressure
P80 – grain size P80 in overflow [mm]
Ec(P80) [%]- total classification efficiency for P80
V_{zn} V_{zw} V_{zp} - volume discharge of overflow, underflow and feed [%]
$\gamma_{w,}$ γ_p - mass yield of overflow, underflow and feed [%]
$\alpha_{w,}$ α_p – density of overflow, underflow and feed [g/dm^3].

Data gathered by the IMNCLASS recording, computing and control system were used for developing the industrial classification process control models [7,8]. Data were selected and gradated as averages from periods of stable plant operation and stable feed (d_{80} grain size variability did not exceed ±15%). The process data for verification were sorted in ascending order by hydrocyclone inlet pressure and presented in Table 6.

IOP Conf. Series: Materials Science and Engineering **641** (2019) 012003 doi:10.1088/1757-899X/641/1/012003

Table 6. Process data.

p [kPa]	**d_{50}** [mm]	**P80** [mm]	**Ec** [%]
80	0.1454	0.0842	85.7
95	0.1574	0.0849	87.6
105	0.1555	0.0833	87.8
110	0.1564	0.0979	84.7
115	0.1684	0.0928	87.2
120	0.1916	0.0989	85.2
125	0.1617	0.0902	86.6
135	0.1689	0.0964	88.8
145	0.2000	0.0994	87.4
150	0.2307	0.1221	86.4

An important aspect of verification of the control system based on the developed models is the continuous analysis of the technological parameters of the classification, e.g. d_{50} split grain, EC (P80) [%] or P80 grain in hydrocyclone transfer.

6.1 Data analysis

The results obtained from ongoing production, i.e. data matrixes gathered and computed by the IMNCLASS recording [4], computing and control system, and data derived from models are the basis of the analysis for the classification system under investigation. To verify and enable the proper assessment of the process data obtained in the actual industrial conditions at a selected classification point, the process (industrial) data were compared with those derived from models. There are presented below examples of the calculations of d_{50} cut size and P80 grain size of hydrocyclone overflow based on linear and polynomial models and based on data obtained by the IMNCLASS control system.

Model 1

d_{50} as a function of *p*; linear model.

d_{50} cut size of hydrocyclone classification depending on feed pressure (for d_O 125 mm inlet).

$$d_{50} = 0.00099p - 0.056R^2 = 68.16[\%]$$

Model 2

d_{50} as a function of *p*; polynomial model.

d_{50} cut size of hydrocyclone classification depending on feed pressure (for d_O 125 mm inlet).

$$d_{50} = 0.000016p^2 - 0.0027p + 0.266R^2 = 76.78[\%]$$

The variability of d_{50} obtained by the IMNCLASS system and derived from models is presented in Figure 4.

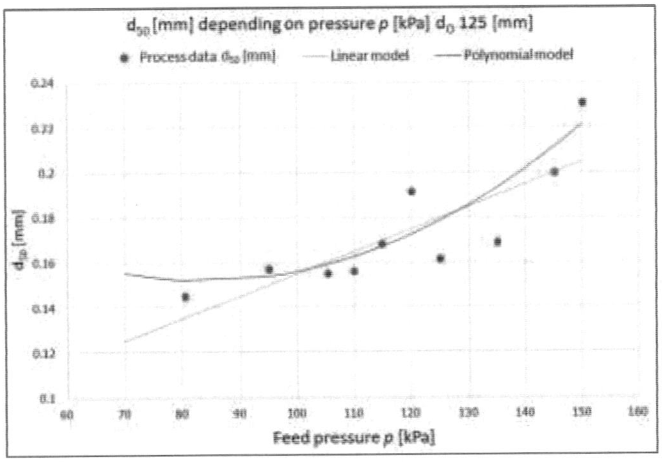

Figure 4. Variability of $d_{50}(p)$ and models 1 and 2 (linear and polynomial).

7. Summary

The studies carried out indicate that it is possible to use the IMNCLASS system for optimising the hydrocyclone classification process. It allows hydrocyclone operation control based on parameters directly connected with feed and classification products. Hydrocyclone operation is characterised by overall hydrocyclone capacity and quantitative product separation in the hydrocyclone. The mentioned parameters depend on hydrocyclone design as well as on the properties of the ore which is being processed. The developed IMNCLASS hydrocyclone classification process control system can be used effectively for assessing this process and as a control system tool. The interrelationships between all physical and process parameters of hydrocyclone operation should be considered. It is of utmost importance when choosing a hydrocyclone for a specified task at the design concept stage and also for adjusting its operation in real-life conditions. Quality improvement and classification technology stability should also have an important effect on circulation changes of product streams directed to further processing and on the results of the operations performed, including finished products. The enrichment process is conducted by a number of machines and devices that do not guarantee the stability of enrichment final indexes despite the advanced control and monitoring technologies used. The specificity of enriched ore results in process variability to which the parameters of individual process operations should be adjusted, and classification optimization is an important action in this field.

References

[1] Trybalski K 2009 *Kontrola, modelowanie i optymalizacja procesów technologicznych przeróbki rud*, AGH University of Science and Technology Press, Kraków

[2] Tumidajski T, Foszcz D, Jamróz D, Niedoba T and Saramak D 2009 *Niestandardowe metody statystyczne i obliczeniowe w opisie procesów przeróbki surowców mineralnych*, IGSMiE PAN Publishing House, Kraków

[3] Nowak Z 1970 Klasyfikacja hydrauliczna w obiegu wodno-mułowym i technologiczne kryterium jej stosowania, Górnictwo 43, Silesian University of Technology, *Zeszyt Naukowy* **288**, Gliwice

[4] Szczerba E, Wieniewski A, Łuczak R, Mańka A and Zachariasz T 2013 Badania innowacyjnego układu klasyfikacji w hydrocyklonach klasyfikująco-zagęszczających w technologii wzbogacania rud miedzi, *IMN Report No 7155/13*, Gliwice

[5] Woch M and Tomaka W 2013 Opracowanie systemu sterowania pracą baterii hydrocyklonów, *IMN Report No 7210/13*, Gliwice

[6] Wieniewski A and Myczkowski Z 2017 Achievements and Participation in the Development of

Mineral Processing and Waste Utilization of the Institute of Non-Ferrous Metals in Gliwice, *Inżynieria Mineralna – Journal of the Polish Mineral Engineering Society, No 2(40), pp. 15-24*

[7] Krawczykowski D 2017 Application of Diffraction Laser Analysis to Monitor Granulation of Copper Ores Processing Products, *Inżynieria Mineralna – Journal of the Polish Mineral Engineering Society, No 1(39), pp. 233–240.*

[8] Niedoba T, Tumidajski T and Surowiak A 2016 Mathematical models of hydrocyclone performance in various copper ores preparation circuits, E3S Web of Conferences, Vol. 8 art. No. 01028, pp. 1–8., https://goo.gl/23FUE4 [2019-07-06]

Acknowledgements

This work was supported by NCBiR - Polish National Centre for Research and Development and KGHM Polska Miedź SA - under CuBR a joint initiative of NCBR and KGHM on the development and implementation of innovative equipment, materials, products and technologies in order to increase the competitiveness of Polish non-ferrous metals industry as a part of the project OPTICLASS Optimization of classification systems in hydrocyclones in Polish copper ore beneficiation (in Polish: Optymalizacja układów klasyfikacji w hydrocyklonach w procesie wzbogacania polskich rud miedzi).

Improving the quality of hard coal products using the state-of-the-art KOMAG solutions in a pulsating jig nod

D Kowol and P Matusiak
Institute of Mining Technology, Division of Preparation Systems, 37 Pszczyńska Street, 44-100 Gliwice, Poland

E-mail: dkowol@komag.eu, pmatusiak@komag.eu

Abstract. Hard coal run-of-mine contains a significant amount of waste rock, which must be removed to improve the quality of the extracted raw material. Coal processing is an integral and extremely important part of the production of commercial assortments. Water pulsating jig is one of the basic devices in which the material is separated. The article presents some possibilities of improving the qualitative and quantitative parameters of the beneficiation products due to design changes and control of the jig beneficiation node.

1. Introduction

A proper operation of the jig beneficiation node depends on many factors, but to a large extent it depends on proper selection of cooperating devices. Improperly selected devices result in ineffective work and, consequently, in a limitation of the ability to obtain the desired parameters of the final products, such as losses of combustible substance in the waste product, ash content and a content of harmful sulphur compounds in the concentrate [1].

There are many methods for obtaining the proper quality and quantitative parameters of the products beneficiated in pulsating jigs. Even a distribution of the feed on the surface of the jig feeding device is an important factor that affects the correctness of a beneficiation process in the pulsating jig. Another important factor is a proper selection and operation at correctness of the beneficiated products collecting device. An adjustment of bucket conveyor's output to the instantaneous load of the dewatered material is an important element of the proper operation of the jig beneficiation node. Operational parameters of the screen deck are the factors having an impact on the water pulsation parameters, and thus the efficiency of the feed separation.

A presentation of a possibility of increasing the jig beneficiation node effectiveness in the scope of technology, design and a control system is the article objective.

2. Feeding the material to the jig

A uniform feed of the material to the water pulsating jig is one of the basic requirements of the beneficiation process. Some disturbances at this stage cause non-uniform loading of the working surface, which results in an decrease of the feed material separation efficiency.

Such conclusions were confirmed by the laboratory tests carried out on the experimental jig at KOMAG. An impact of non-uniform input of the fed material to the jig on the separation efficiency was tested and analysed by changing the feed within granulations 16 – 3 mm as regards its quality and quantity [2,3]. A change in the feed qualitative parameters was obtained by separation of 16 - 3 mm fraction on the 8 mm screen. Thus, it was possible to feed 16 – 8 mm and 8 – 3 mm fractions separately to the working chamber on the left and right side with a uniform output (Test 1). Non-uniform flow of the feed was obtained by its one-sided introduction to the jig working chamber (Test 2). The test results in a form of beneficiation indexes, shown in Fig. 1, indicate that improper preparation of the feed causes a change of beneficiated products parameters.

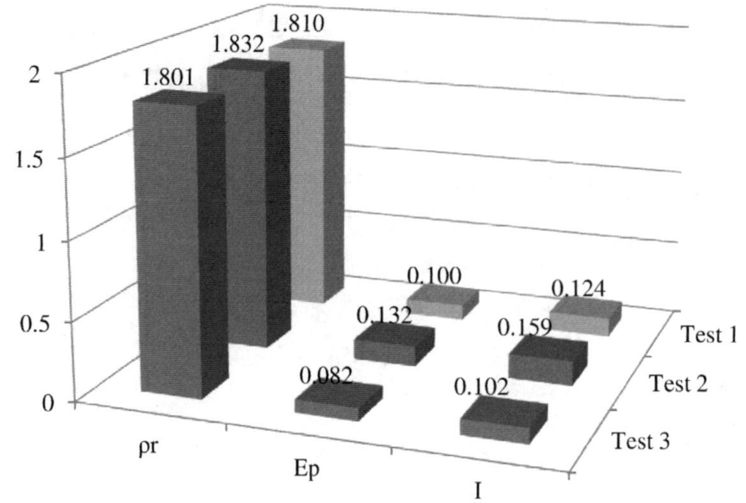

Figure 1 Impact of differentiation of feed on the jig inlet on the separation efficiency [3].

The tests showed that both a non-uniform in-put of the feed on the inlet width (Test 2) as well as quality non-uniformity (Test 1) significantly reduce the efficiency of the beneficiation process in relation to feed in-put (Test 3).

In the case of improper feed in-put, the probability of unplanned production breaks increases due to an excessive accumulation of material which makes its displacement difficult.

The highest efficiency in material distribution is obtained when using the vibrating devices of the width similar to the width of the jig working bed at the same direction as the feed movement.

Feeders and vibrating screens are the most commonly used devices for feeding the material to jigs. When the directions of material feeding and its moving are the same, the vibrating motion allows distribution and obtaining an input layer of similar height and transportation speed. However, a uniform supply of feeders and vibrating screens with raw coal is required.

A non-uniform distribution of the material along the screen width can be caused by feeding the material at the right angle to the longitudinal screen axis. In this case, despite using the additional guiding components on the transfer chute, the material is not averaged along the screen working surface. A non-uniform distribution of the feed on the screen results in its non-uniformity on the feeding chute of the jig trough.

Use of vibrating feeders with a material distribution function is one of the possibilities enabling to improve the quality of the material feed on the width of the devices in the jig beneficiation node. Feeders of this type (Fig. 2) allow to reduce the length of the feeding devices.

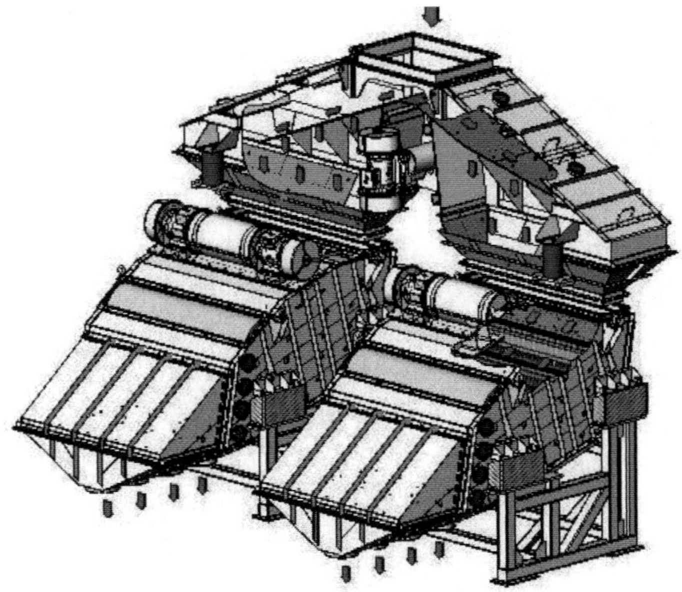

Figure 2 Cross-section of vibrating separator with the central feed and double outlet [1].

3. Solutions of systems for collecting beneficiation process products

Different methods of discharging the heavy fractions from the jig trough surface are used in the design solutions of the systems collecting the bottom product from pulsating jigs. They mainly result from the grain sizes of the feed as well as design assumptions in the aspect of the separation process control or expected load [4].

In the OM fine coal jigs, designed for a beneficiation of the material of grain size distribution 20(30)–0.5(0) mm, feedthrough pipes or sliding bolt pipes are used (Fig. 3). A collecting trough, due to which the material layer is increased over the collecting slot, which is the common feature of these solutions.

The feedthrough pipe is equipped with screens inclined symmetrically towards the collecting trough of rectangular cross-section. A pipe (or angle bar) suspended on moving strings is a component for controlling the degree of feedthrough opening. The bottom product is discharged from the collecting trough through two parallel slots, which can be extended by lowering the pipe (or angle bar) position.

Such a volume control of the discharged material enables to maintain its constant height in the collecting trough. The above mentioned solution is advantageous regarding a stabilization of water pulsating stream flowrate in the products collection zone as well as an accuracy of layer density measurements. Pulsation parameters dependence on a degree of feedthrough slot opening is a disadvantage of this solution [1,5].

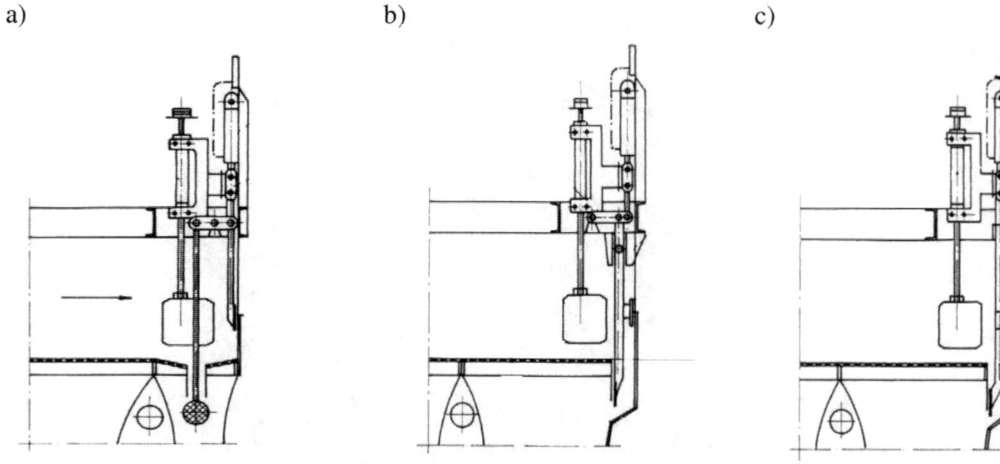

Figure 3 Product feedthroughs in KOMAG coal fines jigs [1,5,6]:
a) pipe, b) lever sliding bolt, c) rectilinear sliding bolt.

A vertical sliding bolt, making the slot opening, is an actuating component in the bottom product collecting system, in which sliding bolt feedthroughs are used. Sliding bolt feedthroughs can be divided into lever ones and straight ones. In the first one a rotation of some system components occurs, whereas in the other one it is a rectilinear movement [1,5,6].

In the OZ grain jigs - (or OS medium-size grain jigs) a collection of the bottom product from beneficiation of coal feeds of grain size distribution 120-20 mm (or 70-0.5 mm) is most often realized with use of key feedthroughs (Fig. 4).

In the above mentioned solution, without the collecting trough, the heavy fraction grains are discharged through a slot placed on the level close to the screen deck surface. The slot appears in the result of simultaneous lifting of the moving threshold equipped with articulating keys and lowering the flap being the screen deck extension. The feedthrough flaps are perforated to ensure pulsating stream flow in the near-the-threshold area and to reduce its flow rate in the collecting slot during the material discharge [1,5].

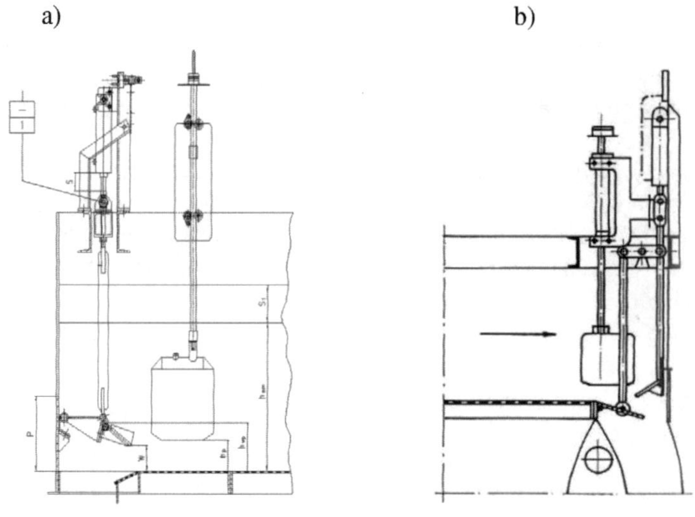

Figure 4 Key feedthroughs for products separated in KOMAG grain jigs (a)
and medium-size grains jigs (b) [1,5,6].

KOMAG continuously develops designs of jigs and their assemblies. Basing on analyses of operational effectiveness of the solutions used in KOMAG jigs, new designs of the bottom products collecting system were developed both for medium-size grain jigs and coal fines jigs.

In a development of the concept for waste fraction collecting system (Fig. 5a) it was assumed that the system will enable oscillating changes in the collecting slot opening. In the case of the same frequency of its operation as the frequency of water pulsation it can be used for controlling an intensity of water flow through a feedthrough slot to ensure a stable discharge of grains irrespective of their amount. In this solution the floating layer measuring sensor system was mechanically separated from the mechanisms controlling the feedthrough.

In the design solution of the products collecting system intended for medium-size grains, a separation of the bottom product collecting trough from the jig boxes, supplied by pulsating chambers is suggested (Fig. 5b). The screen part of the collecting system situated at the feed in-put side is separated from the jig collecting trough. A supply of this part is realized by a separate pulsating chamber having its own system for controlling the flow of pulsating air and bottom water inflow. The above-mentioned control system is coupled with the controller of the collecting system. Similarly as in the case of the solution for a coal fines jig, the layer floating sensor measuring system is mechanically separated from the feedthrough control components [1,7].

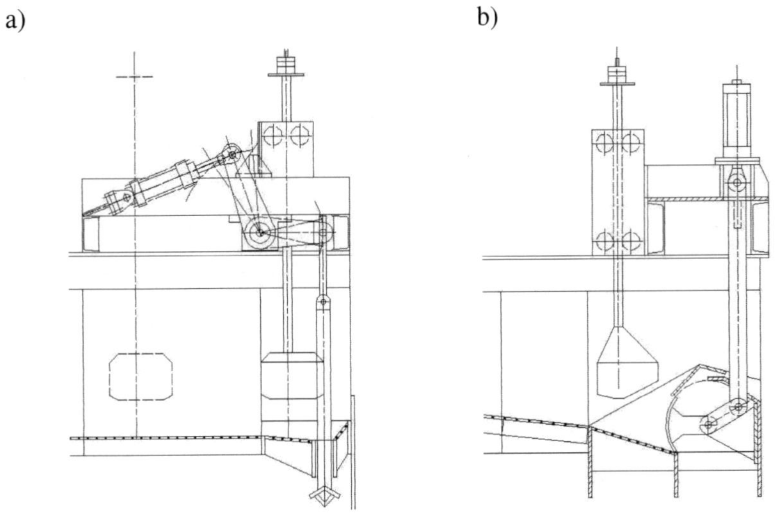

Figure 5 New solutions of the products feedthrough for (a) coal fines jigs and (b) medium-size grains jigs of KOMAG type [7].

4. Control of bucket conveyors

The KOMAG pulsating jigs are equipped with the author's KOGASTER SSWO system for controlling the jig nod. The system for controlling the speed of bucket conveyors, which dewater jig bottom products, is the most important component of this system.

A changeable load of bucket conveyors operating in the jig nod, resulting from changes in jig feeding rate, a change in density distribution of beneficiated material or in the result of operator's intervention, is a characteristic feature of their operation. In this case, a speed of the conveyor should be adapted to the load change to prevent against an excessive accumulation of the material in the conveyor discharge zone.

Use of information from the sensors about jig filling degree, feed stream flowrate as well as weight of the feeding belt and feedthroughs opening degree enables to change the rotational speed of the motor driving the conveyor using the frequency converter. Additionally, the frequency converter informs about the current load of the bucket conveyor [8].

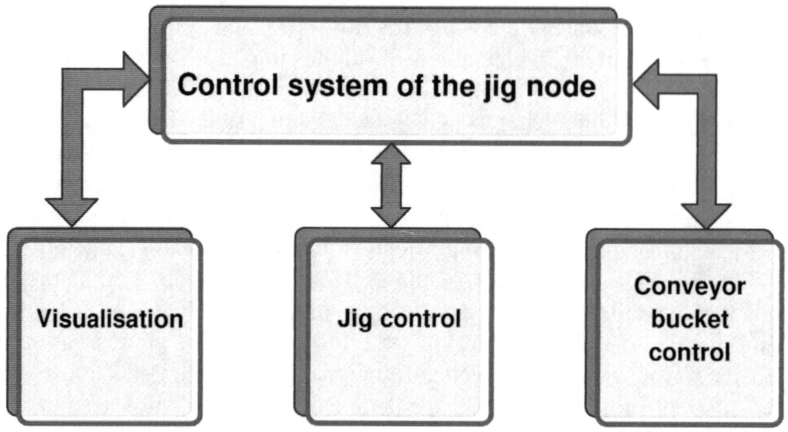

Figure 6 Diagram of the bucket conveyor control system.

Such a system enables exceeding the nominal conveyor output by about 20%, in the case of the nod overloading. The instantaneous increase of the conveyor output enables a quicker discharge of the heavy product from the jig.

In the case, when the amount of the bottom product is less than nominal, it is possible to reduce the conveyor speed, at the same time increasing the conveyor life time (Table 1).

Table 1. Impact of bucket conveyor load on power demand and energy saving [1].

Item	Degree of a bucket filling [%]	Percent of rated power [%]	Energy saving in relation to the rated power [%]
1	0	53.5	46.5
2	20	62.6	37.4
3	40	71.8	28.2
4	60	80.6	19.4
5	80	90.0	10.0
6	100	100.0	0.0

5. Screen deck parameters

Screen decks of pulsating jigs can be one of the controlling components, which support the systems controlling the compressed air and bottom water inflow during a generation of pulsating motion [9,10]. The clearance between screen decks is one of the most important parameters.

The laboratory tests, carried out at the KOMAG Institute of Mining Technology on the experimental jig stand, have shown a significant impact of the screen deck clearance on the separation efficiency of the beneficiated material density fractions. The test results proved that use of screen decks of big clearance enables a more efficient separation of lightweight grains of the concentrate fraction of density <1.5 g/cm^3 (Table 2). A reduction in screen decks clearance results in an increase of separation effectiveness of hypertrophic grains of density 1.5-1.8 g/cm^3 and simultaneously a reduction of separation effectiveness of the concentrate grains (Table 3). An increase in sizes of screen openings showed the same tendency for the screen decks of the comparable clearance.

Table 2. Share of fraction <1.5 g/cm^3 in the concentrate layer [1,9].

Layer		Openings Ø4 mm		Openings Ø 10 mm	
		Clearance coefficient, %			
		22.8	40.4	22.8	40.4
Share of fraction <1.5 g/cm^3	30 s	92.2	98	98	97.9
	45 s	94	100	98	98
	60 s	96	100	98	100

Table 3. Share of fraction 1.5-1.8 g/cm^3 in the interlayer [1,9].

Layer		Openings Ø4 mm		Openings Ø 10 mm	
		Clearance coefficient, %			
		22.8	40.4	22.8	40.4
Share of fraction 1.5-1.8 g/cm^3	30 s	89.8	80.4	71.4	64.6
	45 s	90	82.1	73.5	64.6
	60 s	90	84.3	70.8	65.3

As it can be seen from the above tables an extension of beneficiation time increases a separation effectiveness of the concentrate fraction and reduces an output of hypertrophic grains. A reduction of separation effectiveness of hypertrophic grains, after an extension of beneficiation time indicates that apart from the grains density separation a dimensional separation also occurs.

The results of laboratory tests on impact of screen deck parameters on water pulsating movement and separation effectiveness of coal feed indicates that a proper selection of screen decks design parameters, adequate for the technological conditions, have a positive impact on shaping the characteristics of water pulsating flow [10]. A pulsation pitch and flowrate of water lifting stream during a single pulsation cycle reduces with an increase of water flow resistance through the screens in the result of a reduction of their clearance and opening sizes [3,4].

The factors which affect selection of screen deck parameters for the specified pulsating jig are the following:

- density and grain composition of the beneficiated material,
- quantity and quality of the beneficiated products,
- capabilities of the air and water flow control systems,
- methods for control of the bottom product discharge system.

During a beneficiation of the coal feed of grain sizes in class 20-0.5 mm, under water pulsating movement, a part of heavy fraction grains of small sizes is discharged from the working surface through the screen deck openings. This process, which could be used to increase a separation accuracy of coal feed in a wide spectrum of size classes is not controlled at present.

Changing the volume of compressed air fed to the pulsating chambers in relation to the pressure measured in the under-the-screen part of the jig, is one of the possibilities for controlling a volume of the product discharged through the screen openings. A pressure increase in the above mentioned part of the jig due to a thickness increase of heavy fraction grains layer deposited on the screen surface, after exceeding the set value, will cause a periodical, simultaneous and interdependent increase of water pulsating movement rate and of an amount of discharged heavy product [11,12].

6. Conclusions

Beneficiation efficiency in pulsating jigs depends on many factors in the scope of technological and design solutions as well as control system.

To produce commercial products of the required qualitative and quantitative parameters, a pulsating jig requires among others a uniform input of feed and working media (air, water) as well as a precise control of collecting the separation products.

The suggestions of new design solutions or control possibilities of operational parameters in the jig nod, described in the article, are only a part of the issues aimed at reaching a high beneficiation process efficiency.

KOMAG research projects, realized in collaboration with other scientific organizations, universities and manufacturers and especially with end-users enable a continuous development of jigs as well as an implementation of innovative technological and design solutions.

7. References

[1] Matusiak P and Kowol D 2012 Possibilities of improvement of qualitative and quantitative parameters of products in a jig beneficiation system (Możliwości poprawy parametrów jakościowych i ilościowych produktów w węźle wzbogacania osadzarkowego). KOMEKO 2012 *Innovatve and environmentally friendly techniques and technologies of minerals processing. Safety – Quality – Effectiveness* KOMAG Institute of Mining Technology, pp 115-124

[2] Kowol D and Łagódka M 2012 Impact of quantitative and qualitative differentiation of feed on effectiveness of jig beneficiation process *Gór. Geoinż.* **4** pp 49-56

[3] Kowol D and Matusiak P 2017 Impact of the selected parameters on effectiveness of beneficiation process in water pulsating jigs (Wpływ wybranych parametrów na skuteczność procesu wzbogacania w osadzarkach wodnych pulsacyjnych), *Materiały na konferencję: IV Polish Mining Congress* Kraków 20-22.11.2017 pp 620-629

[4] Matusiak P, Kowol D, Jędo A 2011 Advance in design and technology of hard coal and other minerals separation pulsating jigs (Rozwój konstrukcji i technologii w osadzarkach pulsacyjnych typu KOMAG do wzbogacania węgla kamiennego i innych surowców mineralnych), KOMEKO 2011 Innovative and environmentally friendly techniques and technologies of minerals processing. Safety – Quality – Effectiveness, KOMAG Institute of Mining Technology pp 73-86

[5] Kowol D, Lenartowicz M, Łagódka M 2009 Design solutions of the systems for collection of bottom product in the pulsating jigs (Rozwiązania konstrukcyjne układów odprowadzania produktu dolnego w osadzarkach pulsacyjnych), KOMEKO 2009 *Innovative and environmentally friendly techniques and technologies of minerals processing. Safety – Quality – Effectiveness* KOMAG Institute of Mining Technology pp 225-236

[6] Osoba M and Jędo A 2000 Impact of jigs modernization on qualitative parameters of the beneficiation process (Wpływ modernizacji osadzarek na uzyskiwane parametry jakościowe produktów wzbogacania), KOMEKO 2000 *Produkcja surowców mineralnych z uwzględnieniem problemów ochrony środowiska* Międzynarodowa Konferencja Naukowo-Techniczna XIII pp 1-7

[7] Lenartowicz M, Matusiak P, Jędo A, Kowol D 2010 Development of KOMAG pulsatory jigs (Rozwój osadzarek pulsacyjnych typu KOMAG) *Maszyny Górnicze* **28**(**3-4**) pp 126-132

[8] Jendrysik S, Stankiewicz K, Jasiulek D 2018 KOMAG Innovative solutions in the jig node automation proces (Innowacyjne rozwiązania ITG KOMAG w zakresie automatyzacji węzłów osadzarkowych) *Maszyny Górnicze* **154(2)** pp 65-77

[9] Kowol D, Lenartowicz M, Łagódka M 2010 Laboratory tests of impact of parameters of screen deck on distribution of material in pulsatory jig depending on feed characteristics (Badania laboratoryjne wpływu parametrów pokładu sitowego na rozdział materiału w osadzarce pulsacyjnej w zależności od charakterystyki nadawy) *Maszyny Górnicze* **28**(**1**) pp 35-38

[10] Lenartowicz M, Kowol D, Łagódka M, Matusiak P 2009 Laboratory tests on the impact of screen parameters on the characteristics of pulsatory movement of water in a pulsatory jig (Badania laboratoryjne wpływu parametrów pokładu sitowego na charakterystykę ruchu pulsacyjnego wody w osadzarce pulsacyjnej), *Gór. Geoinż.* AGH **33 (4)** pp 169-175

11] Matusiak P, Łagódka M, Kowol D 2013 Testing the parameters of heavy products discharging process in the pulsating jig (Badania parametrów procesu odprowadzania produktów ciężkich w osadzarce pulsacyjnej) KOMEKO *2013 Innovative and environmentally friendly techniques and technologies of minerals processing. Safety – Quality – Effectiveness* KOMAG Institute of Mining Technology pp 299-310

[12] Kowol D, Matusiak P, Łagódka M 2018 Possibility of increasing the effectiveness of coking coal fines production by increasing separation efficiency in secondary beneficiation of middlings in a pulsating jig (Możliwości zwiększenia efektywności procesu produkcji miałów węgli koksowych poprzez wzrost dokładności wtórnego wzbogacania półproduktu w osadzarce pulsacyjnej) *Maszyny* Górnicze **154(2)** pp 53-64

IOP Conf. Series: Materials Science and Engineering **641** (2019) 012005 doi:10.1088/1757-899X/641/1/012005

Investigation of flotation of salts in their saturated solutions

M Dubiel and T Ratajczak

Wroclaw University of Science and Technology, Faculty of Geoengineering, Mining and Geology, Wybrzeze Wyspianskiego 27, 50-370 Wroclaw, Poland

E-mail: tomasz.ratajczak@pwr.edu.pl

Abstract. Flotation of NaCl, KCl and KPF_6 in saturated aqueous solutions was investigated. The tests were carried out for salt particle sizes of >200, 100-200, 71-100 and <71μm. Flotation tests were performed in a Hallimond flotation cell. In addition, contact angle was estimated using a flotometric method and measured by the sessile drop technique. The angles were 5 degree for NaCl and KCl and 8 degrees for KPF_6. Thus, there was mostly mechanical carryover of particles during the flotation test. However, an increase in the flotation yield of the tested salts with the increase of contact angle was observed.

1. Introduction

The aim of the research was to check the possible natural floatability of selected salts in their saturated aqueous solutions, i.e. to study salt flotation of salt. Commonly salt flotation studies concern flotation of minerals in aqueous salt solutions of various concentrations. As is known that, for substances that are naturally hydrophobic, salt flotation can be used in which there is no need for collecting reagents. Many researchers showed that salt influences the flotation of naturally hydrophobic particles [1]. There are works showing deterioration of salt flotation, especially at salts concentrations below 0.1 M [2-5]. This phenomenon is probably due to the increase in the surface charge of the particles, resulting in a decrease of the interfacial energy at the solid boundary and the aqueous solution of the salt. The decrease of this energy is responsible for reducing the contact angle and thus the deterioration of the floatation. There is usually improvement of the salt flotation at higher salt concentrations [4-9]. This is due to the surface tension of the aqueous solution. The improvement is observed for salts which surface energy is higher than the surface tension of water [1].

Recently, numerous studies on salt flotation were carried out on copper-bearing shale [10-13]. It results from the paper of Kurkiewicz and Ratajczak [14], that the hydrophobicity of copper-bearing shale increases with the concentration of NaCl in the aqueous solution. Smólska and Ratajczak [15] stated that the yield of copper-bearing shale flotation increases along with the surface tension of the aqueous salt solution. Puklińska and Ratajczak [16] confirmed the influence of salt type and concentration on salt flotation of copper-bearing shale. Salt flotation tests were also conducted by Skowrońska and Drzymała [17], who found that the surface tension for the tested concentrations did not affect shale flotation. Bajek and Ratajczak [18] showed that the higher the concentration of salt, the better the flotation. Also, in the paper by Papmel and Ratajczak [19], it was found that along with the increase in the concentration of KCl salt, the yield in the copper-bearing shale concentrate is increasing.

2. Materials and methods

Flotation tests were carried out using NaCl, KCl and KPF_6 having particle size >200, 100-200, 71-100 and <71 µm. Particle fractions of the tested substances were obtained using a laboratory ceramic mortar and a set of sieves with mesh sizes of 200, 100 and 71 µm. Directly before the flotation process, each sample was wetted for 2 minutes with a saturated solution of a given salt and subjected to flotation in a Hallimond cell, which volume was 220 cm^3 and height 36 cm.

Saturated solutions of salts (NaCl, KCl, KPF_6) were prepared on the basis of solubility data [20-25] and experimental testing of the amount of salt dissolved (Table 1). Each of the three solutions was made by dissolving the given amount of salt in 220 cm^3 of distilled water and mixing with a magnetic stirrer for 5 minutes at 500 rpm. The tests were carried out at room temperature 25°C.

Table 1. Concentration of saturated salts solution.

Property	NaCl	KCl	KPF_6
salt weight needed to prepare a saturated solution, g	68.48	61.37	20.46
concentration of saturated solution, M	5.32	3.74	0.50

For the carried out flotation test, the amount of salt representing 100% yield depended on size of particles and is given in Table 2.

Table 2. Weight of salt sample in flotation tests.

Size of particles, µm	NaCl, g	KCl, g	KPF_6, g
>200	2.55	2.16	2.81
100-200	2.38	2.03	2.44
71-100	1.99	1.41	1.78
<71	1.22	1.28	1.41

Flotation was carried out with an air flow of 2.5 dm^3/h. Flotation time was up to 30 min. When the yield was constant for a long period of time, then the test was terminated.

3. Results and discussion

Flotation kinetics

Figures 2 (a-c) show flotation kinetics of NaCl, KCl and KPF_6 in their saturated solutions. The solid line illustrates the approximation of the obtained results with the first order kinetic curve equation (1) [26-28]:

$$\gamma = \gamma_{max}(1 - \exp(-kt)), \quad (1)$$

where:

γ – yield,%,
γ_{max} - maximum yield,%
k – first order flotation rate constant, 1/min,
t - time of flotation test, min.

The values of k, γ_{max} and correlation coefficient R^2 are given in Table 3.

Table 3. Values of k, γ_{max} and R^2 of salt flotation test kinetics.

size of particles, µm	NaCl			KCl			KPF_6		
	k, min^{-1}	γ_{max}, %	R^2, -	k, min^{-1}	γ_{max}, %	R^2, -	k, min^{-1}	γ_{max}, %	R^2, -
>200	0.0010	0	1	0.0914	1	0.8086	0.1044	20	0.9732
100-200	0.1034	32	0.9901	0.1088	43	0.9891	0.1116	46	0.9718
71-100	0.1035	67	0.9814	0.1052	83	0.9760	0.1810	100	0.9977
<71	0.1023	67	0.9851	0.1319	80	0.9144	0.1594	98	0.9940

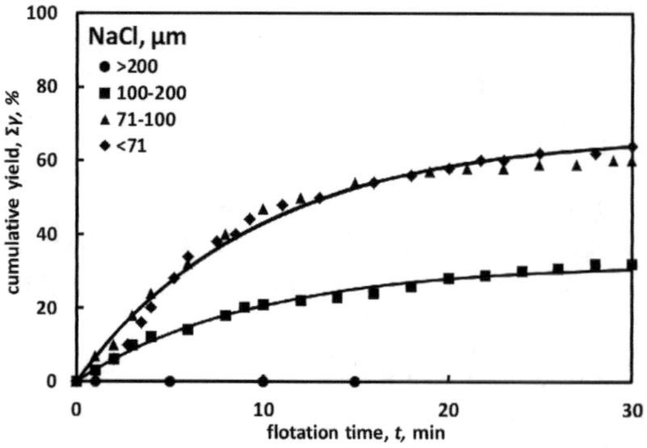

(a)

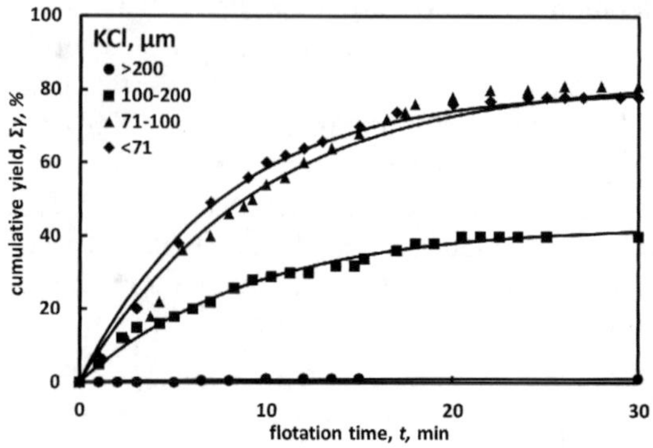

(b)

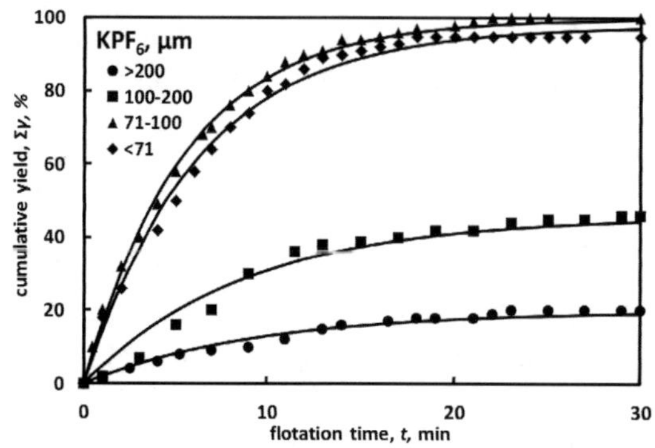

(c)

Figure 1. Kinetics of salt flotation of: a) NaCl, b) KCl, c) KPF_6 in their saturated solutions, depending on particle size.

Figures 1 (a-c) show that the flotation yields of the tested salts are the highest for particle classes below 100 µm. In the case of NaCl (Fig. 1a), the yield for particle size fractions 0-71 µm and 71-100 µm is very similar. The largest observed yield was 67%. For the NaCl particles greater than 200 µm, there was no yield. The yield was constant after about 15 minutes from the start. In the case of KCl (Fig. 1b), the highest yield was obtained for the particle size below 100 µm at the level of 83%. As in the case of NaCl, for KCl with a particle size above 200 µm there was no yield. However, for KPF_6 (Fig. 1c) 100% the yield for the 71-100 µm size fraction was obtained after 21 minutes. Slightly smaller, 98% yield, was obtained for 0-71µm particles. For >200 µm KPF_6 particles the yield was 20%. The highest yield for each particle size fraction was for KPF_6, followed by KCl and NaCl, as shown in Figure 2.

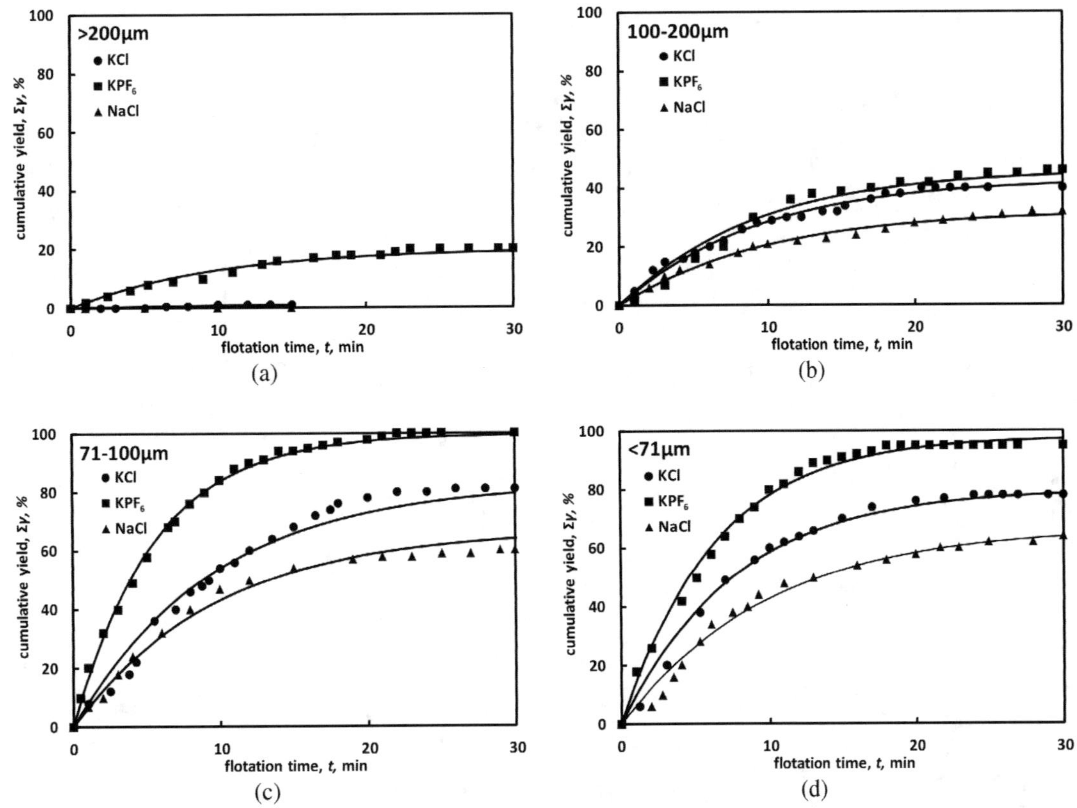

Figure 2. Influence of salt type (NaCl, KCl, KPF_6) on yield in flotation tests in individual particle fractions a) >200 μm, b) 100-200 μm, c) 71-100 μm, d) <71 μm.

Contact angle

The contact angle of the tested salts was determined by the sessile drop and flotometric methods. In case of the first method, bases on placing a drop of saturated salt solution on the surface of the compressed test salt, it was observed that the drop spilled over the entire surface of the prepared salt pellet. It was assumed that the contact angle for each salt tested was near zero or zero degrees, which is also confirmed by the work of Drzymała [28] for NaCl.

Assuming that the observed yields were caused by flotation, not entrainment, the contact angle of the studied salts was determined by using the so-called equation flotometric theory [29, 30]:

$$r_{max} = \left(\frac{3\alpha}{2g(\rho_s - \rho_w)}\right)^{0.5} \cdot sin\left(\frac{\theta}{2}\right), \tag{2}$$

where:

r_{max} - particle radius ($r_{max} = d_{50}/2$), mm, determined from the separation curve (Fig. 4),
α - surface tension, mN/m,
g - acceleration due to gravity, cm/s^2,
ρ_s - density of substance, g/cm^3,
ρ_w - density of solution, g/cm^3.

The particles r_{max} was determined on the basis of approximation of the maximum cumulative yield from the mean particle ($2r_{max} = d_{50}$) of salt (Figure 3). The resulting values are presented in Table 4.

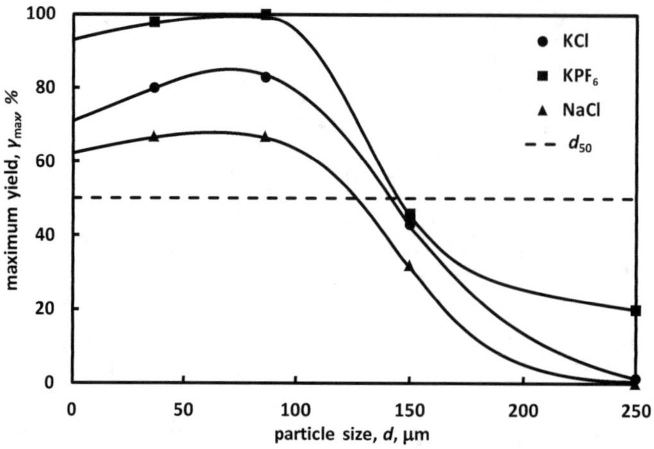

Figure 3. Separation curve of salt.

Table 4. r_{max} values determined form the separation curve (Fig. 4).

Salt	r_{max}, µm
NaCl	62.8
KCl	70.3
KPF_6	72.2

Surface tension values for the saturated salt solutions were determined basing on the literature data (Fig. 4) [1] and were included in Table 5.

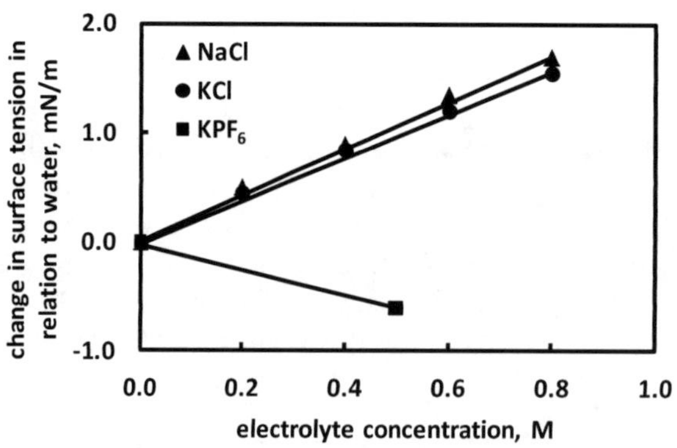

Figure 4. Change in surface tension of the electrolyte solution in relation to water.

Table 5. Surface tension of saturated salt solutions.

Salt solutions	Concentration of solution, M	Surface tension, mN/m
NaCl	5.33	84.11
KCl	3.74	79.99
KPF_6	0.50	72.15

Table 6 shows densities of salts and their aqueous solutions. The densities of salts and solutions were adopted from the Physicochemical Guide [20] and CRC [21], while the density of the saturated solution of KPF_6 was determined using a densymeter (pycnometer).

Table 6. Densities of salts and their saturated solutions.

Salt	Density of salt, g/cm^3	Density of saturated solution, g/cm^3
NaCl	2.16	1.20
KCl	1.98	1.16
KPF_6	2.55	1.10

The resulting values of the contact angle determined with Eq. 2 are shown in Table 7.

Table 7. Contact angle of salts tested.

Salt	Contact angle, Θ,°
NaCl	4.95
KCl	5.24
KPF_6	7.63

The determined contact angles of the tested salts are small, at the level of 5-8°, and confirm great wettability of the surface of these salts. At the same time, the relationship between contact angle (Table 7) and yield of salt (Figure 2) is clearly visible, which is also shown in Figure 5. However, given the very poor hydrophobicity of the salts tested, the increase in flotation can be mostly attributed to the mechanical carryover [31].

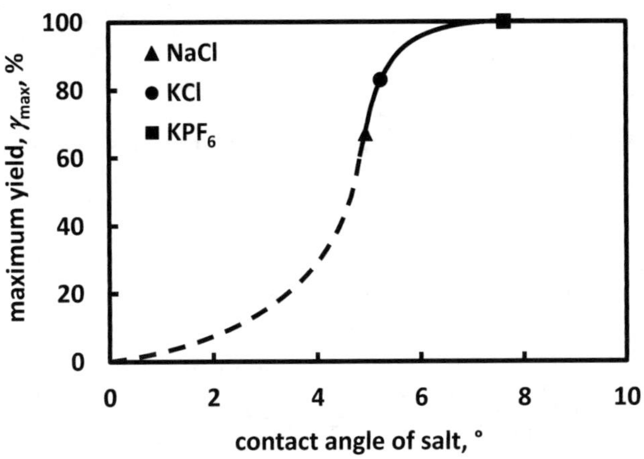

Figure 5. Influence of contact angle on yield flotation salts at particles size 71-100µm.

Comparing the two above methods for determining the contact angle, it can be stated that the flotometric method is much more accurate than the sessile drop. The sessile drop method is an optical procedure that is subject to human error because the human eye is unable to see such small angles.

When investigating the influence of salt density or saturated solutions and the surface tension of salt solutions on yield flotation, one can observe an explicit proportional dependence of salt density and yield (Fig. 6a) as opposed to saturated solution density (Fig. 6b) and surface tension (Fig.6c).

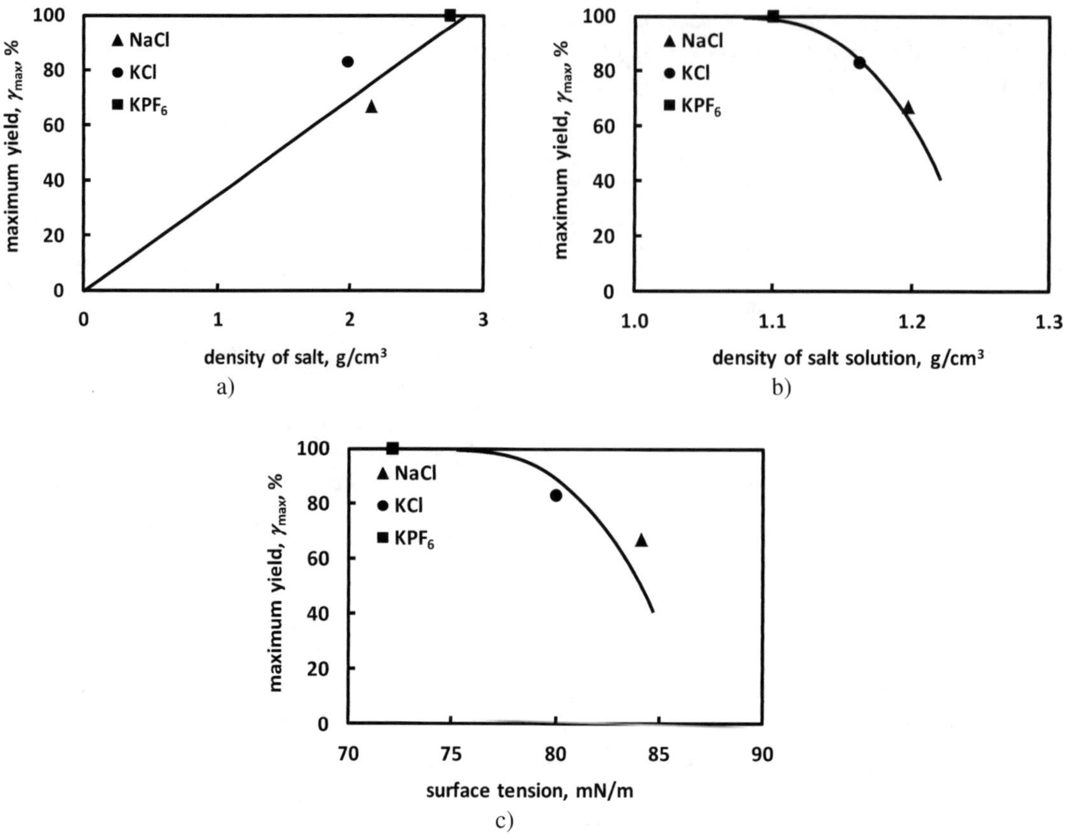

Figure 6. Effect of density of: a) salt and b) saturated solutions; and c) surface tension of salt solutions on yield of salt for 71-100 μm particles size.

Analyzing the results of flotation of the studied salts, it can be seen that the lower concentration of saturated salt solution the higher yields were obtained (Fig. 7). It also resulted in an increase in the process kinetics. KPF_6 salt has the highest kinetics of the process since the value of k is 0.1810 1/min. For comparison, this parameter for KCl is 0.1052 1/min, and for NaCl 0.1035 1/min (Table 3).

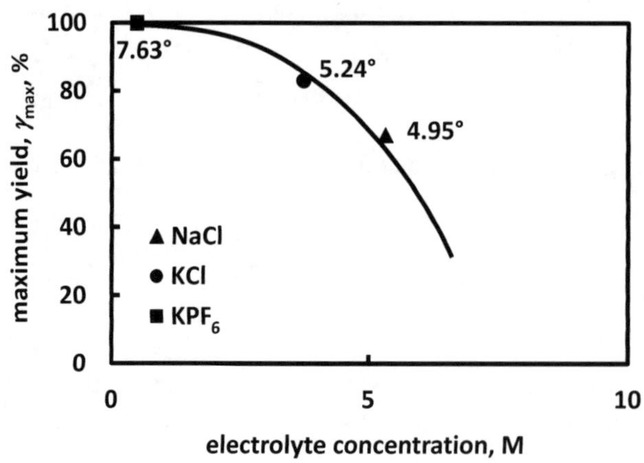

Figure 7. Effect of saturated solution concentrations on salt yield for 71-100 μm size fraction.

It should be added that the reason of differences in flotation of the investigates salts was not caused by the morphology of the salt particles because they were regular in shape (Fig. 8).

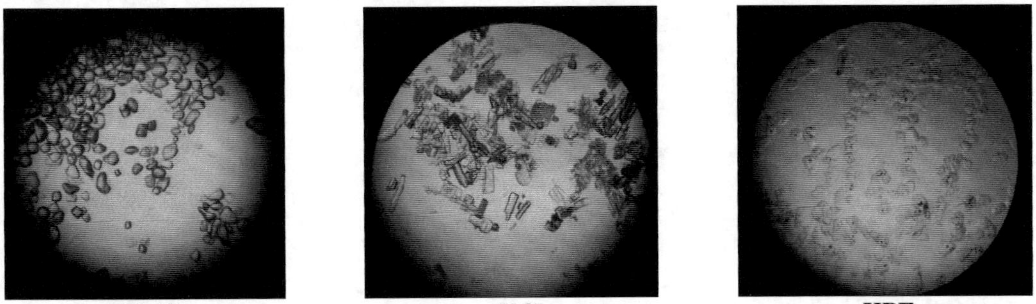

NaCl **KCl** **KPF_6**

Figure 8. Microscopic image of salts (100-200 μm) in their saturated solutions.

4. Conclusions

The work considered the effect of saturated solutions of salts, with different molar concentrations, on flotation kinetics of salts, and also took into account the influence of the size of particles (> 200, 100-200, 71-100, <71μm) on the process kinetics. During the tests, it was found that the kinetics of the process, in addition to the factors mentioned above, is also affected by the salt density, surface tension of the salt and the contact angle. As a result of the research, it was found that:

- NaCl, KCl, KPF_6 are hydrophilic (sessile drop method, Figure 4) or very slightly hydrophobic (5-8°, flotometric method, Table 7), and their flotation is mostly the result of mechanical carryover,
- flotation of salt depends on type of salt, its contact angle, the surface tension of the salt solution and the density and size of the salt particles,
- as the molar concentration of the saline solution increases (Fig. 8), the yield of salt flotation decreases as well as the kinetics of the process. KPF_6 salt having the lowest molar concentration of the solution (0.5M) floated best, while the NaCl, whose molar concentration was over 5M, floated worst,
- larger particles cause much worse entrainment than the smaller ones (Figures 3a-d). Yield was the highest for the 71-100 and <71 μm particles. For KPF_6, 100% of the yield for 71-100 μm particles was achieved (Figure 3c),
- along with the increase in the density of the studied salt, the yield also increased (Fig. 7a), in contrast to the density of the salt solution (Fig. 7b),
- lower surface tension of salt improved salt yield (Fig.7c),
- as the contact angle increased, the yield increased (Fig. 6, 8).

References

[1] Ratajczak T and Drzymała J 2003 *Flotacja solna* (Oficyna Wydawnicza Politechniki Wrocławskiej: Wrocław)
[2] Charłamow W S 1957 *Biuletyn Inst. Mechanobr „Obogaszczenije rud"* **2**, 8, pp 25-30
[3] Li Ch and Somasundaran P 1993 *Energy & Fuels* **7** pp 244-248
[4] Pugh R J, Weissenborn P and Paulson O 1997 *Int. J. Miner. Process.* **51** pp 125-138
[5] Castro S and Laskowski J S 2011 *KONA Powder and Particle Journal*, **29**, 4-15
[6] Kurniawan A U, Ozdemir O, Nguyen A V, Ofori P and Firth B 2011 *International Journal of Mineral Processing* **98** pp 137–144
[7] Laskowski J and Castro S 2015 *International Journal of Mineral Processing* **144** pp 50–55
[8] Lipniarski M, Ratajczak T and Drzymała J, 2015 *III Polski Kongres Górniczy, Mineralurgia i wykorzystanie surowców mineralnych* (WGGG PWr: Wrocław) pp 35–9

[9] Zhang H, 2015 *Physicochem. Probl. Miner. Process.* **51(1)** pp 257–267
[10] Drzymała J and Kowalczuk P B (ed.) 2014 *Łupek miedzionośny* (WGGG PWr: Wrocław)
[11] Kowalczuk P B and Drzymała J (ed.) 2016 *Łupek miedzionośny II*, (WGGG PWr: Wrocław)
[12] Kowalczuk P B and Drzymała J (ed.) 2017 *Łupek miedzionośny III*, (WGGG PWr: Wrocław)
[13] Ratajczak T and Drzymała J (ed.) 2018 *Łupek miedzionośny IV* (WGGG PWr: Wrocław)
[14] Kurkiewicz S and Ratajczak T 2017 *Łupek miedzionośny III* (WGGG PWr: Wrocław) pp 103–109
[15] Smólska M and Ratajczak T 2017 *Łupek miedzionośny III* (WGGG PWr: Wrocław) pp 97–102
[16] Kuklińska M and Ratajczak T 2016 *Łupek miedzionośny II* (WGGG PWr: Wrocław) pp 184–187
[17] Skowrońska A and Drzymała J 2016 *Łupek miedzionośny II* (WGGG PWr: Wrocław) pp 180–183
[18] Bajek K and Ratajczak T 2016 *Łupek miedzionośny II* (WGGG PWr: Wrocław) pp 188–191
[19] Papmel K J and Ratajczak T 2018 *Łupek miedzionośny IV* (WGGG PWr: Wrocław) pp 110–116
[20] Gajewska I, Pietras S, Rudzińska J and Schellenberg A 1974 *Poradnik fizykochemiczny* (WNT: Warszawa) Wyd. II
[21] CRC 1986/87 *Handbook of chemistry and physics, 67th edition* CRC Press Boca Raton USA
[22] Quinn J J, Sovechles J M, Finch J A and Waters K E 2014 *Minerals Engineering* **58** Elsevier Canada
[23] *Safety data sheets KPF_6*, 2016 Sigma-Aldrich (LPK WGGG PWr: Wrocław)
[24] *Safety data sheets KCl* 2017 https://chempur.pl/pliki/karty_charakterystyk/potasu_chlorek.pdf, (29.12.2018r.)
[25] *Safety data sheets NaCl* 2017 http://chempur.pl/pliki/karty_charakterystyk/sodu_chlorek.pdf, (29.12.2018r.)
[26] Brożek M and Młynarczykowska A 2007 *Physicochem. Probl. Miner. Process.* **41**, pp 51-65
[27] Brożek M and Młynarczykowska A 2013 *Physicochem. Probl. Miner. Process.* **49(1)**, pp 341-356
[28] Drzymała J 2009 *Podstawy mineralurgii* (Oficyna Wydawnicza PWr: Wrocław)
[29] Scheludko A, Toshev B V and Bojadjiev D T 1976 *Faraday Trans. I.* **12** pp 2815-2828
[30] Drzymała J 1994 *Int. J. Miner. Process.* **42** pp 153-167
[31] Konopacka Ż 2005 *Flotacja mechaniczna* (Oficyna Wydawnicza Politechniki Wrocławskiej: Wrocław)

Acknowledgements
The work was financed by the Polish Statutory Research Grant

IOP Conf. Series: Materials Science and Engineering **641** (2019) 012006 doi:10.1088/1757-899X/641/1/012006

Evaluation of jig work on the basis of granulometric analysis of particle size fractions of benefication products in purpose of process optimization

A Surowiak, D Foszcz and T Niedoba
AGH University of Science and Technology, Faculty Mining and Geoengineering, Al. Mickiewicza 30, 30-059 Krakow, Poland

E-mail: asur@agh.edu.pl

Abstract. The analysis of hard coal jigging was conducted because of optimal recovery of useful fraction in concentrate and not useful fraction in tailings. The evaluation of the process was conducted on the basis of industrial sampling of coal dust jig and performed granulometric and densimetric analyses of collected products samples in laboratory conditions. In selected size-density fractions of partition products the yields of products were calculated and the amounts of ash and total sulfur were determined. On the basis of the results of granulometric, densimetric and chemical analyses of obtained size-density fractions, balance of partition products and appropriate calculations the beneficiation curves were created which allowed to evaluate the process because of optimization of device work in purpose of achieving higher recovery by possibly highest concentrate quality.
The evaluation of hard coal beneficiation results was done in the paper because of optimal recovery of organic phase in concentrate and mineral components in tailings in aspect of process monitoring. The analysis of obtained characteristics of ability to beneficiation was performed in purpose of selecting optimal technological factors for the needs of optimization of device work.

1. Introduction

The efficiency of beneficiation of mineral raw materials is connected in each case with its susceptibility to beneficiation, so mainly with variation of useful properties of the material being beneficiated in dedicated technological system. This differentiation of properties in aspect of physical, geometrical and other features allows, apart from obvious separation of useful and not useful components, to achieve assumed level of beneficiation which determines economic efficiency of the process. Because of this the necessity of determining optimal beneficiation factors occurs which would make possible to determine the potential ability of material to beneficiation. These actions are necessary in purpose of achieving maximal use of the deposit of certain raw material. Because of the fact that possibly high accumulation of not useful parts in tailings is more and more important the appropriate tools to evaluate efficiency of certain technological process to realize production task are needed to be found [2, 3, 7, 8]. These actions should be concentrated on process optimization in context of changeable parameters of the feed what causes necessity of appropriate process changes adjusting the device work to actual requirements in this range which occur from the characteristics of the feed being directed to beneficiation. This requires detailed analysis of the results of beneficiation process conducted in the device dependably on feed properties allowing to determine optimal work points being appropriate for these changeable properties of the beneficiated product. To analyze efficiency of the partition of the components occurring in raw material the beneficiation curves can be applied, like Fuerstenau curves or Halbich curves which can be used by evaluating the quality of separation products.

The Fuerstenau curve is presented by the relation $\varepsilon_r = f(\varepsilon)$, where

$$\varepsilon = \frac{\alpha-\vartheta}{\beta-\vartheta}\frac{\beta}{\alpha}\cdot 100 \text{ and } \varepsilon_r = \left(100 - \frac{\alpha-\vartheta}{\beta-\vartheta}\cdot 100\right)\frac{100-\vartheta}{100\alpha} \tag{1}$$

It is usually applied by evaluating ores flotation, similarly as Halbich curve which presents relation $\varepsilon = f(\beta)$. Halbich and Fuerstenau curves do not have any extreme points and that is why determination on their basis of extreme beneficiation factors values is impossible.

From the properties of Halbich curve occurs that the characteristic separation point is the point of biggest curvature, marked as point f_H [5]. According to the formula determining the curvature radius it is a point in which second derivative of recovery calculated in accordance to concentrate grade achieves minimal value. According to Kelly and Spottiswood [6] this point can be determined on the basis of maximal value of the parameter $\boldsymbol{f} = \frac{\varepsilon\beta}{100}$ for which the curve tangent to Halbich curve is obtained. For Fuerstenau curve the optimal point can be point of the biggest radius f_F – it is a point in which more gangue starts to occur in concentrate than useful component.

The Fuerstenau curve allows also different ways of determining technologically optimal quality of a concentrate. The point of biggest radius f_F can be determined as in case of Halbich curves or the optimal point F is determined [1], which lies on the crossing of real beneficiation curve with diagonal of identity of useful component recovery in concentrate and recovery of remaining components in tailings. In optimal point F the recovery of analyzed component in concentrate is equal to recovery of remaining components in tailings. The partition efficiency curve based on a sum of recoveries of useful component in concentrate and residuals in tailings achieves extreme value, which is in contrast to curves described above. It can be treated as technological optimal point [3, 4]. The proposed beneficiation characteristics basing on efficiency factor of this process (recovery of useful component in concentrate + recovery of residuals in tailings – 100), because of its parabolic course (clearly visible optimal point for extreme course of factor in function of concentrate quality - f_S) is convenient in application to evaluate obtained beneficiation characteristics, especially when various technologies of beneficiation or various parameters of separation process conductance are to be compared.

2. Materials and methods

The industrial experiment was conducted which was based on sampling of coal dust jig working in three products way in one of coal mechanical processing plant. The samples of concentrate, middlings and tailings were collected and then the densimetric analysis was performed in zinc chloride solutions for all jigging products obtaining fractions of density -1.3; 1.3-1.4; 1.4-1.5; 1.5-1.6; 1.6-1.7; 1.7-1.8; 1.8-2.0 and +2.0 [Mg/m^3]. Each density fraction was screened on appropriate set of sieves what allowed to obtain narrow size-density fractions. In each of them chemical analysis was performed for ash and total sulfur contents. The balance of partition products according to yields and grades of, respectively, ash and sulfur for certain size and density fraction allowed to determine parameters of the jigging feed. The mean ash content in feed was equal to about 46% and mean sulfur content was equal to 4.8%.

The capacity of device work was equal to 500 [Mg/h], amount of delivered bottom water – 218 [m^3/h] and constant number of pulsations was 26 cycles per minute.

3. Results and discussion

The obtained results allowed to calculate coordinates and draw Fuerstenau and Halbich beneficiation curves as well curve of selectivity presenting sum of useful component recoveries in concentrate and of remaining components in tailings in function of component content in concentrate. Additionally, also partition curves for the feed and narrow particle size fractions were calculated and drawn in purpose of comparing preciseness of separation in a jig. These characteristics were presented for the feed and for selected narrow particle size fractions.

The certain characteristics presented in this paper allowed to determine described points in which technological optimum is realized by various criteria. The purpose of presented considerations and conducted calculations was to determine optimal points on beneficiation curves allowing more precise determination of potential possibilities of the material in aspect of obtaining certain values of technological factors of separation process course. In consequence, it makes possible to control the process in purpose of optimization of its results. The calculations were done for individual particle size fractions of the feed delivered to jigging process what allowed to analyze its efficiency in function of processed material particle size distribution.

Figure 1 presents the obtained beneficiation curves with determined points of optimal device work for the feed and Figure 2 shows analogical curves for narrow particle size fractions after jigging. On the basis of the obtained data the coordinates were calculated and partition curves were drawn for the feed and individual particle size fractions what is shown on Figure 3.

a) b) c)

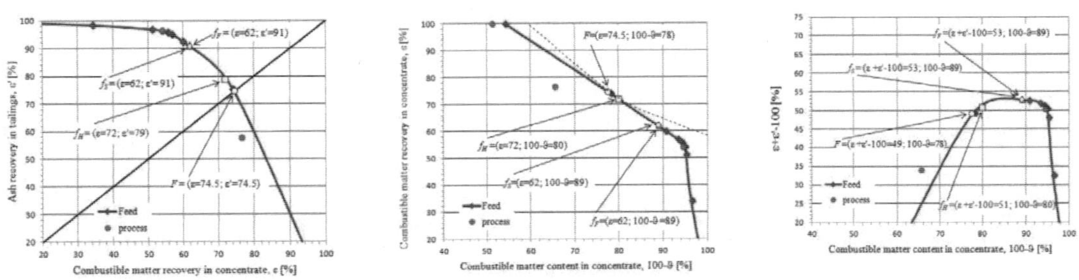

Figure 1. Beneficiation curves for the feed: a) Fuerstenau, b) Halbich, c) curve of beneficiation selectivity.

a) b) c)

fraction < 2.00 mm

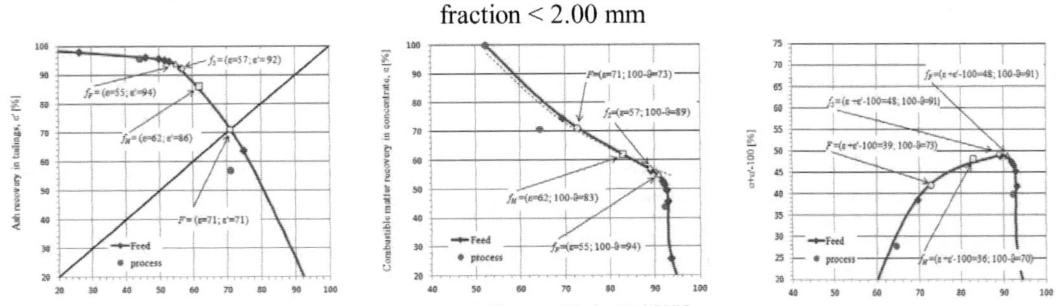

fraction 2.00-3.15 mm

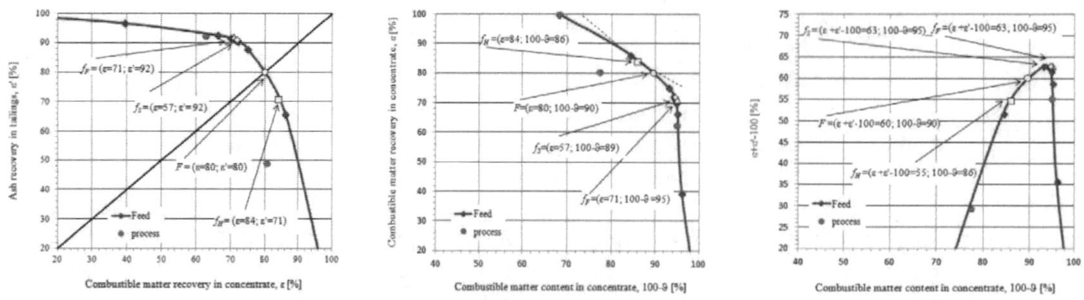

fraction 3.15-5.00 mm

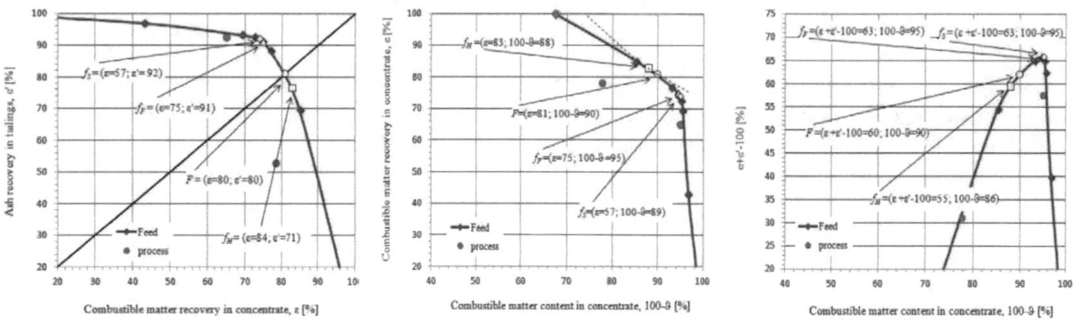

fraction 5.00-6.30 mm

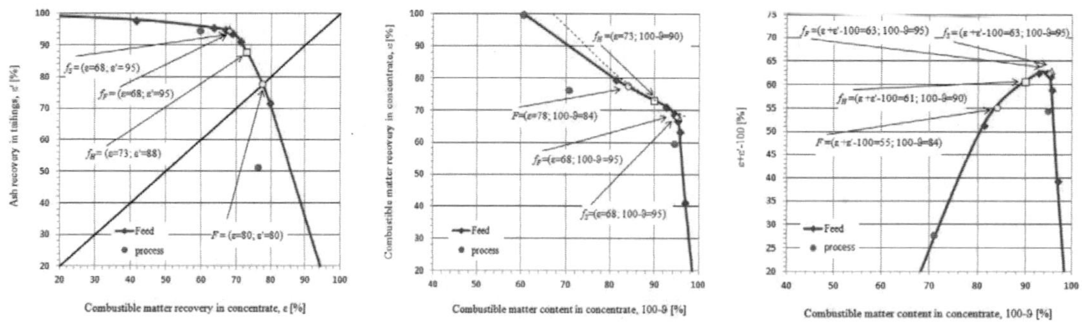

fraction 6.30-8.00 mm

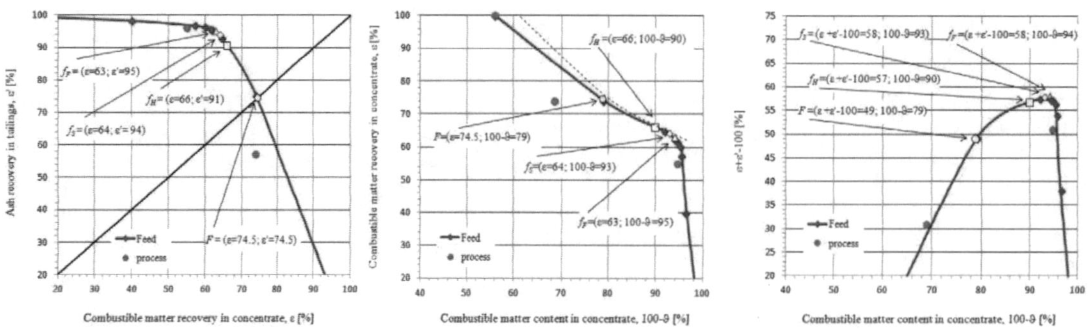

fraction 8.00-10.00 mm

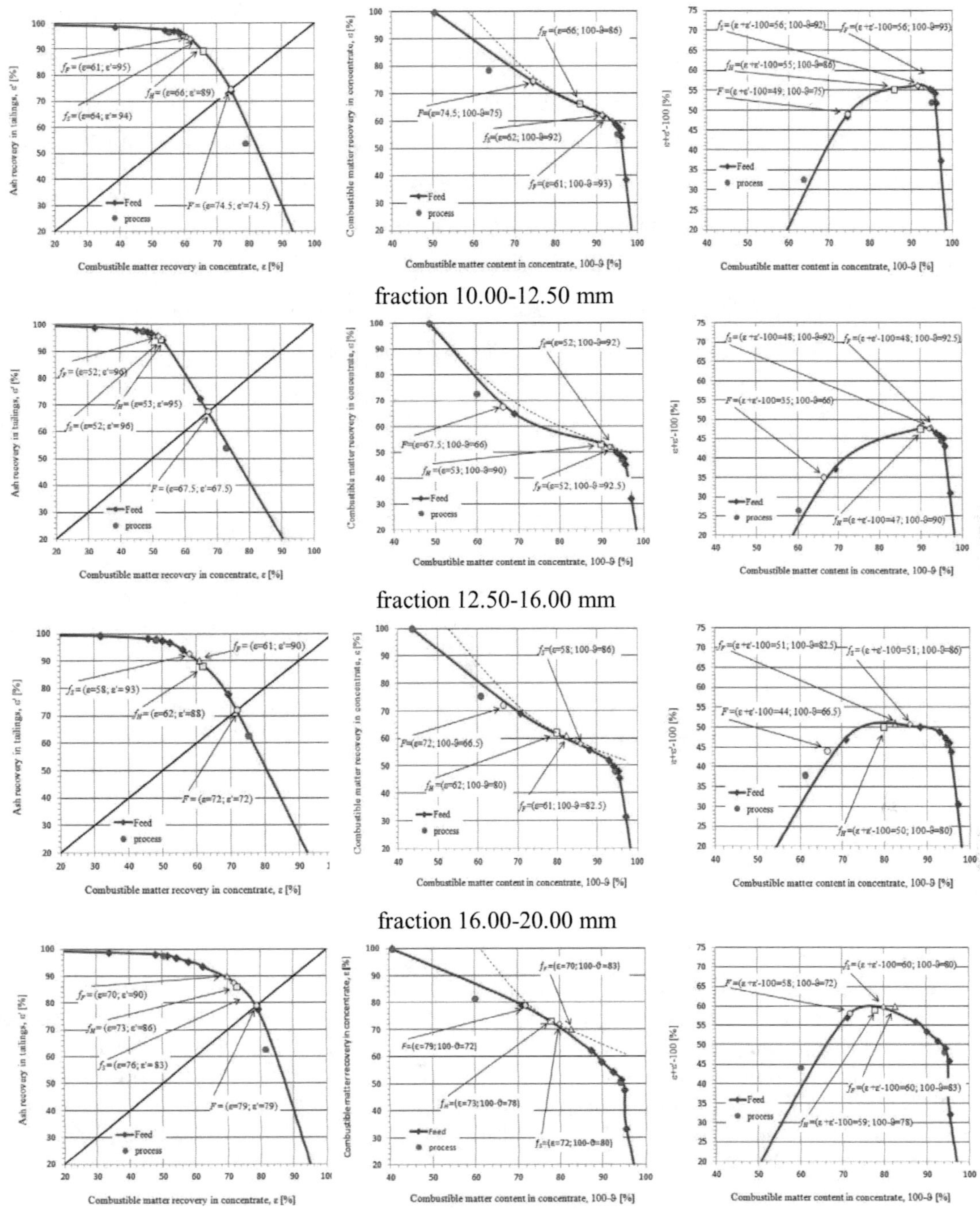

Figure 2. Beneficiation curves: a) Fuerstenau, b) Halbich, c) curve of beneficiation selectivity.

Table 1 contains the values of selectivity factor F and maximal curve radius f_F as well f_H – point of biggest curvature and optimal point for extreme course of relation of the factor in function of concentrate quality – f_S. On the basis of these criteria and partition preciseness factor determined from partition curves – imperfection *I* the analysis of coal dust beneficiation was done in individual particle size fractions. The presented data indicate that the most efficient separation of ash from organic phase occurred in particle size fractions 2.00-3.15 mm and 3.15-5.00 mm. The values of the factors *F* and f_F in these fractions were the highest. In particle size fractions from the range 5.00 till 10.00 mm the results of beneficiation were good too. The lowest values of the factor *F* lower than 70 were observed for particles of size 10.00-12.50 mm and for the finest particle size fraction <2.00 mm which do not suppose to occur in the jigging feed. However, because of the mineral character of the coal and its susceptibility to uncontrolled crushing and soaking fine particles are created which adversely influence on beneficiation effects. The preciseness of partition determined on the basis of partition curves and imperfection factor indicates good separation sharpness, especially for fractions above 8.00 mm.

a) b)

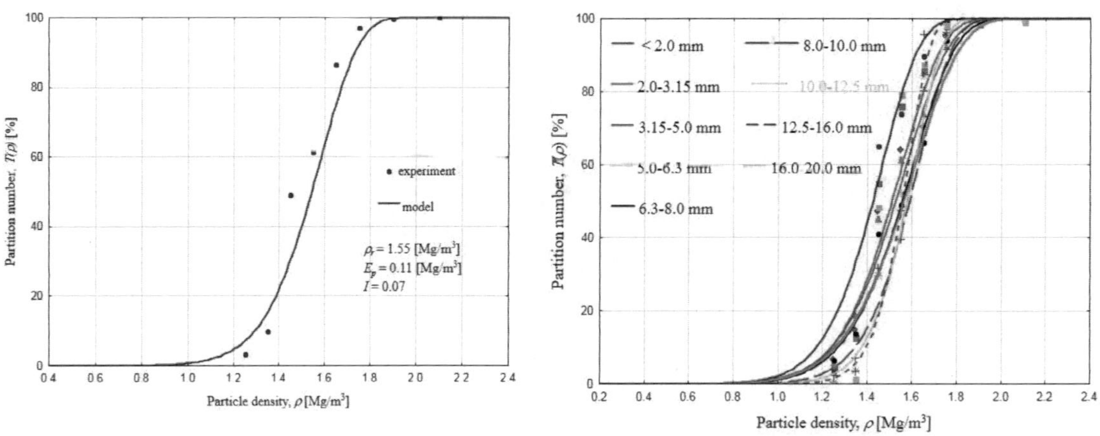

Figure 3. Partition curves a) for feed b) for narrow particle size fractions.

The analysis of correlation between ash content and sulfur content in the feed and particle size fractions presented on Figure 4 and values of correlations index shown in Table 2 indicate strong connection between analyzed parameters, especially in individual fractions 2.00-10.00 mm from the granulation range. It can affect on selective separation of sulfur with mineral phase from coal. This issue will be the subject of future analyzes of efficiency of beneficiation by means of various criteria of evaluation in aspect of control process of coal dusts jigging.

Table 1. Technologically optimal values of the factors determined according to various criteria in particle size fractions.

Benefictaion curve/parameters	Criterion of evaluation	Feed	Particle size fraction [mm]								
			< 2.00	2.00-3.15	3.15-5.00	5.00-6.3	6.30-8.00	8.00-10.00	10.00-12.50	12.50-16.00	16.00-20.00
Recovery of flammable parts in concentrate ε – recovery of ash in tailings ε'	F	74.5	69.5	80	80.3	77.8	74.8	74.8	62.8	71.5	77.8
	f_F	ε=62; ε'=91	ε=55; ε'=94	ε=71; ε'=92	ε=75; ε'=91	ε=68; ε'=95	ε=63; ε'=95	ε=61; ε'=95	ε=52; ε'=96	ε=61; ε'=90	ε=70; ε'=90
Recovery of flammable parts in concentrate ε – flammable parts grade in concentrate 100-ϑ	f_H	ε=72; ε'=80	ε=62; ε'=83	ε=84; ε'=86	ε=83; ε'=88	ε=73; ε'=90	ε=66; ε'=90	ε=66; ε'=86	ε=53; ε'=90	ε=62; ε'=80	ε=73; ε'=78
Sum of recoveries of flammable parts in concentrate and remaining components in tailings ε+ε'– flammable parts grade in concentrate 100-ϑ	f_S	ε=62; ε'=89	ε=57; ε'=89	ε=72; ε'=94.5	ε=74; ε'=95	ε=68; ε'=95	ε=64; ε'=93	ε=62; ε'=91.5	ε=52; ε'=92	ε=58; ε'=86	ε=72; ε'=80
Imperfection	I	0.07	0.08	0.08	0.086	0.09	0.08	0.07	0.06	0.05	0.09

.

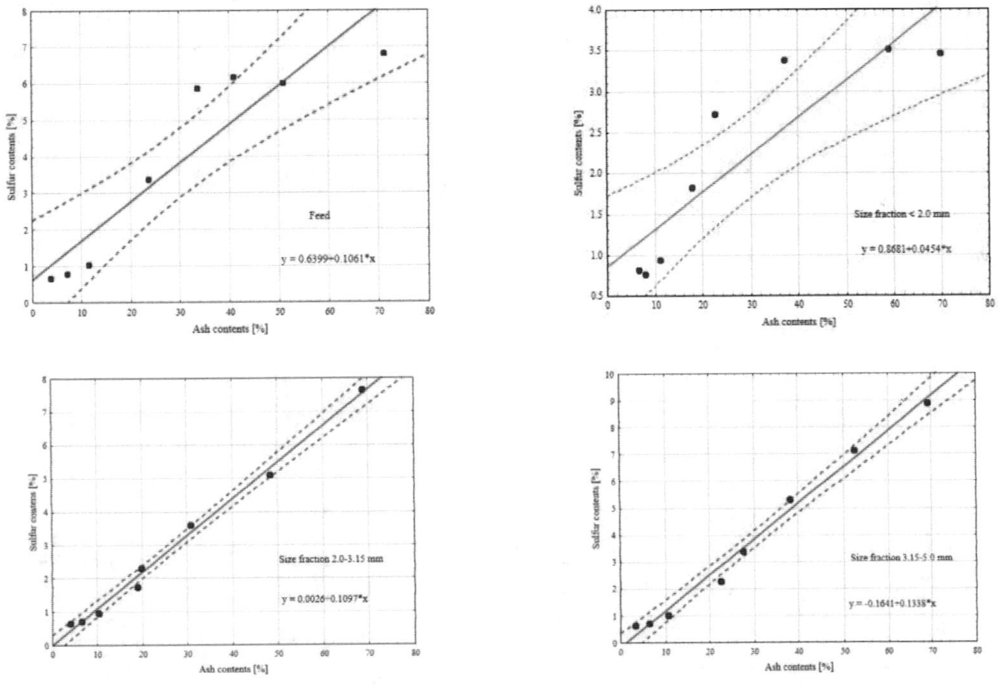

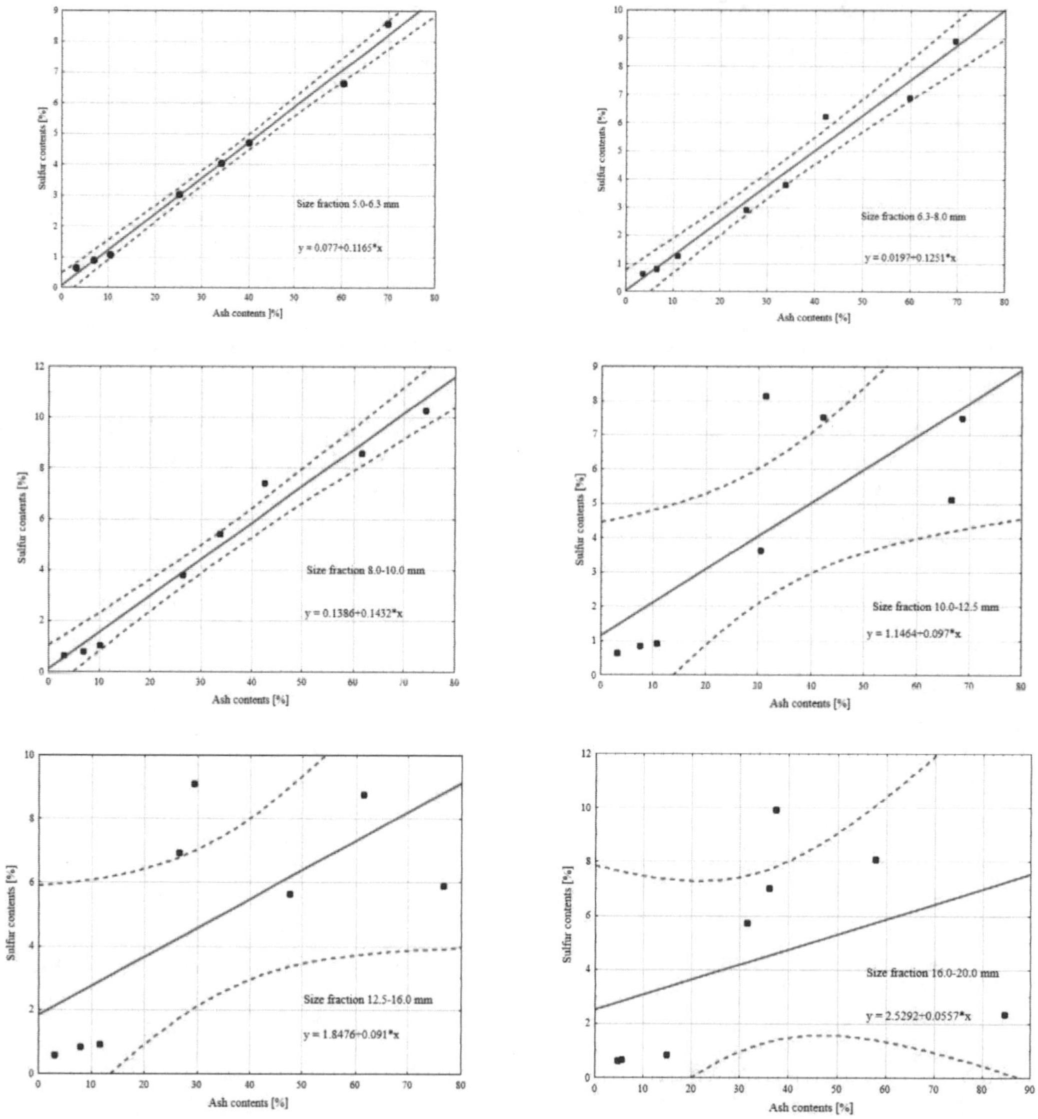

Figure 4. Graphs of linear regressive functions for sulfur contents in function of ash contents.

Table 2. Values of Pearson linear correlation index r between ash contents and sulfur contents for individual particle size fractions and the feed.

Particle size fraction [mm]	< 2.00	2.00-3.15	3.15-5.00	5.00-6.30	6.30-8.00	8.00-10.00	10.00-12.00	12.00-16.00	16.00-20.00	Feed
r	0.889	0.996	0.994	0.996	0.988	0.988	0.762	0.680	0.406	0.926

4. Conclusions

The presented method of jig work evaluation allowed to determine most beneficial values for technological factors of separation process course allowing to control the process in purpose of optimization of obtained results for industrial raw material beneficiation. The conducted densimetric analysis in particle size fractions for the products of three-product jigging allowed to determine conditions in aspect of efficiency of industrial jigging considering particle size distribution of the feed being directed to the process.

The results of analysis indicate that the most beneficial are feed particle size distributions from 8.00 till 16.00 mm giving high efficiency of the process conductance measured by partition sharpness index. The most beneficial values of technological indexes (recovery of useful component) of beneficiation were obtained for sizes 2.00-3.15 mm and 3.15-5.00 mm.

The presented methodology of beneficiation curves shows spectrum of possibilities of selecting an efficient tool to evaluate the beneficiation for both ores and coal. However, it is worthy to pay attention to selection of one criterion of evaluation because the evaluation of the process dependably on various assumed factors can lead to differences in evaluating efficiency of certain process. It has a crucial meaning for the analysis of industrial results which characterize with specific course.

References

[1] Drzymała J., Ahmed H.A.M., 2005. Mathematical equations for approximation of separation results using the Fuerstenau upgrading curves. *International Journal of Mineral Processing*, **76**, 55-65.

[2] Foszcz D., 2013. Zasady określania optymalnych rezultatów wzbogacania wieloskładnikowych rud miedzi. *Wydawnictwo Instytutu Gospodarki Surowcami Mineralnymi i Energią PAN.*

[3] Foszcz D., Niedoba T., Tumidajski T., 2015. Attempt of Determining Optimal Values of Mineral Raw Materials Beneficiation Factors, Inżynieria Mineralna - *Journal of the Polish Mineral Engineering Society*, 2(46), 283-292.

[4] Foszcz D., Niedoba T., Tumidajski T., 2018. A geometric approach to evaluating the results of Polish copper ores beneficiation, *Gospodarka Surowcami Mineralnymi = Mineral Resources Management*, vol. 34 iss. 2, s. 55–66.

[5] Halbich W. 1934. *Űber die Anwendungsmőglichkeiten einiger Netzmittel in der Flotation*. Wűrz-burg: Kondrad Triltsch.

[6] Kelly E.G., Spottiswood D.J. 1982. *Introduction to Mineral Processing.* New York: John Wiley & Sons.

[7] Surowiak A., 2018. The analysis of coal fines separation precision exposed to changeable hydrodynamic parameters of jig work, *Archives of Mining Sciences*, vol. 63 no. 2, s. 437–448.

[8] Surowiak A., 2019, Evaluation of fine coal upgrading effects by means of Fuerstenau curves *Gospodarka Surowcami Mineralnymi = Mineral Resources Management*, vol. 35 iss. 1, s. 5–24.

Acknowledgements

The work was financed by the AGH research subsidy No. 16.16.100. 215.

IOP Conf. Series: Materials Science and Engineering **641** (2019) 012007 doi:10.1088/1757-899X/641/1/012007

Supercritical solvent extraction of lignite combustion products by water and HNO_3 – Rare Earth Elements recovery study

W Urbańczyk[1] and M Lutyński[2]

[1]Cobant GROUP S.A., ul. Grzybowska 2/29, 00-131 Warszawa, Poland
[2]Silesian University of Technology, Faculty of Mining and Geology, ul. Akademicka 2, 44-100 Gliwice, Poland

E-mail: marcin.lutynski@polsl.pl, wu@cobant.eu

Abstract. Coal Combustion Products (CCPs) are anthropogenic materials generated during coal burning in coal-fired power plants and in case of lignite majority of these materials is disposed on land. CCPs contain various metals including Rare Earth Elements (REE). The purpose of this study was to assess if supercritical solvent extraction of CCPs, i.e. fly ash and bottom slag is effective to recover Rare Earth Elements. For that purpose two methods were compared: atmospheric and supercritical solvent extraction with the use of water and 10% HNO_3. Result show that extraction of REE is unjustified when considering efficiency of solvent extraction process and obtained REE concentrations.

1. Introduction

Coal Combustion Products (CCPs) are anthropogenic materials generated during coal burning in coal-fired power plants. These materials are categorized in the following groups: a) fly ash, b) bottom slag, c) bottom slag/fly ash mixtures, d/ gypsum, e) fly ash and dry desulphurization product mixtures [1,2]. Since World's energy generation is based mostly on fossil fuels where lignite and hard coal play a dominant role (according to International Energy Agency over 40% of secondary energy is produced from coal where 3.0% from lignite [3,4]) CCPs should be considered as a resource rather than a waste. For the case of Poland over 80% of hard coal CCPs is utilized for, eg.: concrete or cement production, road foundation construction [5]. In contrary, 65% of lignite CCPs in Poland are considered as a waste and are mostly disposed on land. This is due to the relatively high carbon content of CCPs as a result of incomplete combustion. Hence, there is a limited use of those products in construction industry [7]. Large volumes of disposed CCPs from lignite have an adverse impact on the environment. Land where CCPs are disposed is degraded by the wet form of fly ash storage that prevents dust emission. Another problem is related to the fact that CCPs contain heavy metals such as Cr, As or Pb (that can be leached and migrate to groundwater) and, at low concentrations, Rare Earth Elements (REE) [8].

There were several attempts to use solvent extraction for recovery of metals from lignite fly ash. Authors focused on the use of solvents such as, eg.: citric acid [9], sulfuric acid [10] or mixture of HCl and NaOH [11]. Since the share of lignite in overall electricity production is relatively low available information related to solvent extraction of lignite fly ash is scarce. Nevertheless, sulfuric acid was already used for extraction of lignite fly ash [12,13].

The purpose of this study was to assess if supercritical solvent extraction of CCPs, i.e. fly ash and bottom slag is effective to recover Rare Earth Elements. For that purpose two methods were compared atmospheric and supercritical solvent extraction with the use of neutral or “eco” solvents – water and 10% HNO_3. This approach is sustainable and in accordance with the rules of circular economy where every useful product can be recovered and reused.

2. Materials

For the purpose of the study commercially available lignite Coal Combustion Products were used i.e.: fly ash and bottom slag from one of the polish lignite power plants. Table 1 presents chemical composition of materials used in the study. In Figure 1 SEM images presenting surface morphology of materials are shown.

Table 1. Chemical composition of materials used in the study.

Parameter/Compound, (m/m)	fly ash	bottom slag
LOI,	5,47	48,74
B_2O_3	1,32	0,99
F	0,20	0,09
Na_2O	0,108	0,097
MgO	0,95	0,84
Al_2O_3	24,00	23,80
SiO_2	33,40	47,20
P_2O_5	0,148	0,100
SO_3	3,43	1,33
Cl	0,01	0,01
K_2O	0,16	0,22
CaO	25,30	12,60
TiO_2	0,97	1,32
V_2O_5	0,06	0,04
Cr_2O_3	0,03	0,03
MnO	0,075	0,031
Fe_2O_3	8,11	5,77
Co_2O_3	0,00	0,00
NiO	0,01	0,01
CuO	0,01	0,01
ZnO	0,02	0,01
Ga_2O_3	0,00	0,00
As_2O_3	0,01	0,00
SeO_2	0,01	0,00
Br	0,00	0,00
Rb_2O	0,00	0,00
SrO	0,07	0,05
Y_2O_3	0,01	0,01
ZrO_2	0,04	0,03
Nb_2O_3	0,00	0,00
BaO	0,09	0,06
HgO	0,00	0,00

Figure 1. Surface morphology of a) fly ash, b) bottom slag

3. Methods

Supercritical solvent extraction and atmospheric extraction was carried out for both samples: fly ash and bottom slag. For each test the solid to solvent ratio was 1:2 (w/w). Minimum purity of solvents used in the experiments was 99.9%. In Figure 2 block diagram of experimental procedure is presented.

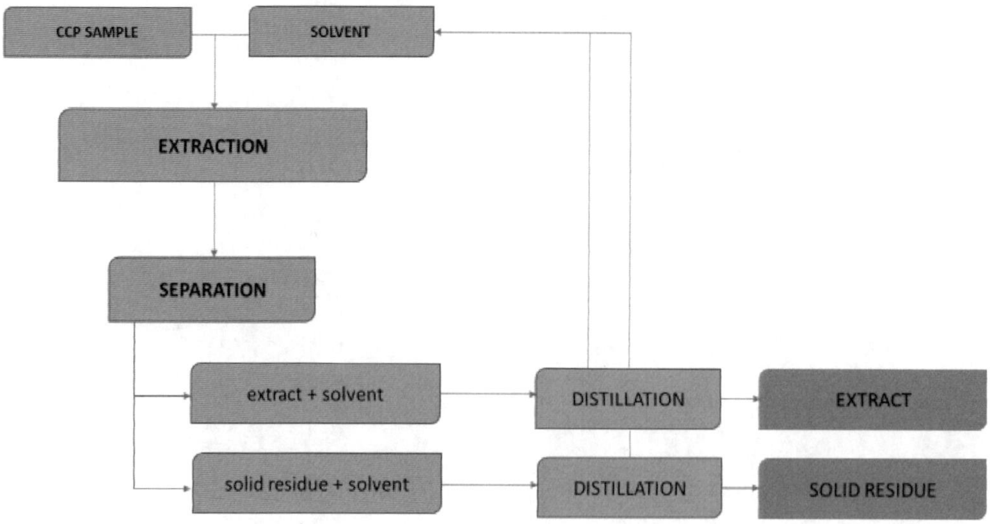

Figure 2. Block diagram of experimental procedure.

In the case of extraction under atmospheric pressure, experiments were carried out in a round bottom flask equipped with a reflux condenser at the temperature of 400°C for 5 hours. Supercritical solvent extraction of CCPs was carried out in interconnected Haas autoclaves presented in Figure 3 [14]. Connection between autoclaves partially eliminated the need for further filtration and as a consequence, lowered the loss of extracts and solid residue. Temperature of the process was kept constant at 400°C with pressure of 20-22 MPa. Duration of the experiments was the same as atmospheric extraction - 5 hours. Obtained extract were subjected for further analysis of metal content using ICP-OES method.

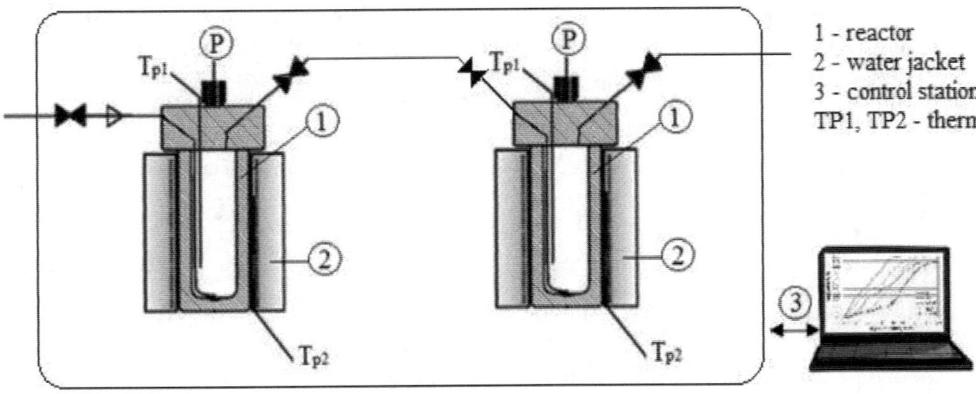

Figure 3. High pressure autoclaves used for the supercritical solvent extraction.

4. Results and Discussion

In Table 2 and 3 mass balance of lignite CCPs solvent extraction processes carried out in the study are presented. Extract yield (*Y*) was calculated with the following formula:

$$Y = \frac{m_{extract} - m_{H2O}}{m_{fly\ ash}} * 100\%$$

Where *m* indicates masses of feed and products in grams.

Table 2. Mass balance of solvent extraction processes under atmospheric pressure of fly ash and bottom slag.

FEED		YIELDS		
Fly ash	– 10 g	solid residue	– 9,4 g	
H_2O	– 20 g	extract	– 20,3 g	*Y* = 3%
		loss	– 0,3 g	
Fly ash	– 10 g	solid residue	– 9,1 g	
10% HNO_3	– 20 g	extract	– 20,6 g	Y = 6%
		loss	– 0,3 g	
Fly ash	– 10 g	solid residue	– 8,4 g	
H_2O	– 20 g	extract	– 21,1 g	Y = 11%
		loss	– 0,5 g	
Fly ash	– 10 g	solid residue	– 7,1 g	
10% HNO_3	– 20 g	extract	– 22,6 g	Y = 26%
		loss	– 0,3 g	

Table 3. Mass balance of supercritical solvent extraction of fly ash and bottom slag.

FEED		YIELDS		
fly ash	– 10 g	solid residue	– 6,1 g	
10% HNO_3	– 20 g	extract	– 22,4 g	*Y* = 24%
		loss	– 0,3 g	
bottom slag	– 10 g	solid residue	– 4,7 g	
10% HNO_3	– 20 g	extract	– 23,7 g	*Y* = 37%
		loss	– 0,2 g	

Results show that a more efficient extraction was with 10% HNO_3 as a solvent for both materials – maximum yield was 37% (m/m). As expected better results were obtained for supercritical extraction under elevated pressure and temperature. Extracts were consequently subjected for further analyses of metal content using ICP-MS technique (see Fig. 4).

Table 4. Metal content of extracts.

	APE, H_2O FA	APE, H_2O BS	ATM, HNO_3 FA	ATM, HNO_3 BS	CSE, HNO_3 BS	CSE, HNO_3 BS
			mg kg^{-1}			
Ag	0,0063	0,0067	0,0070	0,0074	0,0078	0,0081
Al	13,6653	14,6396	15,6140	16,5883	17,5627	18,5371
As	0,0733	0,0701	0,0670	0,0638	0,0607	0,0575
B	4,3727	4,4097	4,4467	4,4836	4,5206	4,5576
Ba	0,0037	0,0037	0,0037	0,0037	0,0037	0,0037
Bi	0,0310	0,0347	0,0384	0,0421	0,0458	0,0495
Cd	0,0012	0,0012	0,0012	0,0011	0,0011	0,0010
Co	0,0011	0,0017	0,0024	0,0030	0,0036	0,0043
Cr	0,0112	0,0146	0,0181	0,0215	0,0249	0,0283
Cu	0,0652	0,0977	0,1303	0,1629	0,1954	0,2280
Eu	0,4414	0,4736	0,5057	0,5378	0,5700	0,6021
Fe	1,2641	1,3296	1,3950	1,4605	1,5260	1,5914
Ga	0,1370	0,1373	0,1377	0,1381	0,1384	0,1388
In	0,0077	0,0078	0,0079	0,0080	0,0081	0,0082
Ir	0,0019	0,0022	0,0026	0,0029	0,0033	0,0037
La	0,0519	0,0556	0,0593	0,0629	0,0666	0,0703
Li	1,1955	1,1991	1,2027	1,2063	1,2099	1,2136
Mg	7,0900	7,4114	7,7328	8,0542	8,3756	8,6970
Mn	0,0767	0,1004	0,1240	0,1477	0,1713	0,1950
Mo	0,0901	0,0938	0,0975	0,1012	0,1049	0,1085
Na	12,4947	12,9659	13,4371	13,9083	14,3795	14,8507
Nb	0,0096	0,0127	0,0159	0,0190	0,0221	0,0253
Ni	0,0328	0,0374	0,0420	0,0466	0,0511	0,0557
P	0,1777	0,1777	0,1778	0,1778	0,1778	0,1779
Pb	0,0375	0,0378	0,0381	0,0385	0,0388	0,0391
Rh	0,0198	0,0202	0,0206	0,0209	0,0213	0,0216
Si	16,6547	17,2025	17,7504	18,2983	18,8462	19,3941
Sm	0,0071	0,1052	0,2033	0,3014	0,3995	0,4976
Sr	0,5372	0,5436	0,5500	0,5564	0,5628	0,5692
Th	0,0484	0,0854	0,1224	0,1594	0,1964	0,2333
Ti	0,0107	0,0117	0,0127	0,0136	0,0146	0,0156
Tl	0,0059	0,0058	0,0057	0,0057	0,0056	0,0055
Tm	0,0005	0,0005	0,0005	0,0006	0,0006	0,0006
V	0,0250	0,0285	0,0320	0,0355	0,0390	0,0425
W	0,0281	0,0318	0,0355	0,0391	0,0428	0,0465
Yb	0,0011	0,0014	0,0018	0,0022	0,0025	0,0029
Zn	0,2710	0,2823	0,2935	0,3048	0,3161	0,3273
Zr	0,0222	0,0259	0,0295	0,0332	0,0369	0,0405

APE – atmospheric pressure extraction, CSE – critical solvent extraction, FA – fly ash, BS – bottom slag

Extracts have a form of a pulp with various metal content including Rare Earth Metals and alkaline metals. Calcium content is not included in the table since the concentration exceeded calibration curve.

This could be explained by the affinity of calcium toward solvents used and high content of calcium in the raw material. Higher yields were obtained in case of bottom slag which can be attributed to the grain morphology (large, porous grains). Content of Rare Earth Elements increases in case of supercritical solvent extraction, eg. Europium (Eu) concentration increased by 36.4%.

5. Conclusions

Results of this study show that recovery of REE is unjustified when considering efficiency of solvent extraction process and REE concentrations. Both fly ash and bottom slag do contain REE such as Samarium or Europium at very low concentrations and it might be difficult to upscale a complex process of solvent extraction to industrial scale. Cost of such process will most probably be higher than the income.

Other potential solutions would be using other solvents such as citric acid or sulfuric acid yet the environmental footprint of such process would be significant.

High LOI indicates high carbon content. Therefore, an alternative is to first separate unburned coal (UC) which is less prone to solvent extraction (it adsorbs solvent) by gravity separation or flotation and later use upgraded material for extraction process.

References

[1] Robl T, Oberlink A, Jones R 2017 Coal Combustion Products (CCPs) Characteristics, Utilization and Beneficiation (Elsevier)

[2] Heidrich C, Feuerborn HJ, Weir A 2013 Coal combustion products: a global perspective *World of Coal Ash Conference*

[3] International Energy Agency. Total Primary Energy Supply (TPES) by source

[4] Eurostat 2017 Generation of electricity by type of fuel, EU

[5] Knaś K, Szymanek A 2018 Potential of anthropogenic materials *XXV International Conference FLY ASH FROM ENERGY*

[6] PGE Mining and Conventional Power. Economy of coal combustion by-products

[7] European Environmental Agency. More from less — material resource efficiency in Europe

[8] Coal's Poisonous Legacy. Groundwater Contaminated by Coal Ash Across the U.S.

[9] Yahya AA, Ali N, Mohd Kamal NL, Shahidan S, Beddu S, Nuruddin MF, Shafiq N 2017 Reducing Heavy Metal Element from Coal Bottom Ash by Using Citric Acid Leaching Treatment *MATEC Web of Conferences*

[10] Wu C, Yu H, Zhang H (2012) Extraction of aluminum by pressure acid-leaching method from coal fly ash *Transactions of Nonferrous Metals Society of China 22(9):2282-2288*

[11] King JF, Taagart RK, Smith RC, Hower JC, Hsu-Kim H 2018 Aqueous acid and alkaline extraction of rare earth elements from coal combustion ash *International Journal of Coal Geology 195(2):75-83*

[12] Bojinova DY, Teodosieva R 2016 Extraction of elements from coal fly ash using thermo-hydrometallurgical method *Journal of Chemical Technology and Metallurgy 51(5)577-587*

[13] Valeeva D, Kunilovab I, Alpatovc A, Mikhailovad A, Goldberge M, Kondratiev A 2019 Complex utilisation of ekibastuz brown coal fly ash: iron & carbon separation and aluminum extraction *Journal of Cleaner Production 218(5):192-201*

[14] Majka M 2018 Tests of thermal and pressure process of coke pitch in the direction of increased yield of oil fractions *Doctoral dissertation, Silesian University of Technology, Faculty of Chemistry*

IOP Conf. Series: Materials Science and Engineering **641** (2019) 012008 doi:10.1088/1757-899X/641/1/012008

Evaluation of groundnut shell as a reductant for microwave reduction of low grade banded iron ore

V Rayapudi and N Dhawan

Department of Metallurgical & Materials Engineering, Indian Institute of Technology, IIT-Roorkee, Uttarakhand-247667, India

E-mail: ndhawan.fmt@iitr.ac.in

Abstract. This study investigates the utilization of low-grade banded iron ore for its utilization as a blast furnace feedstock. The complex association of the quartz-hematite phase and a fine liberation size prohibits the direct use of these ores in the steel production cycle. Conventional reduction experiments using different reductants yielded limited iron enrichment. Microwave carbothermal reduction using economical and abundantly available groundnut shell was investigated using a Taguchi L9 statistical design. The design optimal condition of 900W power, 20 min time and 3% equivalent carbon yielded an enriched iron concentrate with Fe 58% at 85.6% recovery. Characterization studies reveal the formation of sequential hematite, magnetite and wustite formation with groundnut shell dosage. The concentrate obtained can be used as feedstock for blast furnace burden. Microwave reduction was found better in terms of product control than conventional reduction, as fayalite formation was not observed.

1. Introduction

India's steel vision 2030 targets 300 million tons of steel production, which require approximately 550 million tons of quality iron ores (~60% Fe). India does not have enough high-grade hematite ores but possesses abundant resources of banded iron ores namely banded hematite quartzite/Jasper (BHQ, BHJ), banded magnetite quartzite (BMQ) and discarded slimes. During conventional mining of hematite ores, there is a significant generation of banded iron ores, which often ends up in unused stockpile at the mine sites [1, 2]. The iron bands in these ores are of hematite and magnetite along with quartz-rich bands of varying thickness ~0.5 to 1.5 cm. These ores possess different beneficiation characteristics primarily because of negligible alumina content, excessive quartz content and fine liberation size (<100 microns) which makes them hard compared to conventional hematite ores. The iron content in these ores varies from 30-45% and are located in the states of Odisha, Karnataka, Chattisgarh, and Rajasthan, India [1]. The investigations on the beneficiation of BHQ, BHJ, and BMQ are few and includes processing techniques such as the flotation, magnetic separation, jigging and conventional roasting [3, 4]. The carbothermal exposure involves ore reduction in a reducing environment at 500-700°C for partial reduction of hematite to magnetite followed by low-intensity magnetic separation (LIMS) to obtain iron-rich concentrate. The reduction process suffers because of an associated energy penalty but includes a simpler separation step of magnetic separation, and reduced grinding costs due to the increased friability of the roasted ore [5, 6]. The reduction of low-grade iron ores, on an average yields 10-15% increment with 50-70%, Fe recovery [7-9].

BHJ ore resembles taconite ore processed in North America in terms of the banded structure of the iron and quartz phase. However, the absence of the magnetite phase in BHJ makes the beneficiation difficult compared to conventional magnetic processing of taconite ore. The microwave treatment on taconite and magnetite ore causes selective thermal expansion leading to reduced comminution energy along with a cleaner liberation improving the concentrate grade and recovery [10, 11]. The various applications of microwave exposure include faster-controlled temperature ramp-up, enhanced kinetics, rock disintegration, better liberation, and enhanced magnetic properties along with enhanced separation [12-18]. It is reported that oxides-sulfides are good receivers of microwave radiations whereas silicates are poor receptors of microwaves [13]. Since BHJ ore comprises hematite and quartz, it is expected that selective heating of hematite can occur with microwave irradiation. The prime objective of microwave treatment is to selectively transform the hematite phase in the ore to magnetite followed separation in a low-intensity magnetic separator. Unlike conventional ores, BHJ ore consists of alternate bands of hematite and jasper phase in bonded form, therefore, it is expected that the reduction conditions will differ from the ideal thermodynamic conditions [5, 12, 14, 16, 17, 19-21].

It is known that iron oxide can be reduced to Fe, at 700 °C, whereas $Al2O_3$ and SiO_2 cannot be reduced below 1450 °C [19, 23]. The reduction is dominated by the direct reduction (with solid carbon) at the initial stage of reduction and is finally determined by indirect reduction (gaseous CO/CO_2) together with the carbon solution loss reaction [22, 23]. Compared to the reduction of iron oxides in conventional heating, the solid-state reaction occurred at low temperatures for the microwave reduction along with a different sequence of chemical reactions [12, 14, 19]. The microwave electromagnetic field selectively induces the magnetite dissociation which is a strong microwave absorbing material, to produce oxygen gas that can react with solid carbon, to form CO and CO_2 gases. The microwave absorbing power of magnetite diminishes at about 650 °C and reduction to wustite are accomplished below this temperature. It is reported that as the fraction of carbonaceous material increases, the attained temperature increases resulting in the higher reduction ores [12, 19, 24]. This is because the main heat source of microwave heating is carbonaceous material rather than iron oxides. It takes a longer time to initiate the heating reduction than magnetite because hematite is hardly heated from room temperature by microwaves [19]. Microwave reduction is a non-isothermal process and considering this, the effect of reductant dosage, temperature and microwave power on the reduction process is systematically pursued. Previous studies do not emphasize on the carbon requirement, underlying reduction mechanism, and hence lack a systematic approach for the evolution of iron oxides during reduction. There are research works for up-gradation of low-grade iron ores but to the best of author's knowledge, no systematic investigation employing microwave carbothermal reduction is reported on BHJ ore. The purpose of the present study is to evaluate the conventional and microwave-assisted carbothermal reduction for processing of low grade banded iron ore. Further, an attempt is made to evaluate an alternative economical reductant ground nutshell for the enrichment of the low-grade Indian BHJ ore through the carbothermal reduction process. Different reductant parameters such as reductant dosage, time, power, and temperature were evaluated for both the routes. The obtained concentrate through different processes was further characterized to identify the iron enrichment along with underlying phase transformations.

2. Materials and methodology

BHJ ore sample used in this study was procured from a working mine situated in Karnataka, India, assaying 51.8% iron oxide and 46.1% quartz as a significant impurity. The photograph of the as-received sample and corresponding optical micrograph shown in Fig. 1a, b depicts the dispersed and interlocked structure of hematite within the jasper matrix. The XRD spectra are shown in Fig. 1c reflects the hematite and quartzite phase along with the traces of magnetite. The quantitative phase analysis determined by the area under the respective peaks yielded the phase fraction of hematite, quartzite, and magnetite as 47.7%, 51.7%, and 0.5% respectively. The sample was stage-wise crushed using jaw and roll crusher followed by grinding in a laboratory ball mill. The standard riffler sampling method is used for obtaining the representative sample and the effect of particle size on iron grade is shown in Fig. 1d. Particle size below 75 microns possesses higher iron grade suggesting better liberation and is chosen as a representative sample with an overall 38.7 % iron. The overall experimental plan followed is shown in Fig. 2a. The thermo-gravimetric analysis (TGA) is conducted for feed, activated charcoal, and groundnut shell as shown in Fig. 2b reveals a similar behavior with all reductants (activated charcoal and groundnut shell) having a weight loss of approximately 80-85%. The oxidation of reductants around temperature 200° C-550°C caused evaporation of volatile matter and a small weight loss (approximately 4-5%) between 350°C-800°C temperature due to ore dehydroxylation

(e)

Constituent	SiO_2	Al_2O_3	Fe_2O_3	FeO	MnO	MgO	CaO	P_2O_5	LOI
Wt. %	46.1	0.26	51.8	0.43	0.06	0.01	0.02	0.06	1.42

Figure 1. (a) Photograph of hand specimen (b) Optical microscope image (c) XRD spectra (d) Variation in iron grade with particle size (e) Chemical composition of BHJ ore.

The carbothermal reduction experiments were carried out in a refractory grade crucible with lid in a muffle furnace (Carbolite, CWF1200) and microwave unit (LG make, 900 Watts, 2.45 GHz) using charcoal and GNS. The CHNS analysis of the charcoal and GNS reveals the presence of 0.7% nitrogen, 79.6% carbon, 2.1% hydrogen, 0.4% sulfur and 1.2% nitrogen, 44.1% carbon, 5.5% hydrogen, 0.3% sulfur respectively. The GNS sample was procured from the local vendor contains carbon values almost half compared to activated charcoal. GNS was oven-dried for 6h at 70°C moisture prior to pulverization in attritor mill (IKA-A100). The stoichiometric amount of carbon required for the complete reduction of hematite to metallic iron is calculated as 6.03 % according to Eq. (1). The reduced product is water quenched to prevent the re-oxidation of the reduced phases. The quenched sample is subsequently pulverized and subjected to LIMS at 1800 Gauss to recover the magnetic values. The quantitative iron analysis present in the magnetic concentrate is determined using a standard potassium dichromate titration procedure. The change in the magnetic characteristics is evaluated through vibratory sample magnetometer (VSM). The process yield and iron recovery are calculated as shown in Eq. (2-3).

$$Fe_2O_3(s) + 3C(s) + 1/2O_2(g) \rightarrow 2Fe(s) + 2CO(g) + CO_2(g) \quad (1)$$

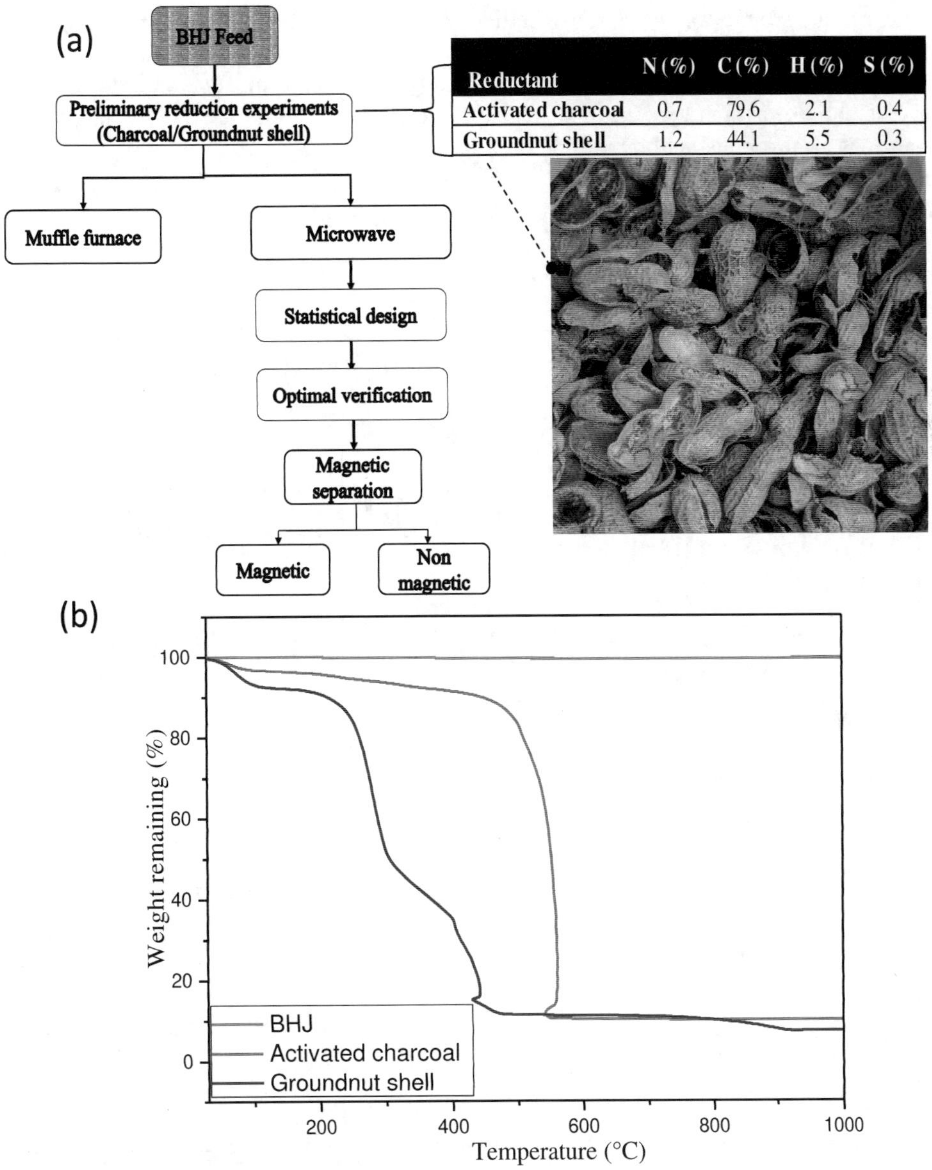

Figure 2. (a) Flowsheet of the experimental procedure followed (b) TGA plot of BHJ, activated charcoal, and groundnut shell feed samples

3. Results and discussion

3.1 Muffle furnace reduction

The preliminary experiments conducted below the temperature of 700°C with charcoal dosage below 9% could not yield suitable iron enrichment as a concentrate, because the reductant and ore mixture was found partially unburnt. Therefore based on literature, the reduction experiments were conducted in a muffle furnace using charcoal and GNS at a fixed temperature of 700°C, 30 min at varying

IOP Conf. Series: Materials Science and Engineering **641** (2019) 012008 doi:10.1088/1757-899X/641/1/012008

reductant dosage (4-12%) whereas stoichiometric value is ~6% as shown in Eq (1). As shown in Fig. 3a, the iron grade lies in between 39-46% and iron recovery of 94-99% with GNS as reductant, however, with ca harcoal, ithe ron grade of 39-56% and iron recovery of 94-99% was attained. The XRD spectrum shown in Fig. 3(b) depicts sa ignificant reduction of hematite to magnetite up to 6% carbon, however, above 6%, the formation of wustite along with magnetite phase was observed. The formation of wustite phase leads to the fall in the iron grade being non-magnetic in nature. The VSM analysis of the feed and the magnetic fractions is shown in Fig. 3c reveals an increase in saturation magnetization value from 5 to ~40 emu/g with the addition of GNS, however, the formation of wustite phase appeared beyond 6%. The quantitative XRD analysis depicts the formation of wustite above 6% carbon, whereas the hematite phase reduces drastically from ~ 54 to 10% and stepwise iron oxide reduction (hematite-magnetite-wustite) was also observed. It should be noted that the saturation magnetization is almost constant beyond 3% carbon.

$$Fe_{Recovery}\% = \frac{(Fe_{Grade} \times Weight)_{magnetic}}{(Fe_{Grade} \times Weight)_{feed}} \times 100 \qquad (2)$$

$$Yield\% = \frac{Weight_{magnetic}}{Weight_{Total}} X\,100 \qquad (3)$$

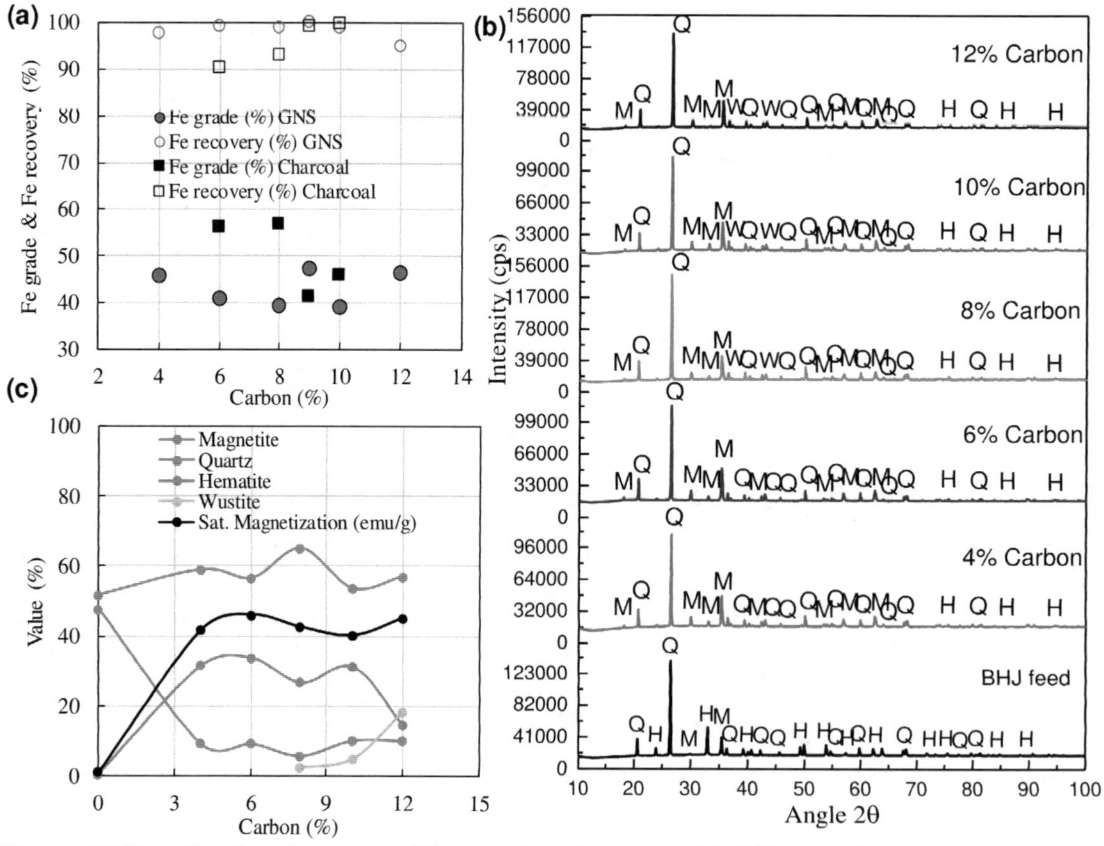

Figure 3 Effect of carbon dosage on (a) iron grade and recovery (b) XRD plot of magnetic concentrate (c) Quantitative phase analysis 700C 30 min in a muffle furnace

3.2 Microwave reduction

Due to limited iron enrichment in the conventional reduction, the microwave reduction was pursued. The experiments were conducted at 900W for 10 min using both charcoal and groundnut shell. The effect of reductant dosage on the iron concentrate parameters is reflected in Fig. 4. The iron grade and recovery show a similar trend with both reductants, however, GNS was found comparable and was hence further pursued to identify the optimal conditions. In both reductants, the grade of concentrate is close to 50% with an iron recovery of more than 90%. The carbothermal reduction process was investigated using a statistical Taguchi-L_9 orthogonal array design using three factors. Power, time, and reductant dosage were the factors considered whereas iron grade and recovery were process responses. The prime objective is to determine an optimal condition, i.e., conditions to maximize iron grade and recovery and evaluating the significant factor. It is important to mention that a residence time of fewer than 10 min, does not lead to the flame formation resulting in unburnt GNS and ore mixture. Each experiment was conducted twice and mean values are reported in the response Table 1. As expected the temperature attained during the design experiments significantly varied from 200-700°C. Fig. 5 show the contour plots for the iron grade, recovery, and temperature with statistically significant experimental factors. It is evident that low reductant dosage is favorable for the higher iron grade at a power of 720-900W. The effect of reductant dosage and microwave power on the concentrate recovery is shown in Fig. 5(b). The iron recovery increases from 84% to 94% and it decreases at both ends i.e., lower and higher reductant dosage. The effect of reductant dosage and power on the attained temperature in the magnetic concentrate shown in Fig. 5(c) depicts that the temperature increases with increasing reductant dosage and at higher power levels. Based on analysis of variance, the sequential order of dominating/influential factors on iron grade, iron recovery, and the temperature is shown in Fig. 5(d).

As expected at higher reductant dosage, both iron recovery, and iron grade falls however higher iron grade is attained at a lower dosage (3-4%) and is in line with conventional reduction. It can be concluded that reductant dosage and time are the most influential factors for both grade and recovery response. It can be observed from Table 1 that increasing reductant dosage leads to an increase in temperature, decreasing grade, and higher iron recovery. The regression equation derived for iron grade and recovery based on experimental response with all the factors is shown in Table 2. The statistical fit "R^2" for the equations indicate the adequateness of the derived model. The plot of means of individual factors of the design for an iron grade, recovery, and the temperature is shown in Fig. 6.

Table 1. Experimental design conditions and their respective response.

S. No.	Reductant (%)	Time (min)	Power (W)	Temperature (°C)	Fe grade (%)	Fe recovery (%)	Yield (%)
1	3	10	540	206	55.85	88.77	58.81
2	3	15	720	285	55.63	84.83	56.43
3	3	20	900	402	58.08	85.61	54.53
4	6	10	720	427	51.38	92.85	66.86
5	6	15	900	693	51.83	94.54	67.49
6	6	20	540	409	49.15	79.29	59.69
7	9	10	900	608	45.57	90.83	73.74
8	9	15	540	384	45.35	97.83	79.82
9	9	20	720	613	49.15	85.49	64.36
10	3	20	900	398	58.1	87.6	55

Table 2. Regression equation for iron grade and recovery based on statistical design.

Iron grade	Grade (%) = 56-1.64 Reductant dosage (%) + 0.119 Time (min) + 0.00475 Power (W) (R^2=0.92)
Iron recovery	Recovery (%) = 91.6 + 0.83 Reductant dosage (%) - 0.735 Time (min) + 0.0047 Power (W) (R^2=0.47)

Temperature (C)	Temperature (°C) = 351 + 39.6 Reductant dosage (%) + 6.1 Time (min) + 0.652 Power (W) (R^2=0.84)

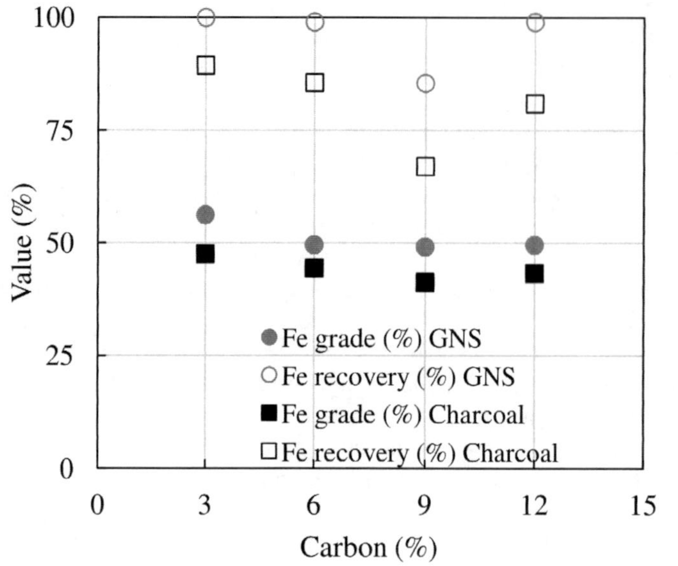

Figure 4. Microwave reduction at 900W for 10 min.

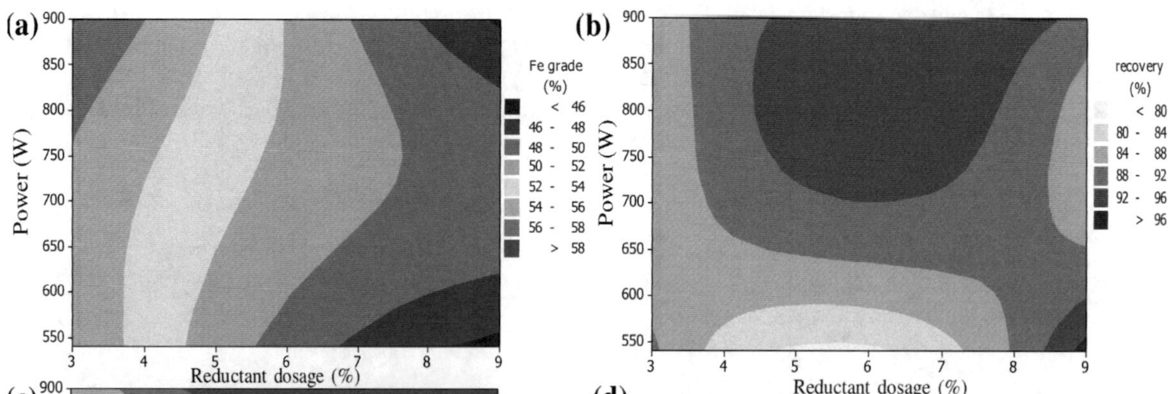

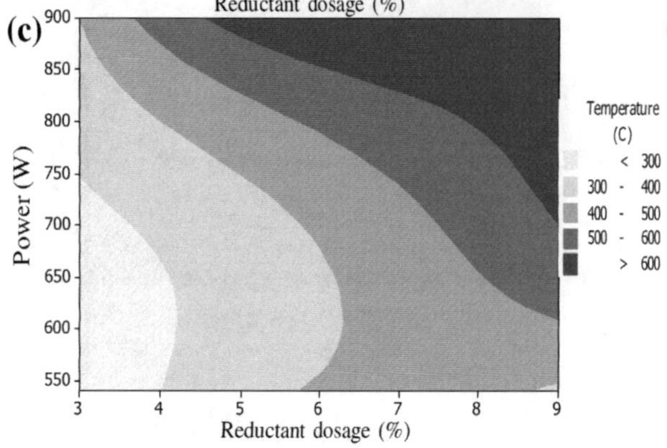

(d)

Response	Impact sequence
Grade (%)	Reductant> Power > Time
Recovery (%)	Time> Reductant> Power
Temperature (°C)	Reductant> Power > Time

Figure 5. Contour plots of significant factors power and reductant for (a) iron grade (b) iron recovery and (c) temperature.

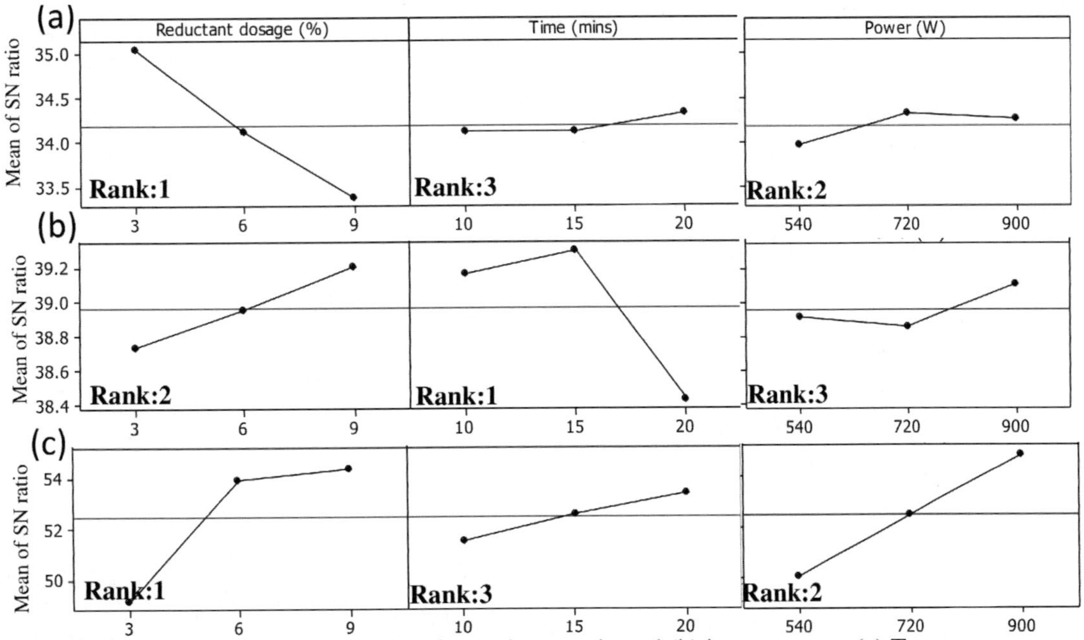

Figure 6. Main effects plot of SN ratios for (a) iron grade and (b) iron recovery (c) Temperature.

For the iron grade, increasing the residence time and power, SN ratio initially increases slightly and on boundary condition, it falls below mean value. However, reductant dosage shows the opposite trend. For iron recovery, increasing the time from low to middle level, the SN ratio increases and on further increasing to the maximum level the value decreases significantly and falls below the mean value. The factor power and reductant dosage show a similar trend as in iron grade, whereas the SN ratio shows an increasing trend. Higher carbon dosage leads to increased absorption of microwaves resulting in high temperature. But for temperature, it shows an increasing trend with all the factors such as reductant dosage, residence time and power.

Fig.7a shows the XRD and VSM analysis of the feed and magnetic concentrate corresponding to run 1, 3 and 5. These experiments were selected as they represent higher iron enrichment in terms of grade and iron recovery. The VSM analysis of the feed and the magnetic concentrate shown in Fig. 7b depicts a distinct difference in the saturation magnetization and is in agreement with iron grade recovery results. The XRF analysis for non-magnetic fractions depicts that silica content is enhanced in the nonmagnetic fraction along with some iron values which are significantly lower compared to the original sample. In all these experiments, hematite and magnetite are the major bearing phases and the magnetic saturation values increased from 4-5 emu/g (feed) to 9 emu/g (concentrate). As shown in Fig.8, the backscattered electron micrograph and EDS atomic percent analysis of as such reduced sample reveals the presence of magnetite, hematite, and cristobalite phases and is in agreement with XRD results. The points marked as 1, 2, 3, 5 reveals the wustite formation with formula Fe_xO_y (x: 1-1.3 and y:1) along with some silica and magnetite.

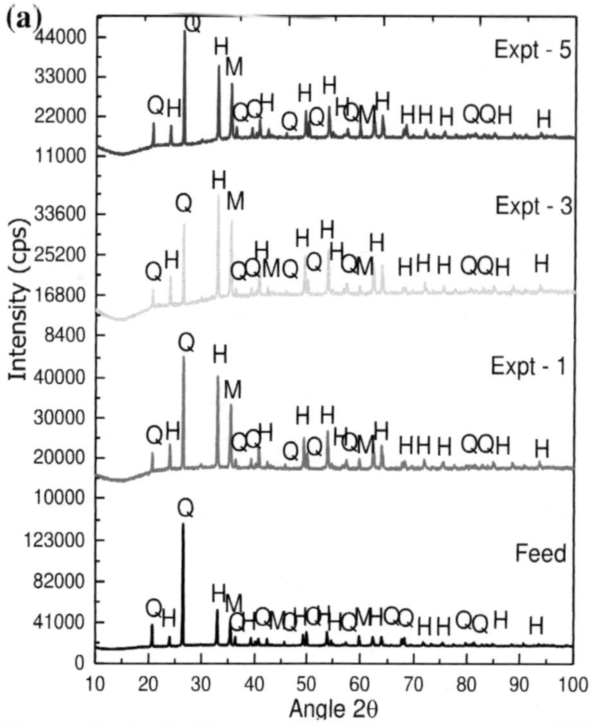

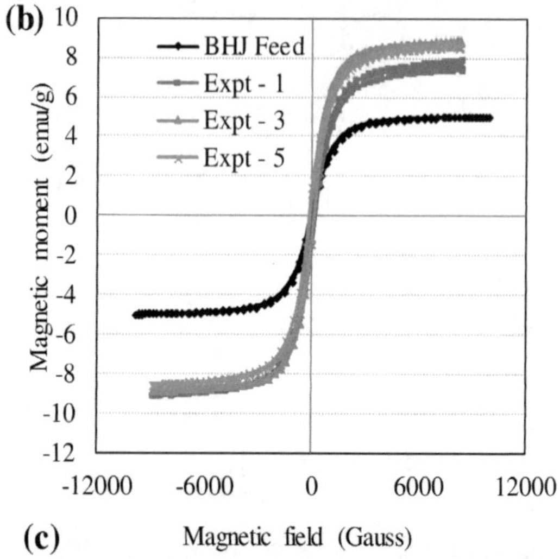

(c)

Component	Feed	Wt. (%) (Non-Mag)		
		1	3	5
Al_2O_3	0.26	0.25	0.21	0.19
SiO_2	46.1	65.69	68.39	66.47
Fe_2O3	51.8	33.08	30.01	32.08

Figure 7. (a) XRD plot, (b) Hysteresis loop (c) XRF of feed and Nonmag fractions of different experiments.

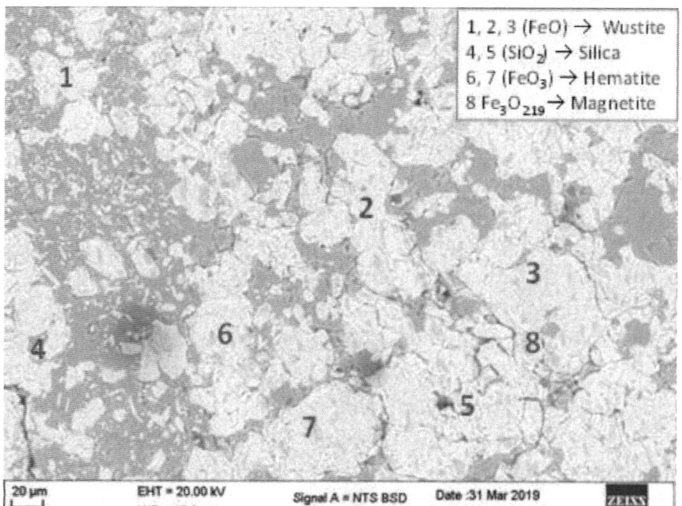

Figure 8. Backscattered electron micrograph and EDS analysis of reduced particles at 900 W, 20 min, 6% GNS.

4. Conclusions

In this study, up-gradation of low grade, banded hematite jasper is investigated. The conventional reduction with charcoal and GNS yielded an iron grade of 39-46% with an iron recovery of 94-99%. The formation of wustite phase inhibits the iron enrichment in the product. The microwave reduction offers suitable iron enrichment and shows a similar trend irrespective of reductants. GNS being economical and abundantly available was evaluated by Taguchi L_9 statistical design optimization. The optimal condition includes 900W power, 20 min time, 3% carbon and yielded a concentrate Fe_G 58.08%, Fe_R 85.61% with a yield of 54.53%. It is concluded that microwave carbothermal reduction employing cheap and abundant reductant GNS offers controlled reduction and the resulting concentrate can be used for blast furnace feedstock.

References

[1] IBM, Indian Minerals Yearbook (Part- III: Mineral Reviews) 2017 56th edition: IRON ORE
[2] Rath S S, Rao D, Dhawan N, Das B, Mishra B K 2014 *Separ. Sci. Technol.* **49** 1927
[3] Das B, Mishra B K, Prakash S, Das S K, Reddy P S R, Angadi S I 2010 *Int. J. Miner. Metall. Mater.* **17** 675
[4] Makhija D, Mukherjee A K, Ghosh T K 2013 Int. J. min. Eng. Miner. Process. **2** 8
[5] Iwasaki I, Prasad M S 1989 Miner. Process. Extra. Metall. Rev. **4** 241
[6] Faris N, Tardio J, Ram R, Bhargava S, Pownceby I 2017 Miner. Eng. **114** 37
[7] Singh S, Sahoo H, Rath S S, Palei B B, Das B, 2015 J. Central. South Univ. **22** 437
[8] Das S K, Prasad R, Singh R P 2018 *Trans. IIM* **17** 1357
[9] Ray N, Nayak D, Dash N, Rath S S 2018 *Clean Technol. Environ. Policy* **20** 1767
[10] Walkiewicz J W, Clark A E, McGill S L 1991 *IEEE Trans. industry applications* **27** 239
[11] Tavares L M, King R P1999 *KONA Powder and Particle J* **17** *163*
[12] Standish N, Huang W 1991 *ISIJ Int.* **31** 241
[13] Kingman S W, Roason N A 2000 J. Microwave and Electromagnetic Energy **35** 144.
[14] Ishizaki K, Nagata K 2008 *ISIJ Int.* **48** 1159.
[15] Pickles C A 2009 Miner. Eng. **22** 1112.
[16] Barani K, Koleini S J, Rezaei B 2011 *Separ. Purif. Technol.* **76** 331.
[17] Omran M, Fabritius T, Elmahdy A M, Abdel-Khalek N A, El-Aref M, Elmanawi A E H 2014 *Separ. Purif. Technol.* **136** 223.
[18] Hartlieb P, Toifl M, Kuchar F, Meisels R, Antretter R 2016 Miner. Eng. **91** 34.
[19] Hayashi M, Takeda K, Kashimura K, Watanabe T, Nagata K 2013 *ISIJ Int.* **53** 1125.
[20] Rath S S, Dhawan N, Rao D S, Das B, Mishra B K 2016 Powder Technol. **301** 1016.
[21] Yu J, Han Y, Li Y, Gao P 2017 Int. J. of Miner. Process. **168** 102.
[22] Han H, Duan D, Yuan P., Chen S 2015 *Ironmaking & Steelmaking*. **42** 542.
[23] Hu M, Wei R, Hu M, Wen L, Ying F 2018 *JOM The J. Mineral. Met. Mater. Soc.* **70** 1443.
[24] Mishra S, Roy G G 2016 Metall. Trans. B. **47B** 2347.

Acknowledgments

The authors would like to thank and acknowledge the funding agency Science Engineering Research Board (SERB) for providing early-career research funds via grant ECR/00874/2016.

IOP Conf. Series: Materials Science and Engineering **641** (2019) 012009 doi:10.1088/1757-899X/641/1/012009

Evaluation of geometric properties of regular and irregular particles of chalcedonite enrichment products from pulsating laboratory jig by means of dynamic image analysis method (DIA)

D Krawczykowski, A Krawczykowska, T Gawenda and A Nad

AGH, University of Science and Technology, Faculty of Mining and Geoengineering, Department of Mineral Processing and Environmental Engineering,Cracow, Poland

E-mail: gawenda@agh.edu.pl

Abstract. The aim of the paper was to evaluate the geometrical properties of regular and irregular chalcedonite particles contained in enrichment products obtained in a laboratory ring jig. Investigative programme included carrying out the tests of aggregate enrichment together with the vision analysis of regular and irregular particles of feed and enrichment products obtained from different layers of the jig bed. Various types of shape coefficients were calculated and the most effective among them for the assessment the particle shape, were selected. The particle size distribution of the feed and their enrichment products according to the minimum Feret's diameter, were also determined. The results obtained by the vision system were discussed in the context of its potential utilization in evaluation of the enrichment process of mineral aggregates in a water jig.

1. Introduction

The quality of mineral aggregates depends on many aspects, concerning their physical and mechanical properties, mineralogical composition and the method of their processing and treatment. Particle size is often regarded as a key parameter, because it preliminary determines an arrangement of technological circuit of their processing, especially in terms of application of specific comminution devices. Such devices operates with different effectiveness, depending the particle size composition of the feed, fines content, material's purity, achieving various technological [5,21], economic [20] and ecological effects [19]. A shape of particle appears to be also a very important feature, that usually classifies particles as regular and irregular ones. The yield of such particles in mineral aggregate products depends, to a large extent, on crushing technology and their geomechanical properties. The aggregate is considered of the highest quality, when it contains cubic particles, i.e. with shape similar to a sphere (regular), while the lower quality aggregate contains flat particles, with a large surface-to-volume ratio (irregular). There are many studies on evaluation of the properties of regular and irregular particles and their impact on the quality of the obtained product aggregates, in particular concretes and asphalt mixtures [4,6,7,12,16,18]. In geomechanics of soils, the shape of particles affects their strength, stability, degree of compaction and other mechanical parameters [3,14]. The particle shape also plays an important role in the technologies of mechanical processing of raw materials, especially in hydraulic classification, gravity beneficiation, and compaction [9,10,15].

IOP Conf. Series: Materials Science and Engineering **641** (2019) 012009 doi:10.1088/1757-899X/641/1/012009

At the same time, the shape of a particle is a contractual term, because it can be determined by means of various methods, according to different classification, with using of different shape factors and measurement techniques. One of the oldest methods of particle shape description is the Zingg classification, which divides the particles into cubic, flat, plane-column and column [11]. Currently, two standards: PN-EN 933-3:2012 and PN-EN 933-4:2008 are commonly used [13].

Some video techniques, utilizing computer image analysis for determination the shape of particles, are also available for application. Significant automation of mechanical stages of measurement (i.e. microscopic) allows to increase the representative number of particles in the measurement, however, the methods based on the microscope utilize 2D image analysis, therefore they generate incomplete information because the analyzed particles are always situated in the most stable position [1,2].

The article tries to apply this technique for evaluation of particle's shape by means of commonly known indices like: Aspect Ratio, Convexity and Circularity. Particle size distributions of regular and irregular particles were also determined, utilizing the minimum Feret's diameter as a measure.

2. Materials and Methods

The Analysette 28 ImageSizer vision system, using a dynamic image analysis, was applied in analyses. The analyzer produces a stroboscopic effect utilizing a pulsating light source, and camera records images at high speed and interchangeable optical systems. The vision system records the images of particles in motion with the speed of up to several hundred objects per second. The measurement is performed for dry particles, falling down in front of the camera lens. The recorded particles are then subjected to computer image analysis, on the basis of which their basic geometrical parameters can be determined. The principle of operation of the vision system is similar to the measurement with using a microscope - the camera records the image of particles, and then the computer software analyzes the shape and size of each particle separately. Microscopic measurement, however, is a static measurement and allows for analyzing of only few particles at a time. The DIA method makes it possible to measure particles in motion. Free movement leads to random orientation of particles and actual shape and size of individual particle can be accurately determined. The continuous feeding of dispersed particles results in reliable and representative measurement results, obtained on the basis of large number of registered particles at a high level of statistical confidence. Thanks to such manner of measurement, about ten thousand images per minute can be analyzed, not just a few. The idea of measurement is shown in Figure 1.

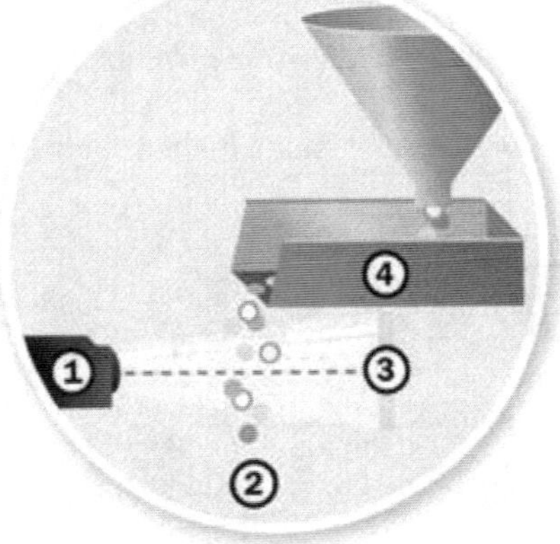

Figure 1. The method of particle size and shape measurement by means of DIA; 1 – camera, 2 – measurement volume, 3 – light source, 4 – feeder (source: www.fritsch.de).

IOP Conf. Series: Materials Science and Engineering **641** (2019) 012009 doi:10.1088/1757-899X/641/1/012009

The feed material was a chalcedonite mineral sample containing regular and irregular particles, the material with some interested properties, especially in terms of densities of individual particles, what determines its wide industrial application [17]. The feed material was initially classified on a slotted bas sieve into narrow size fraction 6.3 – 8 mm, subjected to a vision analysis. The material was then subjected to the enrichment process in a laboratory ring jig, and after 5 minutes of device's operation there were obtained various products located in individual layers of the jig bed [8].

After laboratory experiments involving the enrichment of regular grains and irregular chalcedonite particles in the mentioned particle size class, four products from different layers of the jig bed were obtained. The first product (I) was the bottom one, while the fourth (IV) constituted the upper layer of the material. In addition to the feed, the products of regular and irregular particles enrichment were also subjected to analyzes aimed at determination of differences in geometrical parameters of particles, and thus at examination the effect of aggregate beneficiation. There were specified among others: particle size distributions expressed by the minimum Feret diameter and shape factors: Aspect Ratio AR, Cx (convexity), and C (circularity), according to the formulas:

$$AR = \frac{d_{Fmin}}{d_{Fmax}} \quad (1)$$

$$Cx = \frac{A}{(A+B)} \quad (2)$$

$$C = \frac{4\pi D}{P_c^2} \quad (3)$$

where:
d_{Fmin} – minimal Feret's diameter,
d_{Fmax} – maximum Feret's diameter,
A – convex surface of the particle,
B – concave surface of the particle,
D – particle's surface,
Pc –normalized measure of the number of edges of 0, 45, 90 and 135 degrees in the object (Crofton parameter).

3. Results analysis

Figures 2 and 3 show exemplary shapes of regular and irregular chalcedonite particles from the feed, generated by means of computerized image analysis. An analysis of the shapes of these particles indicates the visible sharpness and irregularity in shapes of irregular particles comparing to regular ones. Extreme lengthening of size proportions for some irregular particles in relation to regular ones in 2D projection as well as their irregular outline, obtained for the same particle size class but separately for regular and irregular particles, indicates for much higher flatness of irregular particles.

Figure 2. Regular particles of chalcedonite feed in particle size fraction 6.3-8mm.

Figure 3. Irregular particles of chalcedonite feed in particle size fraction 6.3-8mm.

Averaged results of the distribution of the three analyzed particle shape coefficients, obtained for the feed with regular and irregular particles, are presented in Fig 4. Analyzing these graphs, it is clearly visible that the coefficient, which apparently indicates differences in chalcedonite particle size, is the circularity (C). Average values of the calculated shape coefficients for feed with regular particles were respectively: ARmean = 0.708, Cxmean = 0.918, Cmean = 0.847, while for irregular ones the results were lower: ARmean = 0.696, Cxmean = 0.914, Cmean = 0.822.

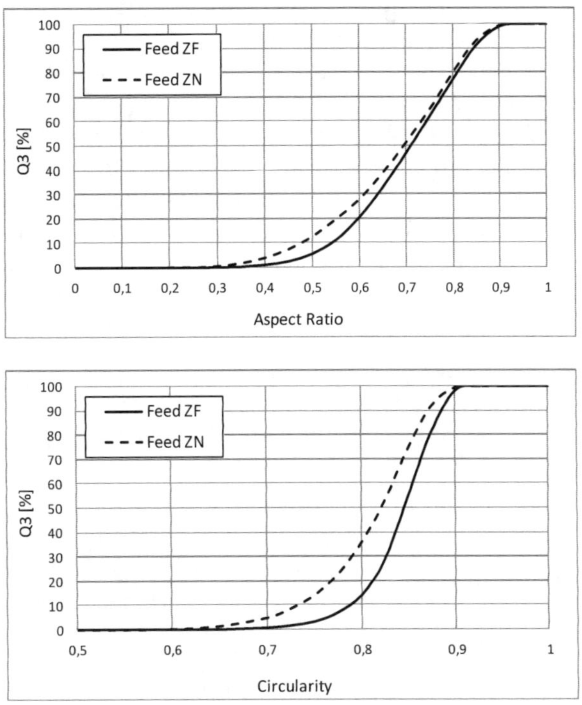

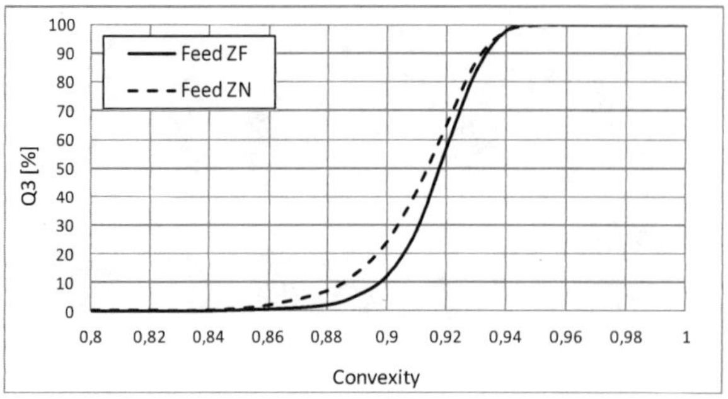

Figure 4. Distribution of selected shape coefficients for regular and irregular particles of chalcedonite feed material .

Analysis of the particle size distribution according to the minimum Feret's diameter d_{Fmin} carried out for the tested feed with regular and irregular particles, prepared on slotted sieves in the particle size class 6.3-8mm, shows the differences in their particle size (Figure 5). The feed material with irregular particles have contained twice as many fine particles (below 5mm). The vision system for these particles has been recording dynamically the smallest third dimension of irregular particles, indicating their flatness, as the minimum Feret's diameter and thus decreased the result of particle distribution. In the area of intermediate particles physically measured on 6.3 mm and 8 mm slot sieves, dynamic image analysis measuring their particle size distribution according to d_{Fmin} underestimates the proportion of irregular particles in the feed. However, it overestimates the yield of these particles in the upper particle size range, close to the size of 8 mm. This is due to the fact that irregular particles are randomly registered by the vision system also in the orientation displaying the two largest dimensions, without capturing the third - the smallest, and that one informs about the flatness (irregularities) of these particles. These two larger dimensions of irregular particles are usually greater than the corresponding dimensions of regular particles within the same particle size class. Differences in the distribution of particles between regular and irregular ones are therefore directly related to differences in their shape. It can be assumed that the differences would be greater by application of the 3D technique, which in each case takes into account the third dimension of the particle, and not only randomly in the case of a convenient orientation of the particle, like in the case of the DIA method.

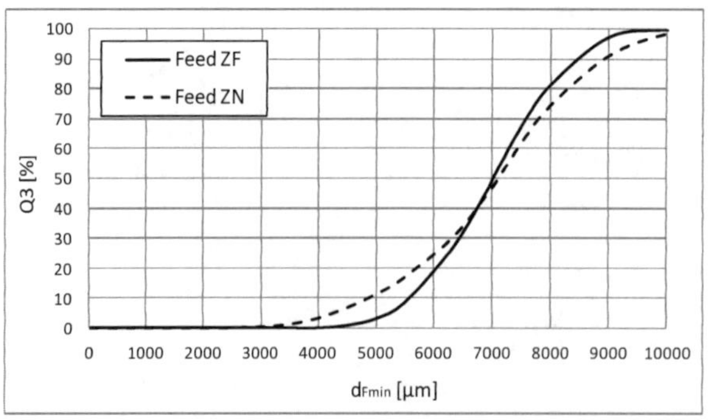

Figure 5. Cumulative particle size distribution functions of chalcedonite feed with regular (ZF) and irregular (ZN) particles.

The products of chalcedonite enrichment, containing regular and irregular particles, were subjected to further visual analyses. A comparative analysis of irregular particles indicates small differences in the particle size of individual enrichment products, but it points on a significantly finer graining in relation to the feed containing irregular particles, especially in the bottom product (I). Fine particles in enrichment products of irregular particles feed could be generated due to mechanical breaking of flat particles, which are also weaker. Confirmation of this phenomenon can also be seen in the variations of the Circularity and Convexity shape coefficients, especially in relation of the feed material to the enrichment products from the lowest layer (I) (Fig. 6). The fine particles that were formed in this way, have to a large extent the circular shapes. This is confirmed (Fig. 7) by concentration of these particles in the upper left corner of the graph (black dots), which are characterized by high values of the C aspect ratio within the fine particles below 4mm. Analyzing the distribution of Convexity coefficient (Fig. 6), it can be also seen that irregular particles of chalcedonite (flat, often fragile with low strength properties) after the enrichment process in the water jig have a smoother surface (higher Cx coefficient in relation to the feed). This may be due to the washing effect of water.

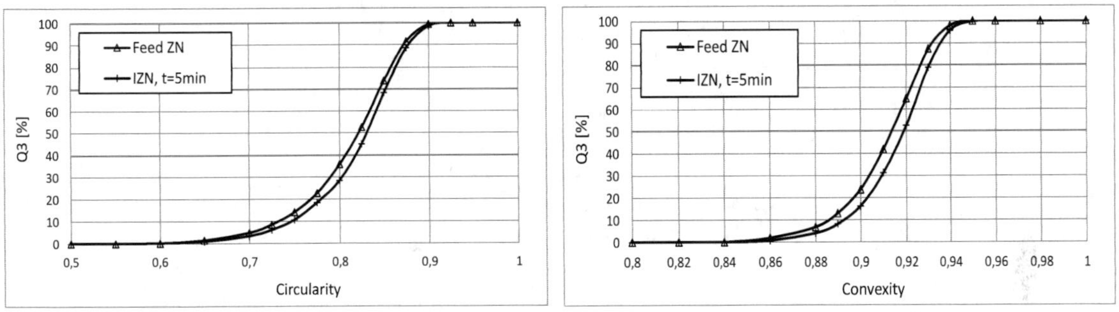

Figure 6. Distributions of the circle and convexity coefficients for the feed particles as well as for enrichment products in the first (I) lowest layer of the jig bed for irregular particles.

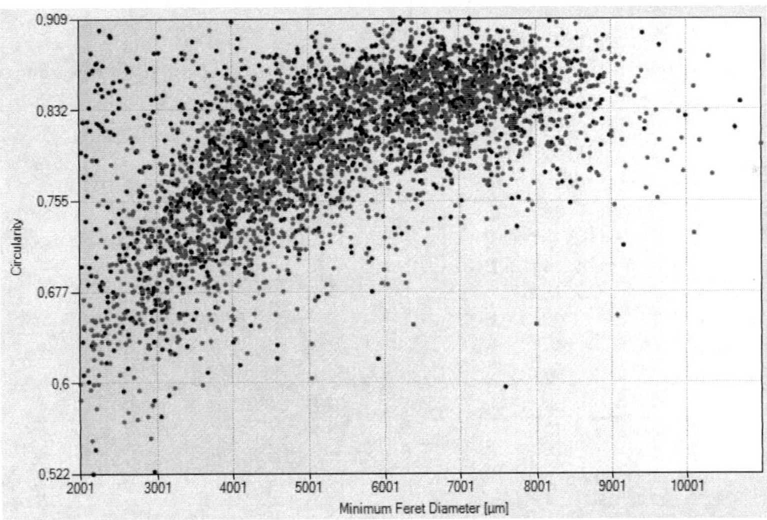

Figure 7. Distribution of circularity coefficient C for the feed with irregular particles and the enrichment product from the lowest layer of the jig, in relationship to the size of particles.

Comparing the shape coefficients of particles in individual layers of the jig there can be seen differences in their values between the lowest (I) and upper (IV) one. Particles in the bottom layer have smoother surface (higher values of Cx coefficient) and a more circular shape (higher C coefficient values), while particles in upper layers have a more irregular surface and less spherical shapes. The speed of sinking for these particles is therefore lower and for that reason they concentrate in the top layers of the jig bed. This shows that the enrichment effect occur even within the same category of regular and irregular particles. In the mixture of regular and irregular particles, the effect of separation, and thus enrichment of the mixture would be stronger.

An analysis of summary figures with the distributions of the Feret's minimum diameters and convexity and circularity coefficients of both studied populations of particles (Figures 8-10) show the differences in particle size, surface structure and the shape of regular and irregular particles for feed and the products. Samples with irregular particles were characterized by a higher yield of fine grains, they had less circular shape as well as irregular surface.

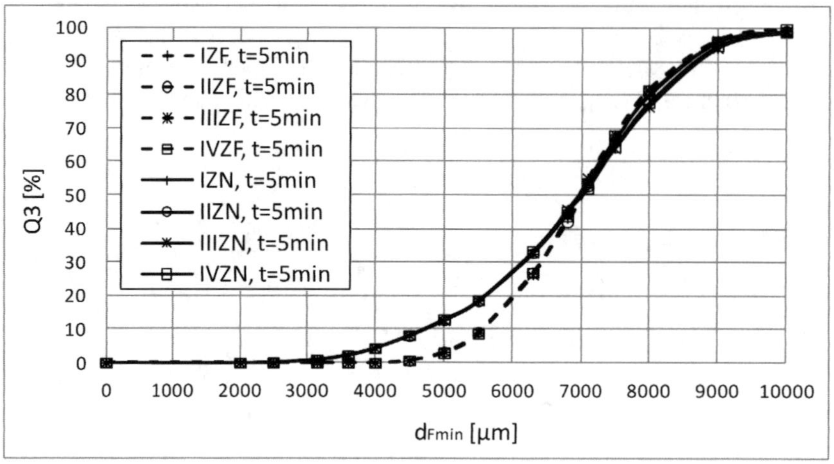

Figure 8. Comparison of particle size distributions of chalcedonite enrichment products for regular and irregular particles.

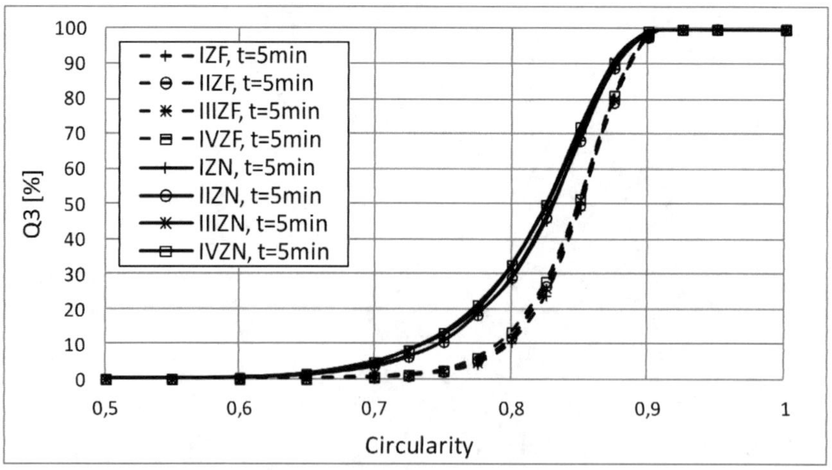

Figure 9. Comparison of Circularity coefficient distributions of chalcedonite enrichment products for regular and irregular particles.

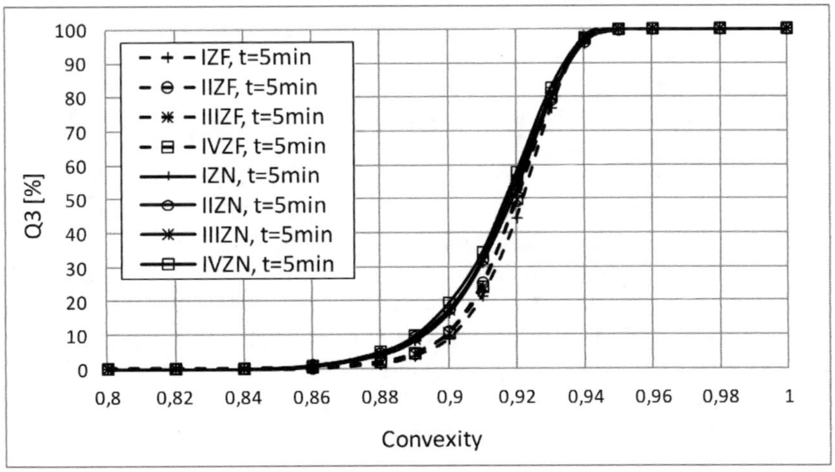

Figure 10. Comparison of Convexity coefficient distributions of chalcedonite enrichment products for regular and irregular particles.

4. Summary and conclusions

The results of investigations show that the shape of particles and a type of measurement method significantly affect the results of particle size measurements by means of vision methods. The dynamic image analysis (DIA) technique gives repeatable and reliable results in terms of the size and shape of chalcedonite particles, differentiating them into regular and irregular grains. The differences in the surface structure and geometry of these particles both for the feed and enrichment products from the individual bed layers of the jig, can be observed. The circularity coefficients C and convexity Cx proved to be the effective coefficients of shape, while the minimum diameter of Feret's Fmin was the effective measure of the size.

These differences could be greater and more visible for a 3D dimensioning technique, which takes into account the particle size distribution and shape of all three dimensions. It seems, therefore, that measurements of the size and shape for irregular (strongly flat) particles should be carried out as far as possible by 3D technique. An application of dynamic image analysis techniques for this purpose, as it was proved in the paper, enables a reliable indication of differences in the geometry of these particles and obtaining representative results, provided, however, a large population of registered particles (minimum few thousand) is used. In such cases, an application of static video measurement technique and the shape of particles, i.e. microscopic image analysis, will be incorrect, because in practice it is difficult to ensure the representativeness of the sample and the registered particles will be placed in the most stable position without the possibility of registering the finest dimension indicating the flatness (irregularities) of these particles. This issue will be a subject of further investigations.

Differences in the structure and geometry of regular and irregular particles between the upper and lower layers of the jig's bed recorded by means of a video measuring system utilizing the DIA technique show that the effect of enrichment of chalcedonite particles occurs even within the same categories of regular and irregular particles.

References

[1] Abbireddy C.O.R., Clayton C.R.I. 2009 A review of modern particle sizing methods. Proceedings of the Institution of Civil Engineers - *Geotechnical Engineering* **162(4)** 193-201

[2] Cavarretta I. 2009 The influence of particle characteristics on the engineering behaviour of granular materials. Ph.D. thesis, Dept. Civil and Environmental Engineering, Imperial College London, London.

[3] Cho G.C., Dodds J., Santamarina J.C. 2006 Particle shape effects on packing density, stiffness, and strength: Natural and crushed sands *Journal of Geotechnical and Geoenvironmental Engineering* **132(5)** 591-602

[4] Fonseca J. 2011 The evolution of morphology and fabric of a sand during shearing. Ph.D. thesis, Dept. Civil Engineering, Imperial College London.

[5] Gawenda T. 2013 The influence of rock raw materials comminution in various crushers and crushing stages on the quality of mineral aggregates *Mineral Resources Management-Gospodarka Surowcami Mineralnymi* **29(1)** 53-65.

[6] Gawenda T. 2015a Innowacyjne technologie produkcji kruszyw o ziarnach foremnych *Górnictwo i Geologia* **22,** Special Issue 1 45-59

[7] Gawenda T. 2015b Zasady doboru kruszarek oraz układów technologicznych w produkcji kruszyw łamanych. Wydawnictwa AGH, Rozprawy Monografie nr **304**, Kraków 1-232.

[8] Gawenda T., Saramak D., Nad A., Surowiak A., Krawczykowska A., Foszcz D. 2019 Badania procesu uszlachetniania kruszyw w innowacyjnym układzie technologicznym *Kruszywa Mineralne* **3** 39-49

[9] Krawczykowski D. 2018 Application of a vision systems for assessment of particle size and shape for mineral crushing products *IOP Conference Series: Materials Science and Engineering* **427** 012013 1–5

[10] Krumbein W.C. 1942 Settling velocity of flume behavior of nonspherical particles. *Transactions of the American Geophysical Union* **41** 621-633

[11] Malewski J. 1984 A comparison of particle shape characteristics of crushed basalt and granite rocks, BULLETIN of the 'assocation internationale de geologie de l'ingenieur, Paris

[12] Malewski J. 2014 Kształt ziaren w produktach kruszenia Kruszywa **3/2014** 52-55

[13] Miśkiewicz W., Utrata A., Trzaskuś-Żak B., Gałaś Z. 2015 Wykorzystanie wskaźników płaskości i kształtu do oceny jakości kruszywa *Przegląd Górniczy* **71(8)** 62–66

[14] Mitchell J.K., Soga K. 2005 Fundamentals of soil behavior. Wiley, New York.

[15] Nad A., Saramak D. 2018 Comparative Analysis of the Strength Distribution for Irregular Particles of Carbonates, Shale, and Sandstone Ore *Minerals* **8(2)** article 37 1-13

[16] Naziemiec Z., Gawenda T., 2006, Ocena efektów rozdrabniania surowców mineralnych w różnych urządzeniach kruszących. VI Konferencja „Kruszywa Mineralne – surowce – rynek – technologie – jakość", Szklarska Poręba, OWPW Wrocław, s. 83-94.

[17] Naziemiec Z., Pichniarczyk P. Saramak D. 2017 Current Issues of Processing and Industrial Utilization of Chalcedonite, *Inżynieria Mineralna* **1** 89-96.

[18] Neville A.M., 2000, Właściwości betonu, Polski Cement, Kraków.

[19] Saramak A., Naziemiec Z., Saramak D. 2016 Analysis of noise emission for selected crushing devices. *Mining Sciences* **23** SI 145-154

[20] Saramak D. 2012 De-agglomeration in high pressure grinding roll based crushing circuits. *Physicochemical Problems of Mineral Processing* **48(1)** 219-226

[21] Wołosiewicz-Głąb M., Ogonowski S., Foszcz D., Gawenda T. 2018 Assessment of classification with variable air flow for inertial classifier in dry grinding circuit with electromagnetic mill using partition curves. *Physicochemical Problems of Mineral Processing* **54(2)** 440-447

Artykuł jest wynikiem realizacji projektu w ramach konkursu NCBiR: konkursu nr 1 w ramach Poddziałania 4.1.4 „Projekty aplikacyjne" POIR w 2017 r., pt.: *Opracowanie i budowa zestawu prototypowych urządzeń technologicznych do budowy innowacyjnego układu technologicznego do uszlachetniania kruszyw mineralnych wraz z przeprowadzeniem ich testów w warunkach zbliżonych do rzeczywistych".* Projekt współfinansowany przez Unię Europejską ze środków Europejskiego Funduszu Rozwoju Regionalnego w ramach Działania 4.1 Programu Operacyjnego Inteligentny Rozwój 2014-2020.

Fundusze Europejskie Inteligentny Rozwój | Rzeczpospolita Polska | Narodowe Centrum Badań i Rozwoju | Unia Europejska

IOP Conf. Series: Materials Science and Engineering **641** (2019) 012010 doi:10.1088/1757-899X/641/1/012010

A method of modeling and control of recycled material to HPGR device in plant scale

Saramak D

AGH, University of Science and Technology, Faculty of Mining and Geoengineering, Department of Mineral Processing and Environmental Engineering,Cracow, Poland

E-mail: dsaramak@agh.edu.pl

Abstract. The aim of the paper is an analysis and assessment of HPGR device effectiveness performance in relationship to the volume of recycled material into press. Analysis was carried out in industrial conditions for HPGR device operating in technological circuit of hard ore processing. Data was collected during six months of HPGR operation. There were determined base characteristics of HPGR crushing operations, as well as relationships between operational parameters of the press and feed properties. It was also determined a model that can be helpful in more effective control of HPGR press. Results of investigation show that too low and too extensive pressure volume results in higher mass of the oversize screening product of HPGR recycled to the press. In order to maintain volume of recycled material according to the plant design the operational pressure of the press should be kept within the range that can be calculated from the proposed model.

1. Introduction

Mineral processing operations in technological circuits of ore processing can be divided into two main types:

- operations of size reduction of the feed material, that aim at liberation useful minerals from the gangue. During (usually) several consecutive stages of crushing and grinding the size of final product from that stage is capable of further treatment in beneficiation processes;
- operations of separation, that are treated as primary ones, because here occurs a concentration of useful minerals in one product (concentrate), while the other (waste) contain mostly the material without useful mineral.

The above classification is a very general characteristics of main idea of mineral processing, without detailed description and distinguishing of further operations within each main type, without a variety of supplementary processes, and finally without analysis of arrangement of technological circuits, what significantly influences throughput and effectiveness of mineral processing.

Operations of size reduction are of significant impact on the recovery of useful mineral, because they entirely determine efficiency of separation, through suitable preparation of feed material for beneficiation operations [2,16]. Operations of comminution are very energy consuming and thus they generate a majority of processing costs, it is estimated, that as high as from 30% to 50%, depending the type of mineral and comminution devices applied [4,13]. For example in Polish copper ore processing, energy cost equals around 30% of total processing costs [3,10].

Apart from energy consumption technological effectiveness of comminution, especially in grinding operations might be a concern, mostly due to the relatively low efficiency of tumble mill operations, where a significant amount of grinding media energy is converter into heat or lost [7,8]. Another problem might be inappropriate design of comminution circuit, especially in terms of nominal throughput of individual crushing and grinding devices and volumes of material stream recycles, what causes not optimal operation of the circuit.

Technological development of comminution methods and application of new technologies of crushing and grinding helps in significant reduction of energy costs. In example, HPGR technology is capable of reducing of as high as even 30-40% of grinding energy comparing to tumbling ball and rod mills [1]. New types of grinding, like vibrating mills and electromagnetic mills also shows potentials in improvement of effectiveness of comminution operations in terms of more favourable fineness and energy savings [14,17].

HPGR technology, designed in mid-70's and developed during next decades [1,11] is regarded as a confirmed method of more efficient comminution of hard ores. Most of concerns concerning the HPGR devices, like increased wear of roll surface, oversize particles, or metal contaminations in HPGR feed, were resolved to some extent. Technological development in rolls production results in constant improvement of the roll's surface servicing time, while systems of tramp metal detectors help in minimizing the risk of roll' damage [12]. However the problems might occur in control of HPGR operation, due to a variety of operational factors that need to be controlled in order to maintain high effectiveness of HPGR work.

Plant operational practice often shows that in case of HPGR ore physical and mechanical properties still can be an issue, because they affect the press throughput and the level of comminution degree index. The presented article deals with the problems of volume of HPGR recycle material and their potential impact on press throughput. Some possibilities of control the level of HPGR recycle are also presented.

2. Materials and Methods

Operational pressure of HPGR is a key-parameter that determines the degree of product fineness. However, the operating pressure level should be suitably selected and maintained during the process. Some results of investigations presented in literature [9] show that too low pressing force might result in less intense comminution. Too excessive pressure in turn, may cause that hard flakes (conglomerate of rock) will be formed in HPGR product. These flakes, despite that they consist in fine particles, are returned to HPGR device. They are too coarse to pass to the undersize product in HPGR screening operation, but at the same time these flakes are too hard to comminute themselves on a screen.

The main aim of the paper was to determine a mathematical relationship between operational pressure (P) and volume of recirculating mass of the product (RF). Investigative programme included analysis of operation of HPGR device in plant condition. The HPGR machine with 100 cm roll's length and nominal throughput (Q) that equalled 100 Mg/h, was crushing the iron ore, and data was collected during 6 months of constant operation. Measurements were performed every 5 minutes. In total more than 50,000 data was obtained. Nominal volume of recycled material was 25%. Figure 1 summarizes a throughput during the analysed time period.

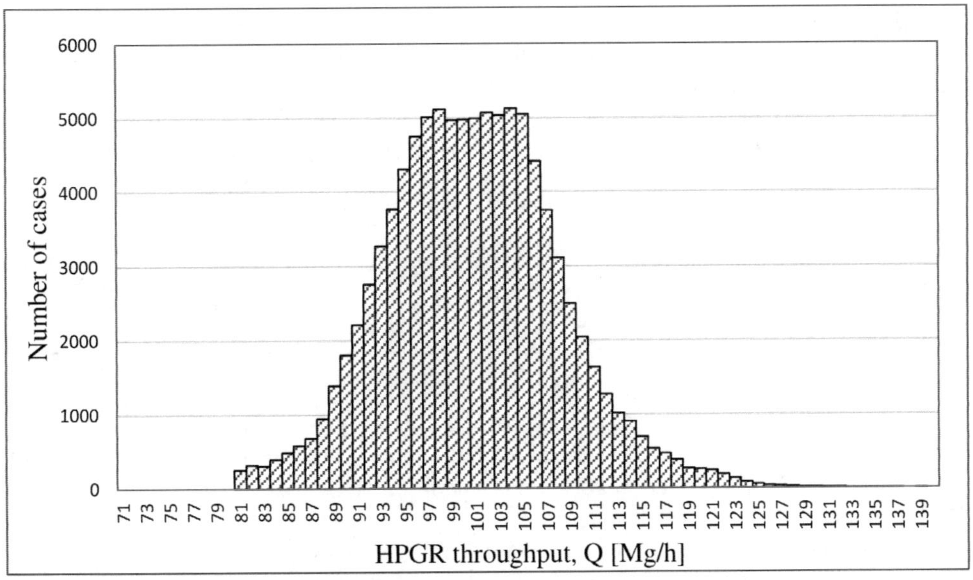

Figure 1. Histogram of press throughput volume in analysed period of time.

Inspecting the figure it can be noticed that the most frequent throughput was between 95 and 105 Mg/h. However it can be also seen that in nearly 50% of cases there were registered throughput lower than 95 Mg/h, and higher than 105 Mg/h.

Figure 2, in turn, shows a histogram of the recycled material. It can be seen that the most frequent values of percentage recycled material were between 20% and 25%, but outside this range there were more than 50% of cases.

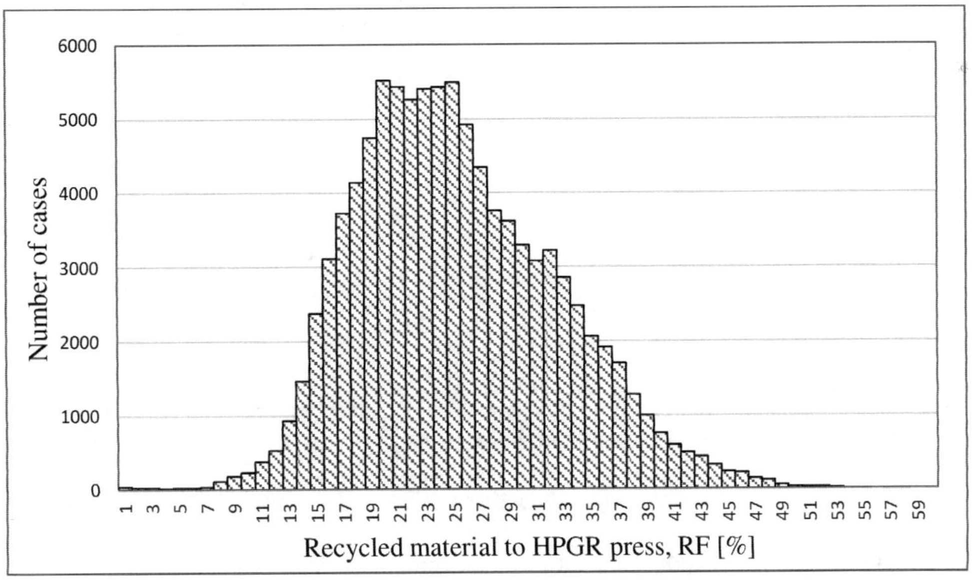

Figure 2. Histogram of the volume of material recycled to HPGR press in analysed period of time.

3. Results of investigations

In the first stage of analysis there were determined linear correlation coefficients between operating pressure and press throughput and recycled material. Results of investigations summarizes Table 1.

Table 1. Values of r-Pearson's correlation coefficient between analyzed parameters.

	Value of r-Pearson correlation coefficient r [%]	
	Throughput (Q)	Recycled material (RF)
Operating Pressure (P)	0.033	0.019
Throughput (Q)	-	0.664

Both coefficient are statistically significant of probability level (1 – α) = 0.95. It should be pointed out that considering the huge dataset (over 50,000 cases) presented correlations are significant, however the lowest value of correlation between (P) and (RF) may indicate that there exists the other type of correlation (non-linear).

In the next stage of analysis there were presented values of operating pressure vs. level of recycled material. To do that the values of RF were averaged in each range of operating pressure every 1 bar. Results are presented in Fig. 3.

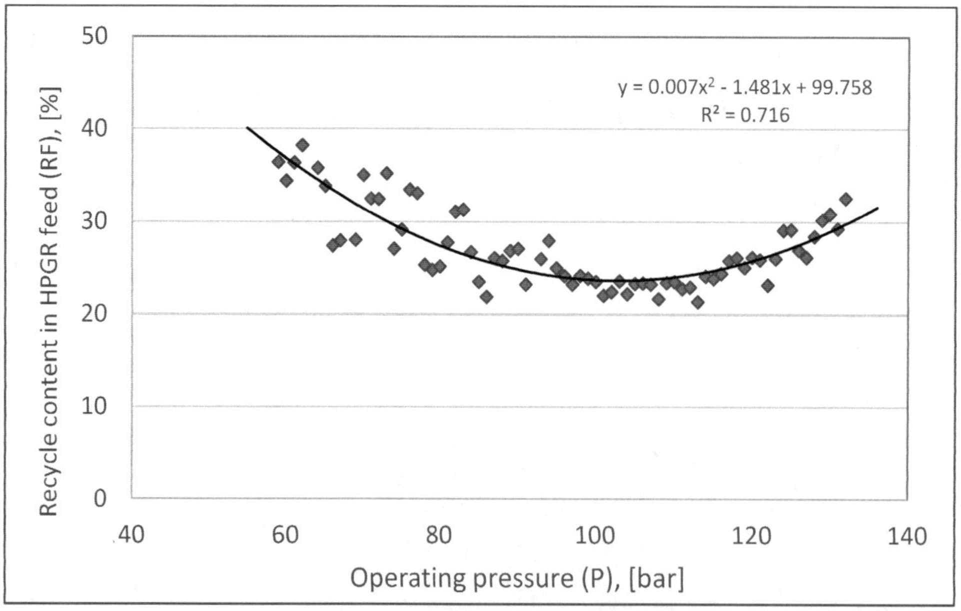

Figure 3. Relationship between operating pressure (P) and volume of recycled material (RF) in the analysed case of HPGR operation.

4. Discussion

Analysis of the Fig. 3 shows that the content of the recycled material in HPGR feed increases together with increasing the operational pressure. On the other hand, too low pressure also causes an increased content of RF in HPGR feed. This case is logical and easy for explanation. When operating pressure (P) is too low, a degree of comminution in HPGR is also lower, because relatively weaker forces act on the material bed in working chamber between the rolls of HPGR press. The HPGR product is coarser, therefore there are more of an oversize particles on the HPGR screen, that are recycled to the press for re-crushing. The case with too excessive pressure can be explained too, but this also depends on the susceptibility of material for conglomeration and forming so-called "flakes". Flakes are a kind of compacted structures of HPGR product that can be formed when very high forces act on the material being comminuted in the press. When the flakes are too hard, to de-agglomerate themselves on the screen, then such structures are recycled to the press. Both cases, described the above, are of a negative impact of comminution effectiveness and HPGR capacity. There are also some other factors influencing formation of flakes (i.e. material moisture), but their analysis is not within the scope of this article.

Results of analysis also show that it is possible to determine a range value of operating pressure for which the HPGR device will be working according to nominal (designed) operational parameters, and thus content of recycled material will not be too high. The model describing the volume of recycled material as a value dependent on operating pressure, can be described as follow:

$$\mathrm{RF} = 0.007 * \mathrm{P}^2 - 1.481 * \mathrm{P} + 99.758 \tag{1}$$

where:
RF – volume of HPGR product recycled to the press, [%],
P – operational pressure, [bar].

Formula (1) has relatively high value of determination coefficient R^2 that equals 0.716. It means that nearly 60% of the phenomenon under analysis (i.e. volume of RF) can be described by means of this model. Considering a huge database (over 50,000 cases) this result can be regarded as very accurate.
Assuming that the maximum content of RF in HPGR feed is known, it is possible to determine such range of operating pressure, for which the RF level will not be exceeded. Calculations can be performed also in opposite way, i.e. what values of operating pressure should be accepted in order to maintain a given value of RF.

5. Summary and conclusions

The presented paper concerned the relationship between operational pressure and volume of recycled HGR product. The research programme confirmed that it is possible to determine a relationship between operational pressing force (P) and HPGR recycled material (RF). The polynomial shape of this curve indicate that both too low and too excessive pressure results in higher content of recycled HPGR product into HPGR feed. This also lead to decreased HPGR efficiency in terms of throughput and achieved comminution degree. It is worth to mention that even though the fineness of crushing products are generally higher together with increasing of operational pressure, it is true within a certain range. Further increases of (P) cause relatively lower increases of comminution degree S_x and a significant content of flakes in HPGR product is becoming a problem with even higher pressure volume.

Results of investigations also show that it is possible to calculate such an operating pressure that maximizes technological effect in terms of the level of recirculated material. The determined functional relationship is true for the investigated type of ore, but it is also possible to adjust the model for the other types of material That may indicate, that a range of optimal value of pressure that maximizes technological (fineness, recycled material) and economical (energy consumption) effects of the press operation, can be determined.

References

[1] Daniel, M J Morrell S 2004 HPGR model verification and scale-up *Minerals Engineering* **17** (11/12), 1149-1161
[2] Gawenda T. 2013 The influence of rock raw materials comminution in various crushers and crushing stages on the quality of mineral aggregates. *Mineral Resources Management-Gospodarka Surowcami Mineralnymi* **29(1)** 53-65

[3] Gawenda T., Saramak D., Foszcz D., Krawczykowski D., Krawczykowska A., Lewandowski D. 2018 An assessment of influence of selected characteristics of feed on the results of ball mill grinding process course for polish copper ores. *Archives of Mining Sciences* **63(1)** 125-137
[4] Hilden M Suthers S 2010 Comparing energy efficiency of multipass high pressure grinding roll (HPGR) circuits *XXV International Mineral Processing Congress (IMPC) 2010, Proceedings* The Australasian Institute of Mining and Metallurgy, Brisbane, 801-811.
[5] Konieczny A., Kasińska-Pilut E., Pilut R. 2009 Problemy technologiczne i techniczne procesu przeróbki mechanicznej rud miedzi w świetle działalności i roli Oddziału Zakłady Wzbogacania Rud KGHM Polska Miedź S.A. *Cuprum* **1,2** 34-46
[6] Krzemińska M., Malewski J. 2011 Energochłonność operacji przygotowania rud do wzbogacania w kopalniach LGOM. *Przegląd Górniczy* **67(7-8)** 143-147
[7] Lowrison G.C. 1974 Crushing and grinding: The size reduction of solid materials. *Butterworths London*
[8] Lynch A.J. 1977 Mineral crushing and grinding circuits. *Elsevier Sci. Publ. Company, N.Y.-Amsterdam-Cambridge.*
[9] Saramak, D., Kleiv, R.A., 2013 The effect of feed moisture on the comminution efficiency of HPGR circuits. *Minerals Engineering* **43-44** 105-111
[10] Saramak D., Młynarczykowska A., Krawczykowska A. 2014 Influence of a high-pressure comminution technology on concentrate yields in copper ore flotation processes. *Archives of Metallurgy and Materials* **59(3)** 951-955
[11] Schönert, K 1979 Aspects of the physics of breakage relevant to comminution *Fourth Tewksbury Symposium,* University of Melbourne
[12] Smit I 2005 Bench scale ore characterization using the High Pressure Grinding Roll *Randol HPGR Workshop 2005*, Perth, August 22
[13] Thromans D. 2008 Mineral comminution: energy efficiency considerations. *Minerals Engineering* **21(8)** 613-620
[14] Tomach P. 2017 Study of intensification of the milling process in the vibratory mill. *Przemysł Chemiczny* **96 (9)** 1893-1897
[15] Tumidajski T., Kasińska-Pilut E., Gawenda T., Naziemiec Z., Pilut R. 2010 Investigation of grinding process energy consumption and grindability of lithologic components of polish copper ores. *Mineral Resources Management-Gospodarka Surowcami Mineralnymi* **26 (1)** 61-72
[16] Wolosiewicz-Glab M., Ogonowski S., Foszcz D., Gawenda T. 2018 Assessment of classification with variable air flow for inertial classifier in dry grinding circuit with electromagnetic mill using partition curves. Physicochemical Problems of Mineral Processing **54 (2)** 440-447
[17] Wolosiewicz-Glab, Marta; Ogonowski, Szymon; Foszcz, Dariusz 2016 Construction of the electromagnetic mill with the grinding system classification of crushed minerals and the control system. *IFAC PAPERSONLINE* **49 (20)** 67-71

Acknowledgments
The paper was the result of AGH UST statutory work no. 11.11.100.276.

IOP Conf. Series: Materials Science and Engineering **641** (2019) 012011 doi:10.1088/1757-899X/641/1/012011

The efficiency of engaged capital in the WIG-mining index

Kruk S

Cracow University of Economics, Department of Economics and Organization of Enterprises, Rakowicka 27, 31-510 Krakow, Poland

E-mail: kruks@uek.krakow.pl

Abstract. The main goal of the article is to analyse the relationship between the level of debt and the level of efficiency of using the invested capital. The article is based on the analysis of the subject literature and the use of financial analysis tools. The analysis confirmed the relationship between the debt ratio and Return on Invested Capital. Conducted considerations should be treated as a starting point for further in-depth analysis regarding the impact of the capital structure on the effectiveness of the enterprise.

1. Introduction

The volatility of business processes and the associated instability of the environment doesn't have a local character, but global. This translates into business conditions which force enterprises to undertake activities aimed at proper adaptation to the changing environment. All this is related to the creation of new conception and assumptions oriented at improving the efficiency and effectiveness of operations. In connection with this, the goals and concepts of management are constantly evolving. Nowadays it is assumed that the main goal of business management is to increase its market value [1], which leads to the maximization of the owner's benefits. These benefits are manifested in the form of dividends and / or long-term increases in the value of shares, which should be higher than the increase in inflation. It should be noted that this goal can only be achieved if the postulate of survival and development is realized, as this determines the implementation of the other objectives of the enterprise. The necessity to implement such a formulated postulate dominates especially during periods of instability of the economic system and downturn. In addition, it should be noted that the indicated goal is correlated with the goal expressed in terms of neoclassical, understood as maximizing profit. Profit as a source of paid dividends is related to the benefits of the owners.

However, the main objective, formulated as maximizing the owner's benefits, causes a number of controversies, the source or this is the approach to interest groups. The attention is drawn to the fact that the company should not act only to increase its value and maximize the benefits of the owners. Company is an integral part of society, so in the process of its activity the needs and interests of other stakeholder groups should be taken into account. Shareholders, as the last group of interest, after creditors, contractors, local and central authorities benefit in the generated value [2]. In addition, in well-run enterprises, value is created not only for owners.

The level of achievement of objectives set by the business owners, including the increase in the value of the enterprise and the profitability of the invested capital, can be determined using detailed financial measures, among which the following should be mentioned [3]:

- Earning Before Interests and Taxes – EBIT or Net Profit,
- Return on Invested Capital - ROIC,
- Return on Equity – ROE,

- Economic Value Added – EVA,
- Net Cash Flow – NCF,
- the current value of the enterprise – market or economic,
- Market Value Added – MVA.

Using mentioned measures, it is possible to set to what extent the company's activity determines the improvement of its financial results and the fulfilment of investors' expectations.

In this work, the interest is covered by the Rate of Return on Invested Capital which reflects the effectiveness of the capital made available to the enterprise by its owners and creditors. Because enterprises in Poland are eager to use foreign capital, the question is whether changes in its involvement translate into the effectiveness of using the invested capital. Thus, the purpose of the article was to check whether there are links between the debt ratio of enterprises and the effectiveness of capital employed. Therefore, a research hypothesis was put forward that assumes that changes the Debt Ratio translates into a change of Return on Invested Capital in the subsequent period.

2. The engaged capital

In the economic sense, capital means resources of produced goods that are not consumed on an ongoing basis and which have been left to continue production. Sometimes this concept is related to the aspect of human capital, understood as the skills acquired by people in the course of gaining experience or training. In the aspect of credit or loans, capital is identified with the amount of a loan or loan [4]. In the context of accounting, capital is identified with the concept of net assets, defined by the Accounting Act as assets of an enterprise less its liabilities, and therefore corresponding to its own capital (fund). However, in the analysis of the method of financing the entity, capital in a simplified way is understood as the sum of funds entrusted by investors for financing the activity.

In general, the capital financing the enterprise's activity is divided into equity and foreign capital. Equity capital is divided into share capital, supplementary capital and provisions. Foreign capital, on the other hand, includes long-term liabilities, i.e. those which maturity date is longer than one year and short-term liabilities which maturity date is not longer than one year. Every investor expects measurable benefits when deciding on the involvement of his capital in the company. Shareholders are interested in receiving dividends and increasing the value of shares, while donors of foreign capital are expected to receive a certain amount of interest. A. Duliniec draws attention to the fact that the basic measure of the effectiveness of the capital employed is Return on Invested Capital ratio. This indicator shows the profitability of equity investments in the enterprise carried out by the owners and creditors. It illustrates changes resulting from the operating activity of the company. It needs to be stressed that it is insensitive to the leverage effect. It is assumed that it should be at least equal to the rate of return expected by investors. Its level can be related to the weighted average cost of capital level. If Return on Invested Capital exceeds the weighted average cost of capital level, it means that the effects related to capital involvement exceed the costs of its acquisition and therefore the value of this capital is multiplied. And the level of Economic Value Added will take positive value [5]. If the rate of Return on Invested Capital would be lower than the level of the weighted average cost of capital, it means that the operational efficiency of the invested capital is lower than the costs of its acquisition, and therefore it will translate into a negative level of Economic Value Added.

Invested Capital can be defined as the sum of cash invested by investors, but the sources of their origin are irrelevant [6]. It includes both own capital and foreign capital. At the same time, it does not include liabilities from which interests are not paid, including, for example, liabilities towards suppliers, payroll liabilities, interest-free loans, etc. According to T. Dudycz, when determining the value of invested capital, investments in progress, including advance payments, should not be included in the estimation of the invested capital because they do not contribute to the profit before they are used. The capital invested should therefore be determined according to the following formula [7]:

$$\begin{gathered} \textit{Invested Capital} = \textit{Total assets} - \textit{Intangible goodwill} \\ + \textit{Capitalized operating lease} - \textit{Non interest bearing liabilities} \\ (\textit{short term liabilities excluding loans and borrowings and from issuing debt securities}) - \\ \textit{Passive Accruals} - \textit{Provisions for liabilities} - \\ \textit{Fixed assets under construction including advances} \end{gathered} \tag{1}$$

E. Maćkowiak emphasizes that the invested capital includes ordinary equity, preferred shares, minority share packages, interest-bearing debt and the current value of operating lease [8].

3. Metodology and data

The companies listed on the Warsaw Stock Exchange and qualified for the WIG-mining sector as at June 24, 2019 were admitted to the study. This sector has been taken into account, as it is one of the most important industries and is closely related to the energy security aspect of the country and the issue of environmental protection. The following entities were included: Lubelski Węgiel Bogdanka SA (BOGDANKA), Jastrzębska Spółka Węglowa SA (JSW), KGHM Polska Miedź SA (KGHM), and Prairie Mining Ltd (PRAIRIE). The financial statements based on which the research was conducted were taken from the Notoria Serwis SA database, an enterprise dealing, among others, in the collection and delivery of financial data. The time range of the research was limited by the availability of data and covered the years 2012-2018, which was caused by the lack of availability of the data of the company Pairie Mining Ltd. For the purpose of the analysis, consolidated reports were adopted due to the lack of annual report for Prairie Mining Ltd., which is listed on the Warsaw Stock Exchange since September 2015. It is worth noting that in the companies BOGDANKA, JSW and KGHM the main shareholder is the State Treasury. However, PRAIRIE has Australian roots and is also listed in Australia and London.

Return on Invested Capital has been determined as the Net Operating Profit After Taxes over Invested Capital relationship:

$$ROIC = \frac{NOPAT}{IC} \quad (2)$$

where:
ROIC – Return on Invested Capital
NOPAT – Net Operating Profit After Taxes
IC – Invested Capital

NOPAT was calculated by adjusting operating profit by income tax. Net operating profit after taxes indicates the effects that were obtained from the basic activity of the company, and therefore the one for which it was established [9]. It therefore shows the company's ability to generate income from capital that has been involved in operational assets. At the same time, the origin of capital is not important [3]. Because the tax is calculated from the level of operating profit, it is called the adjusted one, because it does not take into account the benefits obtained by the company and resulting from the use of foreign capital of an interest nature.

The Invested Capital was calculated as equity capital increased by foreign capital on an interest basis. However, its book value was determined, not the market value. In order to calculate the invested capital, the following categories have been adopted, listed in the reports available on the Notoria service: equity shareholders of the parent, non-controlling interests non-current liabilities from derivatives, non-current loans and borrowings, non-current liabilities from bonds, non-current liabilities from finance leases, other non-current liabilities, liabilities from derivatives, financial liabilities (loans and borrowings), bond liabilities and liabilities from finance leases. Because it is important to adopt the value of capital, which was related to the company in individual considered periods, the value of invested capital from the beginning of the year was taken into account for calculations within a given year.

The Debt Ratio was calculated as the relation of sums of liabilities to the value of total assets. This indicator shows the level of involvement of foreign capital in financing the company's assets. Its level illustrates the size of the company's financial risk, and therefore if it reaches too high a level, it implies a risk of losing the ability to service debt. According to the golden rule of financing, it should amount to 50 percent, however, because many enterprises need a larger share of debt to develop their business, it is assumed that it should be in the range of 57-67% [10].

IOP Conf. Series: Materials Science and Engineering **641** (2019) 012011 doi:10.1088/1757-899X/641/1/012011

4. Results and analysis

Net operating profit after taxes was calculated as operating profit adjusted by income tax - tab. 1.

Table 1. NOPAT in WIG-mining index in the years 2012-2018 (in thousands of PLN)

Specification	2012	2013	2014	2015	2016	2017	2018
BOGDANKA	215 249	315 266	344 090	293 475	-264 239	191 976	686 289
JSW	2 193 885	1 059 642	163 539	-627 588	-3 155 760	183 546	2 524 365
KGHM	10 717 920	5 244 750	3 541 320	2 773 440	-3 900 960	-2 607 390	1 035 990
PRAIRIE	921	-41	-3 563	-5 645	-5 644	-4 147	-4 619

Sources: Own study based on Notoria Serwis S.A.

Analysis of data presented in tab. 1. allows to conclude that the companies in question in most cases showed positive effects on the basic activity. The best situation was recorded in BOGDANKA, and the worst in PRAIRA, which in six out of 7 periods considered showed a loss at the operating level, which was caused by low level of sales revenues and high remaining operating costs and relatively high in relation to the level of sales revenues, general management costs. In addition, BOGDANKA showed a systematic increase in the operating profit in 2012-2015. During this period, revenues from sales grew faster than the costs of obtaining them. Other entities in the period indicated a gradual decrease in the level of net operating profit after tax. The critical period was 2016, when all analyzed enterprises showed a loss at the operational level. In the last two years, in the following companies: BOGDANKA, JSW and KGHM, there was an increase in revenues from core operations in relation to costs related to operating activities.

The level of invested capital is presented in tab. 2. As part of the capital invested, none of the companies reported non-current liabilities from finance leases and liabilities from finance leases during the period under consideration.

Table 2. Invested capital in WIG-mining index in the years 2011-2017 (in thousands of PLN)

Specification	2011	2012	2013	2014	2015	2016	2017
BOGDANKA	2 483 646	2 737 374	3 081 763	3 337 989	2 844 017	2 915 762	3 223 646
JSW	8 872 300	8 839 800	8 668 700	8 797 700	5 556 100	5 759 700	7 599 700
KGHM	24 558 000	25 027 000	26 017 000	31 519 000	28 601 000	25 440 000	25 977 000
PRAIRIE	19 236	24 230	13 013	21 332	9 399	18 152	19 479
Average	8 983 295	9 157 101	9 445 119	10 919 005	9 252 629	8 533 403	9 204 956
St. dev.	11 033 035	11 203 818	11 614 459	14 202 005	13 096 200	11 512 223	11 604 990

Sources: Own study based on Notoria Serwis S.A.

The highest level of invested capital in all analyzed periods was demonstrated by KGHM. At the same time, this entity showed the highest value of equity. PIRAIRIE showed the lowest value of equity, however, it should be noted that this company financed its operations mainly by equity. There were no long-term liabilities in any of the periods considered, while in the area of short-term liabilities, financial liabilities appeared only to a small extent in the last three considered periods.

The situation of PRAIRE company is different, which can be explained by the different specificity of this entity. This company has been listed on the Warsaw Stock Exchange since 2015. In 2012, it obtained a license for the exploration of hard coal deposits and since 2012 it has been focusing on the Jan Karski hard coal project in the Lublin Coal Basin. In 2014, exploratory drilling was completed and at the beginning of 2018, the results of tests showing the presence of type 34 coking coal with low ash content were announced. Additionally, in 2016, the company acquired the Dębieńsko Coal Mine to extract coking coal type 35. The presented situation undoubtedly translates into a negative level of operating profit.

In tab. 3. the level of the Return on Invested Capital ratio was presented.

Table 3. Return on invested capital in WIG-mining index in the years 2012-2018

Specification	2012	2013	2014	2015	2016	2017	2018
BOGDANKA	8.67%	11.52%	11.17%	8.79%	-9.29%	6.58%	21.29%
JSW	24.73%	11.99%	1.89%	-7.13%	-56.80%	3.19%	33.22%
KGHM	43.64%	20.96%	13.61%	8.80%	-13.64%	-10.25%	3.99%
PRAIRIE	4.79%	-0.17%	-27.38%	-26.46%	-60.05%	-22.84%	-23.71%
Average	20.46%	11.07%	-0.18%	-4.00%	-34.94%	-5.83%	8.70%
St. dev.	17.70%	8.66%	18.82%	16.75%	27.20%	13.47%	24.71%

Sources: Own study based on Notoria Serwis S.A.

The rate of Return on Invested Capital in the analyzed enterprises decreased in 2012-2016. In 2012, KGHM showed the highest ROIC level. It amounted to 43.64%, which means that one zloty of invested capital brought benefits corresponding to 43.64% of their value. In 2016, all analyzed entities showed
a negative level of ROIC, which means that in the analyzed entities the invested capital was not used effectively. In medium terms, the rate of return on invested capital showed positive values in three of the seven periods considered. From the perspective of the rate of return on invested capital, BOGDANKA should be assessed most positively, as in six of the seven periods analyzed, the capital employed in the company brought the desired results.

The worst performance in the indicated range was demonstrated by the PRAIRIE company, which only in the first of the analyzed periods recorded a positive level of operating profit, and thus a positive ROIC level. The level of debt ratio in the WIG-mining index companies is presented in tab. 4.

Table 4. The debt ratio in WIG-mining index in the years 2012-2018

Specification	2011	2012	2013	2014	2015	2016	2017	2018
BOGDANKA	30.35%	34.11%	36.12%	42.17%	41.75%	39.68%	30.23%	25.00%
JSW	37.99%	39.05%	39.75%	52.71%	66.69%	64.67%	45.23%	38.64%
KGHM	23.68%	35.47%	33.08%	36.77%	44.47%	52.42%	47.88%	48.37%
PRAIRIE	0.64%	0.45%	5.80%	4.63%	9.90%	6.02%	43.81%	26.77%
Average	23.17%	27.27%	28.69%	34.07%	40.70%	40.70%	41.79%	34.69%
St. dev.	16.12%	18.00%	15.50%	20.71%	23.38%	25.27%	7.89%	10.94%

Sources: Own study based on Notoria Serwis S.A.

In medium terms, the share of liabilities and provisions for liabilities increased in subsequent periods. Their highest level was achieved by companies in 2014-2017. In 2017, liabilities and provisions for liabilities corresponded to 41.79% of the value of assets. This was the result of a significant increase in the debt ratio in the PRAIRIE company. The indicated company incurred Financial liabilities (loans and borrowings) during the period and benefited from trade payables which was much larger than in previous years. In addition, in the area of non-current cases, it showed a significant level of non-current provision.

The purpose of the study was to check whether, along with the change in debt, the rate of return on the capital invested changes. Comparison of changes in the Debt Ratio and the rate of Return on Invested Capital allows to conclude that the change in the Debt Ratio in a given year did not translate into
a change in the rate of Return on Invested Capital in the same period.

However, it should be noted that the change in the rate of debt preceded the change in the rate of return on invested capital in the following year, with the change taking the opposite direction in 19 of the 24 cases considered. In 2011-2018:

- an increase in the Debt Ratio preceded the fall of Return on Invested Capital in the next period in 12 of the 24 cases considered,
- the decline in Debt Ratio preceded the increase of Return on Invested Capital in the next period in 7 out of 24 cases considered,
- the decline in Debt Ratio preceded the fall of Return on Invested Capital in the next period in 3 out of 24 cases,
- increase in debt ratio preceded the increase of Return on Invested Capital in the next period in one case.

Therefore, it should be stated that the change in the size of debt affects the change in the effectiveness of the use of capital employed, while in the vast majority of cases it takes the opposite direction.

5. Conclusions

Efficiency is considered as the most important manifestation of rational management, which is one of the conditions for survival on the market [11]. Economic efficiency is defined by the relation of results to expenditures necessary to bear in order to obtain specific effects.

This study attempts to indicate whether the change in the size of debt translates into a change in the Return on Invested Capital. As key findings, it should be pointed out that in 79.17% of cases the change in debt ratio preceded the change in Return on Invested Capital in the next period. In over 63.16% of cases, the increase in debt translated into a decrease in the efficiency of invested capital, and in 36.84% of cases the decline in debt translated into the increase of Return on Invested Capital. This implies the legitimacy of conscious shaping of the capital structure and the use of foreign capital in a way that enables the company to improve the efficiency of its operation, manifesting itself, inter alia, an increase in the level of profit from operating activities, thus improving the efficiency of using the capital employed.

However, due to the relatively small research sample, it seems reasonable to conduct analogous tests for other indices listed on the Warsaw Stock Exchange. In order to obtain confirmation of the conducted analyses, it would be recommended to identify companies with a positive and negative operating profit level, and then carry out analogous considerations in such grouped entities.

References

[1] Damodaran A 2017 *Finanse korporacyjne. Teoria i praktyka* (Gliwice: Wydawnictwo Helion) p 50
[2] Kruk S 2019 Efektywność zainwestowanego kapitału w spółkach sektora WIG-budownictwo *Przedsiębiorczość i zarządzanie* 1 p 218
[3] Duliniec A 2007 *Finansowanie przedsiębiorstwa* (Warszawa: Polskie Wydawnictwo Ekonomiczne) p 52, 75
[4] Gajdka J 2002 *Teorie struktury kapitału i ich aplikacja w warunkach polskich* (Łódź: Wydawnictwo Uniwersytetu Łódzkiego) pp 18-19
[5] Young D 1997 Economic Value Added: A Primer for European Managers *European Management Journal* 15 p 335-343
[6] Stewart G B 1990 *The Quest For Value: The EVA Management Guide* (New York: HarperBusiness) p 86
[7] Dudycz T 2005 *Zarządzanie wartością przedsiębiorstwa* (Warszawa: Polskie Wydawnictwo Ekonomiczne) p 156
[8] Maćkowiak E 2009 *Ekonomiczna wartość dodana* (Warszawa: Polskie Wydawnictwo Ekonomiczne) p 67
[9] Salaga J, Bartosova V and Kicova E 2015 Economic Value Added as a Measurement Tool of Financial Performance *Procedia Economics and Finance* 26 p 484-489
[10] Sierpińska M, Jachna T 2007 *Metody podejmowania decyzji finansowych. Analiza przykładów i przypadków* (Warszawa: Wydawnictwo Naukowe PWN) p 89
[11] 2009 *Pomiar i ocena procesów kreowania wartości w badaniu efektywności przedsiębiorstwa*

ed R Borowiecki (Kraków: Fundacja Uniwersytetu Ekonomicznego w Krakowie) p 13

Acknowledgments

The publication was financed from the funds granted to the Faculty of Management, Cracow University of Economics within the framework of the subsidy for the maintenance of research potential.

Factor analysis in determining the quality of coal

T Niedoba, P Pieta and A Surowiak

AGH, University of Science and Technology, Faculty of Mining and Geoengineering, Department of Mineral Processing and Environmental Engineering,Cracow, Poland

E-mail: tniedoba@agh.edu.pl

Abstract. The separation of coal material of three types of coals originating from three various Polish hard coal mines (types 31, 34.2 and 35, according to Polish nomenclature, which were steam coal, semi-coking coal and coking coal) into particle size fractions and then into particle density fractions was done and then the following parameters were measured for each particle size-density fraction: combustion heat, ash contents, sulfur contents, volatile parts contents, analytic moisture. In this way a 7-dimensional vector of data was created. Using methods of factor analysis the important features of coal were selected, which decide about their membership to individual types. To evaluate the appropriateness of the applied method the Bartlett's sphericity test as well coefficient of Kaiser-Mayer-Olkin (KMO) were used. To select important factors the Kaiser criterion and Cattell's scree test were used. The obtained results were compared with the results obtained in previous works by means of observation tunnels method. The results showed which particular features are crucial to define the type of coal what is also important to select appropriate method of its enrichment.

1. Introduction

Mineral raw materials which are beneficiated in purpose of their using characterize with many factors describing their features. In case of coal, these features are among others ash contents, sulfur contents, combustion heat, volatile parts contents or analytic moisture. The features mentioned above decide about coal quality also in economical aspect. Because of that the preciseness of determining values of these features is very important.

The most often researched properties of the coal are combustion heat, ash contents, sulphur contents, volatile parts contents and moisture. These features are very often highly correlated but also can occur independently . The selection of the necessary factors which influence on individual properties is the goal of the paper. To this purpose three types of coal (according to Polish nomenclature – coal types 31 (steam coal), 34.2 (gas-coking coal) and 35 (orto-coking coal)) were selected to the investigation which were divided into particle size and density fractions. The classification of coals is presented in Table 1.

Table 1. Classification of coal types according to Polish nomenclature [21].

Coal type	Coal number	Volatile parts contents [%]
Steam coal	31	Above 28
Gas-steam coal	32	Above 28
Gas coal	33	Above 28
Gas-coking coal	34	Above 28
Orto-coking coal	35	20-31
Meta-coking coal	36	14-28
Semi-coking coal	37	14-28
Thin coal	38	14-28
Anthracite coal	41	10-14
Anthracite	42	3-10
Meta-anthracite	43	Till 3

The whole group of considered factors were measured for each size-density fraction [14].
The following variables were considered (X_i = 1, 2, …, 5).
X_1 – combustion heat [cal];
X_2 – ash contents [%];
X_3 – sulfur contents [%];
X_4 – volatile parts contents [V^a];
X_5 – moisture [W^a].

2. Materials and methods

The considered types of coal originated from three various Polish coal mines and all of them were initially screened on a set of sieves of the following sizes: -1.00, -3.15, -6.30, -8.00, -10.00, -12,50, -14.00, -16.00 and -20.00 mm. Then, the size fractions were additionally separated into density fractions by separation in dense media using zinc chloride aqueous solution of various densities (1.3, 1.4, 1.5, 1.6, 1.7, 1.8 and 1.9 g/cm^3). The fractions were used as a basis for further consideration and additional coal features were determined by means of chemical analysis. In purpose of appropriate identification of coal type many parameters are being measured which describe coal quality. For each density-size fraction such parameters as combustion heat, ash contents, sulfur contents, volatile parts contents and analytical moisture were determined, making up, together with the mass of these fractions, seven various features for each coal.

The example of obtained data is presented in Table 2.

Table 2. Data for size fraction 14.00-12.50 mm – coal, type 31.

Density [Mg/m^3]	Mass [g]	Combustion heat [cal]	Ash contents [%]	Sulfur contents [%]	Volatile parts contents V^a	Analytical moisture W_a
<1.3	308.6	7048	6.41	0.72	34.32	3.23
1.3-1.4	292.5	5859	19.61	0.7	29.22	3.36
1.4-1.5	36.1	2948	16.55	0.76	28.92	3.87
1.5-1.6	10.7	5117	26.10	1.55	31.08	3.40
1.6-1.7	25.6	4467	35.78	2.28	26.71	2.40
1.7-1.8	139	3920	37.20	1.23	29.24	2.19
1.8-1.9	12.7	3078	48.20	1.13	24.05	2.23
>1.9	601.2	457	86.53	0.40	9.30	0.91

The measurements of X_i were performed for each size-density fraction. Because of the fact that the individual features were measured in various units their standardization was done.

In purpose of selecting significant factors influencing on individual variables, the factor analysis method was applied. To evaluate adequacy of applying factor analysis to this problem two criteria were used: Bartlett's test and Kaiser-Mayer-Olkin coefficient (KMO) [1, 2, 10, 11, 21].

The reduction of variables is done through the Cattell's scree criteria and criterion of sufficient proportion which suggest to apply such number of factors that they explain together at least 85% of variance of all observed variables [22].

3. Results

Applying Bartlett's test it occurred that for all researched cases the value of the test was significantly higher than the critical values on significance level being equal to α=0.0005. The lowest value of the test U was obtained for coal, type 35 in particle density fraction (1.9-2.0) and was equal to 84.74, while the critical value on this level is equal to 31.42. It can be said then that zero hypothesis (that correlation matrix is a unit matrix) should be rejected for all particle size and density fractions.

Furthermore, it can be noticed that in almost all cases the value of KMO coefficient was higher than 0.5. Only for density fraction lower than 1.3 g/cm^3 for coal, type 34.2 and density fraction (1.6-1.7) for coal, type 35 it occurred to be slightly lower than 0.5. That means that the results of Bartlett's test and the values of KMO coefficient gave strong basis to apply factor analysis.

In the work, the reduction of variables is done through the Cattell's scree criteria and criterion of sufficient proportion which suggest to apply such number of factors that they explain together at least 85% of variance of all observed variables [22].

The correlation matrix of the factor Z_j with variable X_i is obtained by creation of matrix Z, which elements are numbers

$$z_{ij} = \sqrt{\lambda_j} a_{ji}, \qquad i,j = 1,2,\dots,5. \tag{1}$$

where: λ_i – i^{th} eigenvalue of correlation matrix; a_{ji} – elements of matrix A which fulfills the condition $A^T = R$, where R is correlation matrix of variables X_j.

The square of number z_{ij} is the percentage of variance changeability explained by the factor Z_j. For example, considering coal, type 31 from the particle size fraction (10-12.5) it is obtained that matrix Z is in form

$$Z = \begin{bmatrix} -0.9813 & 0.1331 & -0.0962 & 0.0676 & 0.0747 \\ 0.9828 & -0.1017 & 0.1145 & -0.0767 & 0.0700 \\ -0.0667 & -0.9963 & -0.0484 & 0.0246 & 0.0033 \\ -0.9793 & -0.0651 & -0.0297 & 0.1893 & -0.0019 \\ -0.9620 & -0.1035 & 0.2487 & 0.0063 & -0.0029 \end{bmatrix} \tag{2}$$

The eigenvalues of the correlation matrix are in this case numbers λ_1=3.8177; λ_2=1.0355; λ_3=0.0875; λ_4=0.0488; λ_5=0.0105.

The plot of scree is presented on Figure 1.

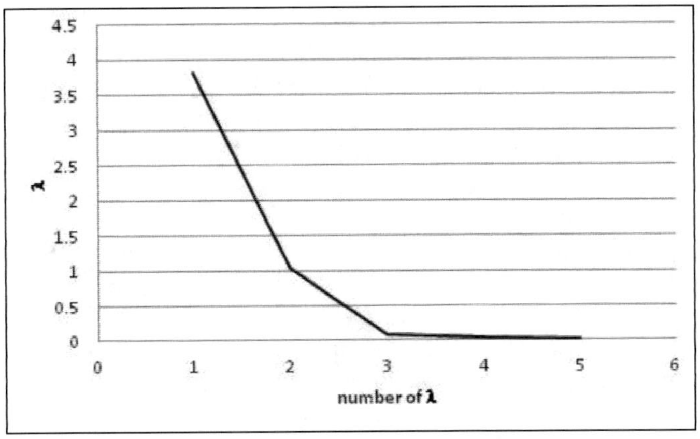

Figure 1. Cattell's scree plot for coal, type 31, particle size fraction (10-12.5)

On the basis of the presented Cattell's scree plot only these factors remain which are located to the left from the point in which a mild decline of eigenvalues is observed. In this case these are factors Z_1 and Z_2.

The group of factors (Z_1, Z_2) explain 98.07% of changeability of combustion heat, 97.12% of changeability of ash contents, 99.71% of changeability of sulfur contents, 96.33% of changeability of volatile parts contents and 93.62% of changeability of moisture.

It is obtained then that factor Z_1 is responsible for variables $\{X_1, X_2, X_4, X_5\}$ and factor Z_2 for variable X_3.

Let consider the particle density fraction (1.6-1.7) of coal, type 34.2

The matrix Z is in form

$$Z=\begin{bmatrix} 0.8566 & -0.4196 & -0.1506 & -0.1824 & 0.3643 \\ -0.5854 & -0.6574 & 0.3863 & 0.1622 & 0.1400 \\ 0.5544 & -0.7491 & -0.2733 & 0.1882 & -0.2073 \\ -0.7229 & -0.5915 & -0.1757 & -0.2615 & -0.0447 \\ -0.4385 & 0.1454 & -0.8755 & 0.0956 & 0.0961 \end{bmatrix} \quad (3)$$

The eigenvalues of correlation matrix in this case are numbers λ_1=2.0993; λ_2=1.5404; λ_3=1.0443; λ_4=0.1727; λ_5=0.1433. The plot of Cattell's scree is presented on Figure 2.

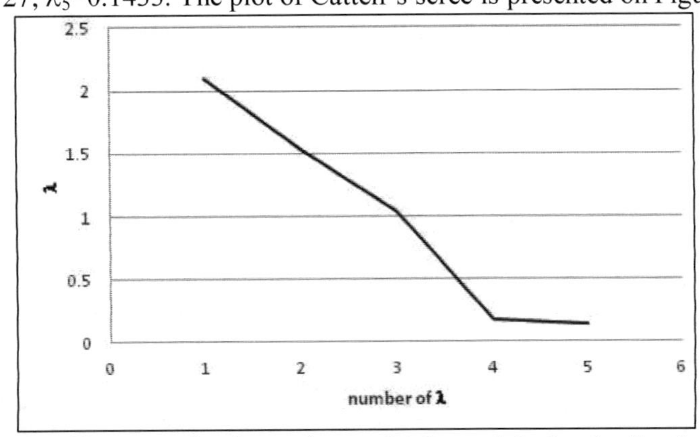

Figure 2. Cattell's scree plot for coal, type 34.2, particle density fraction (1.6-1.7)

The Cattell's scree plot suggests to take factors Z_1, Z_2 and Z_3 into consideration. The same factors explain sufficient percentage of changeability of all observed variables. Group of factors (Z_1, Z_2, Z_3) explains 93.25% of changeability of combustion heat, 92.41% of ash contents, 94.32% of sulfur contents, 90.33% of volatile parts contents and 97.99% of moisture, while factor Z_1 is related to variables X_1, X_2, X_3, X_4; factor Z_2 to variables X_2, X_3, X_4 and factor Z_3 to variable X_5.

Another criterion of limiting number of factors is determination of amount of percent of total variance explained by chosen factors (most often it is required to not be lower than 85%). In this case, for coal type 31, factors Z_1 and Z_2 explain 93.14% of variation of variable X_1 (combustion heat), 96.65% of variation of variable X_2 (ash contents), 99.00% of variation of variable X_3 (sulfur contents), 91.14% of variation of variable X_4 (volatile parts contents) and 89.14% of variation of variable X_5 (analytic moisture). For coal type 34.2, factors Z_1, Z_2 and Z_3 explain 95.21% of variation of variable X_1, 97.48% of variation of variable X_2, 99.95% of variation of variable X_3, 86.72% of variation of variable X_4 and 99.68% of variation of variable X_5. Finally, for coal type 35, these factors explain 98.21% of variation of variable X_1, 98.39% of variation of variable X_2, 99.87% of variation of variable X_3, 95.57% of variation of variable X_4 and 99.00% of variation of variable X_5.

The influences of individual factors on considered variables in all fractions of individual types of coal are presented in Tables 3-8. It was assumed that changeability of each feature should be explained by factors in at least 85%.

Table 3. Influence of factors on properties of coal, type 31 by particle size fractions.

Feature	0.5-1	1-3.15	3.15-6.3	6.3-8	8-10	10-12.5	12.5-14	14-16	16-20
				Combustion heat					
Z_1	97.49	95.39	97.57	97.63	94.13	96.29	81.52	95.41	99.89
Z_2							11.42		
				Ash contents					
Z_1	86.47	95.55	90.68	99.34	95.86	96.58	97.33	97.65	99.28
				Sulfur contents					
Z_1	95.74	68.65	94.59	7.99	5.00	0.04	2.31	22.45	2.06
Z_2		30.83		91.96	94.63	99.26	90.13	77.28	97.19
				Volatile parts contents					
Z_1	94.71	95.60	84.65	88.34	93.41	95.90	96.09	88.56	86.71
Z_2			12.11						
				Moisture					
Z_1	93.25	95.21	75.25	95.19	95.90	92.34	79.90	97.35	94.22
Z_2			18.16				7.00		

Table 4. Influence of factors on properties of coal, type 34.2 by particle size fractions.

Feature	0.5-1	1-3.15	3.15-6.3	6.3-8	8-10	10-12.5	12.5-14	14-16	16-20
Combustion heat									
Z_1	97.89	97.73	88.58	65.37	94.14	86.65	82.95	95.90	91.83
Z_2				6.96					
Z_3				27.60					
Ash contents									
Z_1	97.37	96.35	99.52	93.33	94.53	91.83	87.25	91.83	85.34
Sulfur contents									
Z_1	97.51	62.60	1.84	9.92	31.49	54.43	20.79	6.25	52.26
Z_2		16.74	95.29	88.37	65.15	11.59	72.53	91.43	44.28
Z_3		5.85				31.21			
Volatile parts contents									
Z_1	61.29	86.22	92.58	93.91	90.68	77.51	68.14	84.89	82.95
Z_2	25.35					11.59	26.65	0.09	14.36
Z_3								7.59	
Moisture									
Z_1	22.21	49.29	30.33	89.20	70.39	24.35	38.26	64.02	66.19
Z_2	73.23	32.06	3.01		16.54	69.87	49.75	8.34	29.99
Z_3		4.23	66.48					21.64	

Table 5. Influence of factors on properties of coal, type 35 by particle size fractions.

Feature	0.5-1	1-3.15	3.15-6.3	6.3-8	8-10	10-12.5	12.5-14	14-16	16-20
Combustion heat									
Z_1	92.23	98.46	96.29	92.87	90.70	97.12	97.49	92.14	84.89
Z_2									13.80
Ash contents									
Z_1	92.23	98.01	76.47	95.29	91.75	96.80	96.68	93.89	95.08
Z_2			12.64						
Sulfur contents									
Z_1	12.18	4.59	6.48	1.16	24.70	2.23	0.02	4.32	26.79
Z_2	70.66	77.03	34.07	97.02	52.67	69.80	67.99	75.00	62.85
Z_3	15.35	18.35	48.24		21.51	27.23	31.84	16.42	
Volatile parts contents									
Z_1	78.35	87.90	99.64	92.14	76.51	92.23	84.54	87.60	87.19
Z_2	6.88				13.64		8.93		
Moisture									
Z_1	15.14	36.10	54.49	40.60	44.32	0.04	2.74	1.15	15.94
Z_2	68.49	29.89	31.16	13.81	46.37	89.85	63.66	83.50	72.35
Z_3	14.06	26.68		43.74			33.50	15.26	

Table 6. Influence of factors on properties of coal, type 31 by particle density fractions.

Feature	<1.3	1.3-1.4	1.4-1.5	1.5-1.6	1.6-1.7	1.7-1.8	1.8-1.9	1.9-2.0
				Combustion heat				
Z_1	86.99	87.47	35.10	84.97	59.66	28.46	87.94	75.69
Z_2			60.40	8.15	20.53	63.98		27.82
Z_3					9.15			
				Ash contents				
Z_1	92.42	94.03	82.88	70.94	83.86	82.04	75.15	51.62
Z_2			1.33	25.38	11.19	0.02	9.01	36.33
Z_3			3.12			17.05	0.01	
Z_4							15.30	
				Sulfur contents				
Z_1	7.82	17.61	35.58	64.03	36.52	18.13	1.60	40.24
Z_2	56.73	80.64	48.87	4.86	36.97	67.04	87.51	54.30
Z_3	34.85		14.49	17.92	23.87			
				Volatile parts contents				
Z_1	89.88	87.01	73.80	68.22	21.16	71.84	18.36	74.33
Z_2			0.03	1.26	43.08	13.03	42.04	16.73
Z_3			0.06	6.83	35.45	1.06	38.69	
Z_4			24.75	23.66				
				Moisture				
Z_1	1.87	79.85	63.42	46.36	93.10	60.04	39.66	66.11
Z_2	67.24	0.09	5.97	37.93		5.84	34.95	0.07
Z_3	30.74	18.61	27.06	15.37		31.75	0.06	37.06
Z_4							24.35	

Table 7. Influence of factors on properties of coal, type 34.2 by particle density fractions.

Feature	<1.3	1.3-1.4	1.4-1.5	1.5-1.6	1.6-1.7	1.7-1.8	1.8-1.9	1.9-2.0
				Combustion heat				
Z_1	68.90	21.37	75.81	52.56	73.37	99.60	91.83	83.37
Z_2	13.54	70.82	1.03	28.72	17.60			7.68
Z_3	14.35		20.48	13.13				
				Ash contents				
Z_1	80.94	83.39	89.18	73.41	34.26	13.14	87.25	6.51
Z_2	6.02	10.66		3.69	43.21	23.72		86.19
Z_3	18.01	4.79		9.90	14.92	46.22		
Z_4						5.34		
				Sulfur contents				
Z_1	18.36	83.26	63.64	53.96	30.73	51.60	37.05	95.39
Z_2	64.78	11.15	8.70	0.06	56.11	48.00	52.91	
Z_3	16.30		23.41	31.76				
				Volatile parts contents				
Z_1	82.88	71.58	56.23	11.26	52.25	1.46	75.65	87.32
Z_2	15.10	0.06	0.01	81.28	34.98	72.72	19.64	
Z_3		26.70	34.32			14.75		
				Moisture				
Z_1	49.75	47.22	2.97	43.19	19.22	43.02	40.90	64.67
Z_2	25.45	42.22	86.52	8.72	2.11	32.11	48.26	24.86
Z_3	20.63			39.77	76.65	4.38		
Z_4						20.13		

Table 8. Influence of factors on properties of coal, type 35 by particle density fractions.

Feature	<1.3	1.3-1.4	1.4-1.5	1.5-1.6	1.6-1.7	1.7-1.8	1.8-1.9	1.9-2.0
				Combustion heat				
Z_1	36.22	94.80	58.46	93.14	55.65	88.39	59.42	99.70
Z_2	47.32		0.17		43.09		18.46	
Z_3	13.34		37.14				8.12	
				Ash contents				
Z_1	36.62	97.91	15.03	94.01	71.14	76.54	77.59	59.87
Z_2	47.32		56.07		23.93	9.48	5.65	32.02
Z_3	13.34		27.41				3.76	
				Sulfur contents				
Z_1	22.05	40.51	16.48	9.04	21.90	75.06	27.98	57.54
Z_2	70.30	54.61	37.22	78.17	16.54	10.15	53.01	26.44
Z_3			17.61	7.79	54.39			0.02
Z_4			25.56					
				Volatile parts contents				
Z_1	94.78	55.74	4.00	49.97	28.64	39.06	31.14	26.50
Z_2		31.34	42.35	19.51	44.55	35.14	10.68	44.03
Z_3			20.81	15.70	11.12	13.42	51.94	12.22
Z_4			31.70		4.93			9.95
				Moisture				
Z_1	70.12	23.27	86.19	7.81	27.96	5.03	52.51	6.35
Z_2	14.68	1.38		33.79	44.98	68.92	18.25	0.21
Z_3	11.48	72.67		48.87	20.76	25.99	1.18	89.98
Z_4							17.51	

4. Conclusions

Because of the fact that the most often three factors occur in individual fractions and considering power of relations between individual properties the investigated variables can be divided into three subsets. First one contains combustion heat, ash contents and volatile parts contents, second one contains sulfur contents and the third one contains moisture. In scientific works [3, 4, 5, 6, 7, 8, 9, 12, 13, 14, 15, 16, 17, 18, 19, 20, 23, 24], through application of various visualization methods it was claimed that features being sufficient to identify coal type are sulfur contents, moisture and volatile parts contents. The conducted analysis confirms these results. The selection of variable X_4 (volatile parts contents) occurs from the fact that this variable is explained by other factor than mutual factor with variables moisture and combustion heat.

References

[1] Comrey A. L. 1973. *A first Course in Factor Analysis* New York Academic Press

[2] Dobosz M. 2001. *Statistical analysis of research results* Akademicka Oficyna Wydawnicza Exit Warsaw [in Polish]

[3] Jamróz D. 2009. Multidimensional labyrinth - multidimensional virtual reality. In: Cyran K., Kozielski S., Peters J., Stanczyk U., Wakulicz-Deja A. (eds.): *Man-Machine, Interactions,* AISC Heidelberg Springer-Verlag **59** 445–450

[4] Jamróz D. 2014a. Application of Multidimensional Data Visualization in Creation of Pattern Recognition Systems, In: Gruca A., Czachórski T., Kozielski S. (eds.), *Man-Machine, Interactions 3* AISC Switzerland Springer International Publishing **242** 443-450

[5] Jamróz D. 2014b. Application of multidimensional scaling to classification of various types of coal, *Archives of Mining Sciences* **59(2)**, 413-425
[6] Jamróz D. 2014c. Application of multi-parameter data visualization by means of autoassociative neural networks to evaluate classification possibilities of various coal types *Physicochemical Problems of Mineral Processing* **50(2)** 719-734
[7] Jamróz D., Niedoba T. 2014. Application of Observational Tunnels Method to Select Set of Features Sufficient to Identify a Type of Coal *Physicochemical Problems of Mineral Processing* **50(1)**, 185-202
[8] Jamróz D., Niedoba T. 2015a. Application of multidimensional data visualization by means of self-organizing Kohonen maps to evaluate classification possibilities of various coal types *Archives of Mining Sciences* **60(1)**, 39-50
[9] Jamróz D., Niedoba T. 2015b. Comparison of selected methods of multi-parameter data visualization used for classification of coals *Physicochemical Problems of Mineral Processing* **51(2)** 769-784
[10] Kline P. 1994. *An easy Guide to Factor Analysis* Routledge London.
[11] Lawley D.N., Maxwell A.E. 1971. *Factor Analysis as a Statistical Method* London Butterworths.
[12] Niedoba T. 2009. Multidimensional distributions of grained materials characteristics by means of non-parametric approximation of marginal statistical density function *AGH Journal of Mining and Geoengineering* **4** 235-244 [in Polish].
[13] Niedoba T. 2011. Three-dimensional distribution of grained materials characteristics, in *Proceedings of the XIV Balkan Mineral Processing Congress* Tuzla Bosnia and Herzegovina **1** 57-59.
[14] Niedoba T. 2013a. *Multidimensional characteristics of random variables in description of grained materials and their separation processes* Wydawnictwo Instytutu Gospodarki Surowcami Mineralnymi i Energią PAN Kraków [in Polish].
[15] Niedoba T. 2013b. Statistical analysis of the relationship between particle size and particle density of raw coal *Physicochemical Problems of Mineral Processing* **49(1)** 175-188
[16] Niedoba T. 2014. Multi-parameter data visualization by means of principal component analysis (PCA) in qualitative evaluation of various coal types *Physicochemical Problems of Mineral Processing* **50(2)** 575-589
[17] Niedoba T. 2015. Application of Relevance Maps in Multidimensional Classification of Coal Types *Archives of Mining Sciences* **60(1)** 93-106.
[18] Niedoba T. Jamróz D. 2013. Visualization of multidimensional data in purpose of qualitative classification of various types of coal *Archives of Mining Sciences* **58(4)** 1317-1333
[19] Niedoba T., Pięta P., Surowiak A. 2018. Analysis of distributions of various coal types properties by means of statistical methods *IOP Conference Series: Materials Science and Engineering* art. 012008 **427** 1-5
[20] Niedoba T., Surowiak A. 2012. Type of coal and multidimensional description of its composition with density and ash contents taken into consideration, in *Proceedings of the XXVI International Mineral Processing Congress* **1** 3844-3854
[21] Sobolewski A., Micorek T., Winnicka G., Heilpern S. 2016. Proposal of Polish Coking Coal Classification, *The Polish Mining Review* **72(10)** 38-43 [in Polish]
[22] Stanisz A. 2007. *Easy Course of Statistics, vol. 3* Statsoft Krakow Poland [in Polish]
[23] Surowiak A. 2013. Investigation of hard coal beneficiation destined to gasification process in fluidized bed gas generator *The Polish Mining Review* **69(2)** 239–244 [in Polish]
[24] Surowiak A. 2014. Influence of particle density distributions of their settling velocity for narrow size fractions *Mineral Resources Management* **30** 105-122 [in Polish]

Acknowledgement
The paper is a result of statutory project no. *16.16.100 215.*

IOP Conf. Series: Materials Science and Engineering **641** (2019) 012013 doi:10.1088/1757-899X/641/1/012013

Innovative technological circuits for regular aggregates production

Tomasz Gawenda

AGH University of Science and Technology, Faculty of Mining and Geoengineering, Department of Environmental Engineering, Mickiewicza 30 Av., 30-059 Krakow, Poland

E-mail: gawenda@agh.edu.pl

Abstract. The aim of the article is to discuss possibilities of production of aggregates with increased content of regular particles, on some well-known examples, as well as presentation of methods of aggregate production, which was not previously present in the industry. Traditional aggregate production circuits require application of three or four grinding stages (depending on the particle size of the feed), but for fine particle fractions of aggregates irregular grains occur on average approximate content of 10%. The innovative technological circuit can produce the aggregates with the content below 3% irregular grains, even in a single- or two-stage crushing circuit.

1. Introduction

The processing of rock materials is currently more and more challenging in aspect of final products quality. The specific market requires big amounts of products of narrow particle size distribution and specified shapes (cubic ones) by possibly low permitted share of elongated or flat particles. The physicochemical properties of the material depend on location of exploitation and because of that they are unchangeable while desired size and shape of particles or surface's texture are possible to achieve dependably on applied processing methods during their production (especially comminution) and can directly influence on other features.

The most important rock materials for road and civil engineering are aggregates being produced from magmatic rocks. The basalt and melaphyre aggregates find wide applications in construction of upper layers of road surface. These layers, transferring huge dynamic loads and being directly abrading and under influence of disadvantageous atmospheric conditions should be constructed of aggregates of low abrasion, highly durable and resistant to water and frost [1]. Besides, these aggregates should characterize with particles shape being closed to spherical or cubic ones, have sharp edges and coarse fracture planes.

In civil engineering most of aggregates built of magmatic rocks is used to produce high quality concretes and special concretes. Also here the most desired are regular particles of spherical or cubic shapes because particles of other shapes have bigger surface requiring enlarged amount of concrete and water., Furthermore, flat and elongated particles have tendency to orientate in one plane what is connected with possibility of creating air voids [2]. The growth of flat particles contents influences on growth of free spaces what causes necessity of increasing the amount of mortar in concrete and in this way influences on increased amount of consumed concrete. Their significant share in the aggregate influences badly on durability of a concrete.

The ratio of particle width and their coarseness has also very important influence on particles durability. The irregular particles, especially flat ones indicate the biggest abrasion. It was stated that especially high influence of irregular particles on aggregates durability occurs by their contents of 25-50%. For example, the durability of basalt aggregate is lower by 55% when the share of irregular particles is equal to 50% [1]. So, both the granulometric distribution and particles shape decide about the quality of the aggregate. Also physicochemical properties, like resistance to comminution determined by abrasion in ball mill Los Angeles are important. The regular particles have lower susceptibility to comminution (lower value of LA factor), lower absorbability, abrasion what is related to concrete's or road surface's durability [3,4].

J. Malewski noticed the problems of defining measure of shape and interpretation of particles shape factors [5]. He defined the particles shapes, like spherical, cubic, elongated or flat. To avoid discrepancies in evaluating particles shapes and interpretation of the results the following norms were used in the conducted researches: PN-EN 933-4:2008. Investigations of geometrical properties of aggregates - Part 4: Determination of particles shape – shape coefficient and PN-EN 933-3:2012. Investigations of geometrical properties of aggregates – Part 3: Determination of particles shape by means of flatness factor [6,7].

2. Possibilities of increasing share of regular particles in mineral aggregates

Undoubtedly, the appropriate choice of the crushers with exploitive parameters influence on possibilities of increase of regular particles share. Other important features are amount of comminution stages and sort of technological systems.

To produce aggregates in purpose of getting particles of beneficial shape the cone granulators and impact crushers (cubisers) are being used. Cone granulators characterize with special shape of crushing chamber ensuring multiple comminution of individual particles and usually slightly lower jump and higher rotations what ensures that particles have longer way to pass in working chamber. To produce grits in cone granulators is necessary equip the installment with buffer containers which should get feed to these crushers by covering their total working chamber. In this way the optimal comminution is achieved and inner cone is protected against abrasion caused by material's fall from height.

The especially interesting are impact crushers with vertical shaft. The progress in material branch allows to use them also to crushing very hard materials. Furthermore, the way of feeding (system stone – stone) in such devices limits consumption of working parts of the crusher. Cubisers are more and more often used in aggregates production, especially concerning limestones and dolomites. However, products of impact crushers indicate the contents of finest fractions (like <2 mm) much higher than in case of jaw or cone crushers.

It is worthy to remember that improperly selected device parameters influence on its exploitation, like energy or working parts consumption which influence on quality of the products (shape and size of particles).

Technological systems have their task in processes of comminution and classification conducted in mineral processing plants. The quality of obtained products depends not only on appropriate selection of comminuting devices but also on cooperating ones (classifiers), dependably on sort of processed material. Assuming certain technological process we usually consider work characteristics of individual devices which depend among others on physicochemical properties of the feed and values of constructive and steerable parameters of the devices. The obtaining of good results depends also on way of process conducting (amount of comminution stages, technological cycles, steering on material flow streams to selected devices etc.).

It occurs that comminution of material in crushers with closed circuit is more beneficial because during material's return the filling of crushing chamber is higher and flat, naturally physically weaker particles are crushed easier what influences on their better shape. The appropriately designed comminution systems with closed circuit allow to control material's flow and also to get better quality of products. According to conducted investigations [8] the contents of flat particles in product after stabilization of material's flow in closed circuit was, dependably on particle fraction, lower by 4-15% than for product being crushed in open circuit (without return).

In paper [9] the conditions and results of four-stage systems of comminution in two selected basalt aggregates production plants located in Lower Silesia were presented. Table 1 presents sorts of crushers being installed on individual comminution stages in plants A and B, their comminution degrees and shape coefficients of products particles.

Table 1. S80 and S50 comminution degrees and shape coefficients K, obtained on consecutive crushing stages [9].

	Type of crusher	S_{80}	S_{50}	K [%]
Plant A	jaw JM st-1	4.6	4.2	21.0
	cone Svedala Superior S3000 st-2	2.5	3.6	38.0
	cone Svedala Hydrocon H4000 st-3	2.3	2.1	14.3
	impact Barmac MK st-4	1.5	1.8	6.0
Plant B	cone Krupp st-2	4.2	3.6	-
	cone Svedala Hydrocon H4000 I st-3	2.3	2.8	-
	cone Svedala Hydrocon H4000 II L1 st-3	1.2	1.6	13.3
	cone Svedala Hydrocon H4000 II L2 st-3	1.2	1.4	10.0
	cone Svedala H3000 L1 st-4	2.2	2.9	16.3
	cone Svedala H3000 L2 st-4	2.3	2.5	16.4
	impact PSP Dragon st-3 L1	1.1	1.3	7.2

The shares of irregular particles in individual particles fractions of comminution products are shown on Figure 1 (plant A) and 2 (plant B). Figure 1 shows that there is very high content of irregular particles (>60% for particle size fractions <16 mm) after crushing conducted in cone crusher S3000 (second stage). This content significantly lowers in following comminution stages, especially after using cubiser Barmac. From the analysis of data presented on Figure 2 it occurs that the lowest contents of irregular particles are obtained for product of comminution in impact crusher Dragon (third stage) and the share of such particles in fraction >16 mm is the lowest after crushing in H3000 crusher (fourth stage).

The data presented in Table 1 allow to determine dependencies between shape coefficient and comminution degree. This relation was presented on Figure 3. As it is visible the highest comminution degrees are typical for crushers working in initial stages of the process. However, better shape coefficients can be obtained for particles of products obtained in following stages by lower comminution degrees. The very high value of *K* for S_{50}=3.6 occurs from the particularly high amount of irregular particles in fraction <16 mm after comminution in cone crusher S3000, what was described above

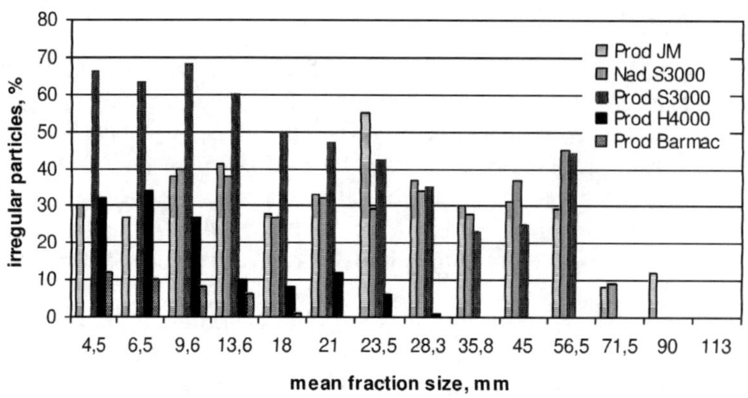

Figure 1. Irregular particles share (shape coefficients) in individual particle size fractions of comminution products – plant A [9].

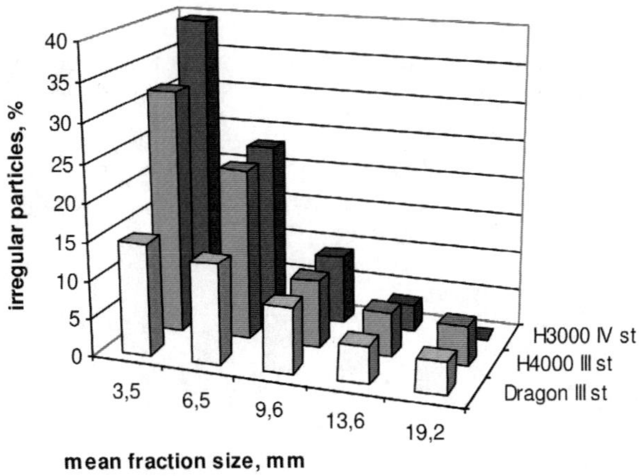

Figure 2. Share of irregular particles (shape coefficients) in individual particle size fractions of chosen comminution products – plant B, summer period [9]

Analysis of efficiency of multistage comminution on example of basalt rocks allows to make some important conclusions. The shape coefficient of particles in impact crushers products is lower than shape coefficient of the products of cone crushers. However, in cone granulators is possible to get particles fractions of low (even lower than the one obtained in impact crushers) contents of irregular particles but under condition that the outlet gap is properly selected. The size of this gap is crucial in context of not only granulation but also of comminution products particles shape. For each fraction of the aggregate there is optimum size of outlet gap by which the most appropriate particles shape can be achieved. This value is closed to the size of required fraction. The shape coefficient in comminution products lowers with lowering of comminution degree, It is possible then to ensure appropriate shape of comminution products particles through application of bigger amount of comminution stages in aggregates production technology. It can be noticed especially for final comminution. Unfortunately, it is connected with purchase of higher amount of devices and more expensive exploitation.

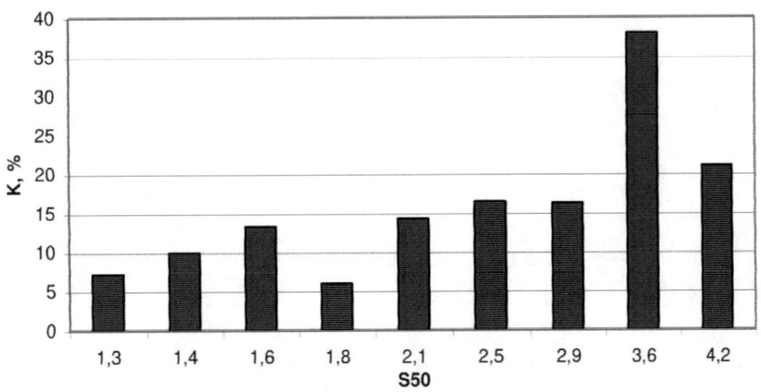

Figure 3. Influence of the shape coefficient on comminution level [9]

It occurs that comminution processes with return of material not only bigger than cut point but even fine one (being called also as bed) are being used in mineral aggregates production in purpose of lowering contents of irregular particles. Such investigations were carried out by Metso Minerals in cone granulators producing grits [10]. To this purpose two three-stage systems were used. In first system (Figure 4) two first stages of crushers work in open circuits. Cone granulator on third stage works in closed system with full charge. All devices are joined in the way ensuring maximization of capacity which was equal to 262 Mg/h. As it is shown on Figure 4 fine flat particles occurring in feed will not be crushed in any crusher and we will obtain a product of low quality. The comparison of irregular particles contents for both systems is presented in Table 2.

The second system (Figure 5) presents the situation where jaw crusher works on first stage in open system. The other crushers work in closed system while cone granulator on third stage works also with full charge as it was shown on Fig. 4. However, such system characterizes with lower capacity which was equal to 171 Mg/h but maximum contents of regular particles are obtained. It is worthy to notice that lower product from second sieve deck of first screen is on this scheme joined with lower product of first deck and being directed to cone granulator.

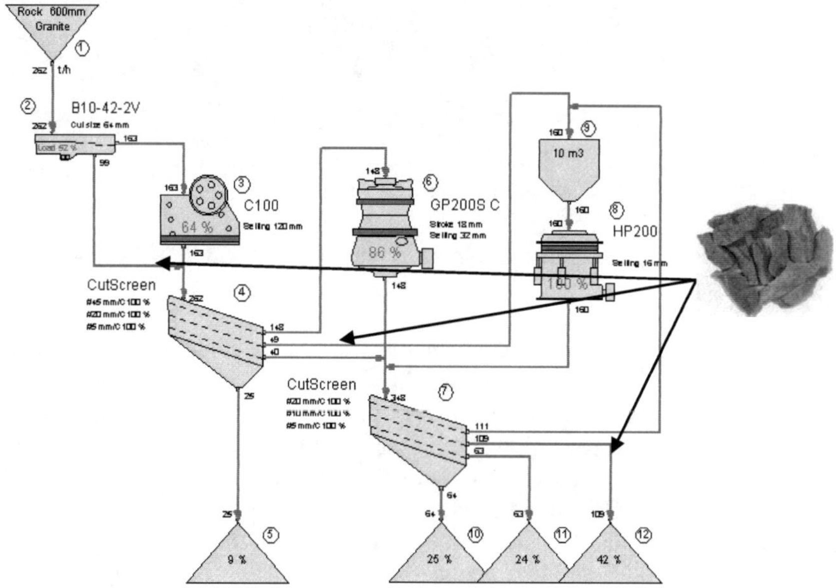

Figure 4. Triple-stage system with non-selective material flow [10]

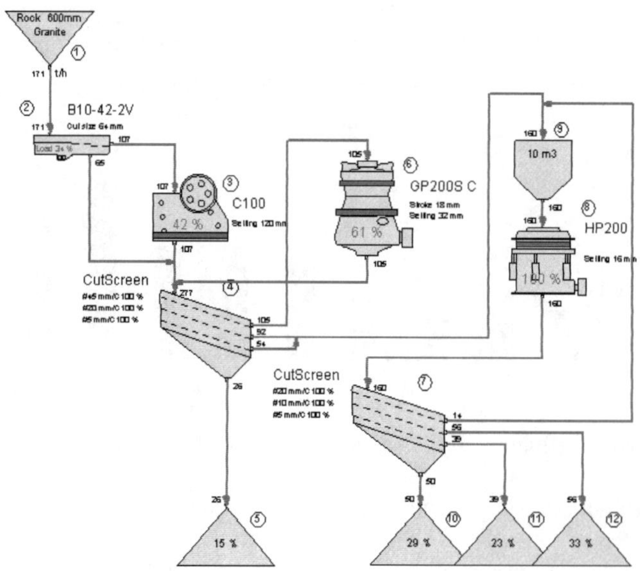

Figure 5. Triple-stage system with selective material flow [10]

Table 2. Irregular particles content for products after different crushing stages for different technological systems [10].

Crushing stage	Percentage of irregular particles contents in fractions			
	Non selective system		Selective system	
	5/10 [mm]	10/20 [mm]	5/10 [mm]	10/20 [mm]
II	50	30	n/a	n/a
III	20	15	15	10
Final product	34	22	15	10

The process of selective comminution with return of fine material (with bed) is beneficial in production of mineral aggregates in cone granulators but it is necessary to remember that in such case the excessive comminution should be avoided (too many comminution degrees) because it may lead to creation of fine dusts in the products. Also, the rules of selection of particle size distribution of the feed must be respected for such crushers to avoid too large shares of fine particles being lower of outlet gap size. Badly selected parameters of screen working before the crusher can influence on improper particle size distribution of the granulator's feed. This issue was discussed in the paper [11].

3. Innovative technological systems to produce aggregates of increased contents of regular particles

The most popular technological solutions in relatively small rock materials processing plants, especially ones producing recycled aggregates from wastes, are mobile and stationary installations equipped with one or two comminution stages. While stationary installations work in closed systems, mobile one work usually open systems with one crusher, preferably of jaw type, eventually cone or impact one. Such solution is caused mainly by economic reasons of small enterprise what make the quality of the product worse. Despite there are mobile installations on the market which allow material to return, like it is in SBM MP enterprise which offers device of Remax type equipped with rotary impact crusher, not many plants have this type of installments.

To make the technological process of aggregates production more efficient in simple installations is possible to equip the system with additional multi-product screen with slotted sieve and return the lower product to additional comminution process. Figure 6 presents the scheme of such innovative system designer by the Author which serves to production of aggregates of increased amount of regular particles, which idea of invention was reported to Patent Office [12].

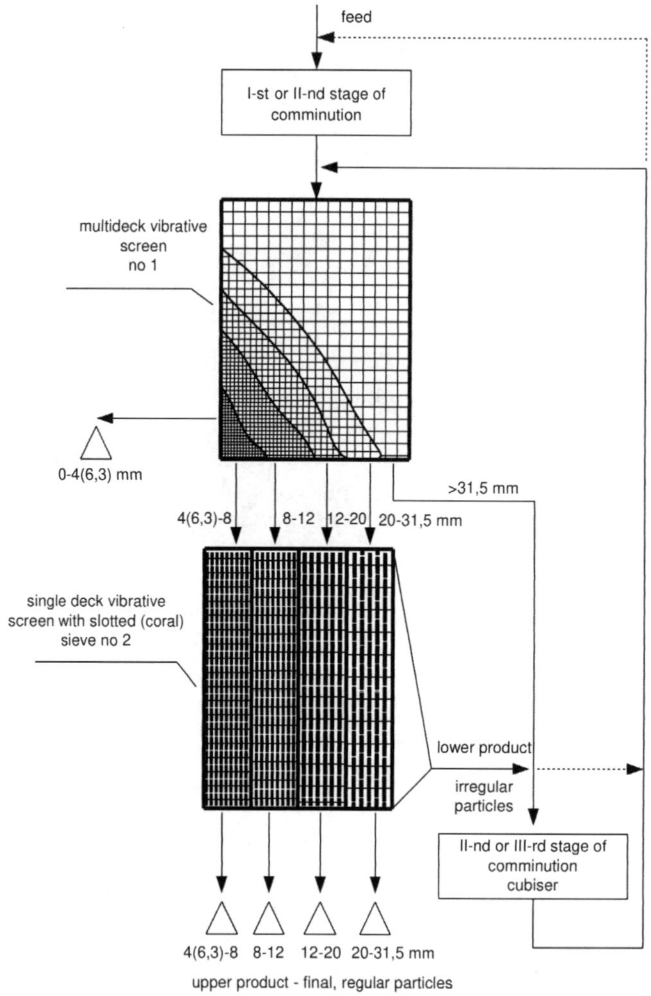

Figure 6. Idea of the aggregate production circuit with a closed recirculation for selective screening and crushing operations [12,13].

The system was thought in the way ensuring that even with only one crusher (for exampole of jaw type), despite it is not beneficial concerning quality of products is possible to get final aggregates with contents of no more than 2-3% of irregular particles. Such system requires only application of vibrative screens with sieves of quadratic mesh no 1 and slotted mesh no 2 (Figure 6) cooperating in pelting way in return with crusher being located in first or second stage. The task of multideck screen is to classify aggregates into narrow particle fractions which would occur to single deck multi-product screen with slotted sieve and then the irregular particle are being sieved (lower product) and returned again to comminution. The irregular particles can be comminuted in the same crusher or on secondary stage of crushing by impact, for example in cubiser what will affect positively on quality of the product. The contents of irregular particles in final products will depend on capacity of the screen with slotted sieve and especially on relation between narrow particle fraction range and size of the slot in sieve. This sieve should be selected according to the rule $d_{max}/2$ what means half of maximum size of certain fraction's particle. Because share of irregular particles lowers with growth of particle fraction and efficiency of screening grows for coarser particles then sieving of irregular particles in coarser fractions will be easier and more efficient. That is why in laboratory investigations conducted in KIŚ AGH according to the scheme presented on Figure 6, the finest particles size fraction (6.3-8 mm) was investigated to verify correctness of the idea and to determine the maximum contents of irregular particles which could occur in final products.

The dolomite used in tests came from the Skała I rock mine [14]. Particle size distribution of the material was within the range 0-100 mm. The material comminuted in jaw crushers of L44.41 type and Eko-Lab type was classified on vibrative two-deck screen in the way ensuring selection of narrow particle fraction 6.3-8 mm. This fraction contained about 80% of regular particles and 20% of irregular ones. In combination of the pelting system of screens with quadratic and slotted mesh, 2 types of the following slotted sieves were used in purpose of determining the efficiency of sieving of irregular particles.

- metal wire of mesh 4x20 mm shaped lengthwise (MD lengthwise),
- polyurethanic of mesh 4x20 mm shaped lengthwise (PU lengthwise).

Schemes of investigations were presented in Figures 7 and 8, while the results are shown in Table 3.

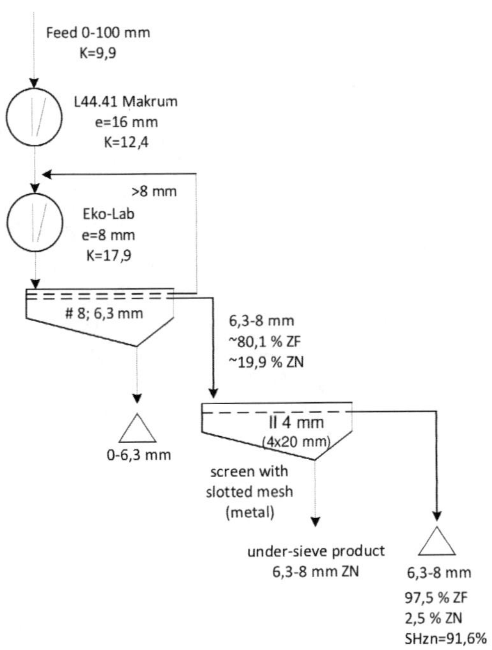

Figure 7. Scheme of investigations with irregular particles screening on a slotted wire screen [14]

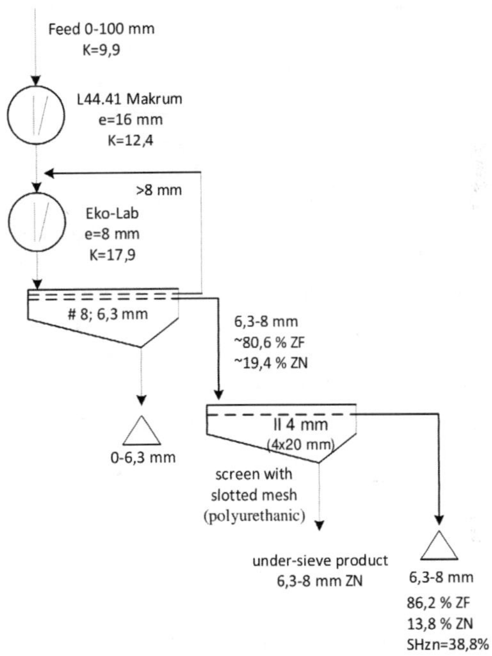

Figure 8. Scheme of investigations with irregular particles screening on a polyurethane screen [14]

Table 3. Distribution of regular (ZF) and irregular (ZN) particles in 6.3-8 particle size fraction in relationship to the type of the sieve [14].

Type of sieve	Yield (%)		Yield (%)				Contents in final product (%)		Recovery (%)	Efficiency (%)
	γ_g	γ_d	γ_g ZF	γ_d ZF	γ_g ZN	γ_d ZN	ZF Pk	ZN Pk	ε_{ZN}	SH_{ZN}
MD lengthwise 4x20 mm	81.8	18.2	79.8	0.3	2.0	17.9	97.5	2.5	8.3	91.6
PU lengthwise 4x20 mm	91.9	8.1	79.2	1.4	12.8	6.6	86.2	13.8	60.4	38.8

The test results show that after application of the slotted screen in the tested technological circuit it is possible to obtain mineral aggregates with irregular particles content below 3%, instead of 20%.

The most favorable slotted screen appeared to the wire one. The above results confirm outcomes achieved in the work published by Gawenda [13], where for both tests the contents of irregular particles (ZN Pk) equaled about 3% at the Hancock's technological efficiency of 92%.

Polyurethane sieves cannot be used for such a screening process due to their low coefficient of clearance (low recovery of regular particles: 60%, high content of irregular particles in the final product: 14% and low screening effectiveness: 39%).

According to the idea of producing aggregates of increased contents of regular particles in system of closed circuit of selective pelting process of screening and comminution, it is possible to lower contents of irregular particles from several dozen % till at least 2-3% in each particle fraction. Even by enlarging slots of sieve from 50% to 60-70% of maximum particle size of certain fraction it will be possible to eliminate almost every irregular particle from the products causing increase of the returned material in the system. After joining narrow particles fractions is possible to obtain also aggregates of other granulation range, like for example 0-31.5 mm.

Comparing comminution effects which were achieved in industrial conditions in selective system of Metso Minerals with cone granulators where, according to Table 2, the contents of irregular particle was equal to 15% for related particle fraction 5-10 mm is worthy to notice that obtained results are almost five times higher. Also, in system to produce basalt aggregates (Figure 2), in cubiser Dragon on third stage of comminution 13% of ZN was achieved in fraction 5-8 mm and in cone granulators of type H3000 and H4000 Svedala on third and fourth stages even 23% of ZN. So, these values are more than 8 times higher.

An alternative solution to the presented technological concept is the AGH-patented circuit for the production of aggregates with two crushers and a multi-deck screen for the grain classification and selective separation of irregular aggregates (PL 231748B1) [15]. The idea is shown in Figure 9. The circuit consisting of crushers contains one multi-deck screen in which the feed is separated into narrow particle size classes that are further separated into regular and irregular particles on a slotted screens placed at the bottom deck of the screen.

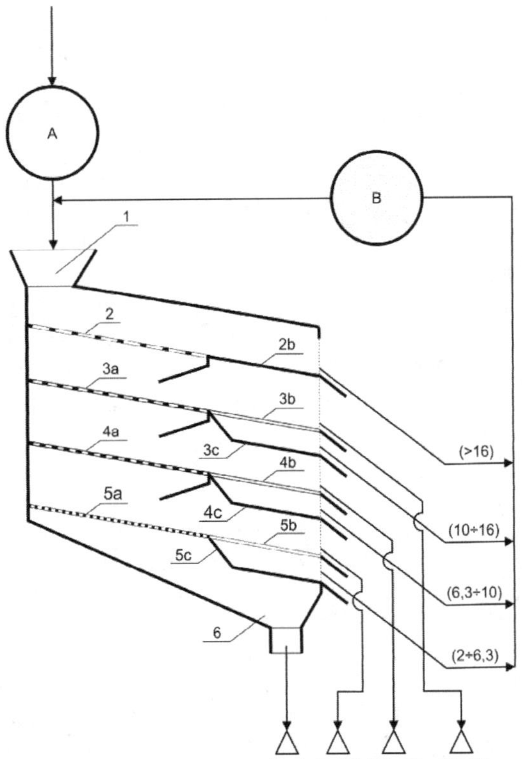

Figure 9. Circuit for separation of regular and irregular particles according to PL 231748B1 [15]: A, B - crushers; 1 - hopper; 2, 3a, 4a, 5a - decks of fractional sieves; 2b, 3b, 4b, 5b – decks of slotted screens; 3c, 4c, 5c - chutes of irregular particles, 6 - chute of fine particles.

The efficiency of screening depends on sort of slotted sieve and slots size in ratio to the range of granulation of sieved fraction, dynamic parameters of vibrative screen and also on sort of applied crusher. By impact crushers applications with vertical shaft and limitation of amount of comminution stages in closed circuit, for example from four to three stages, certainly less amount of irregular particles will circulate. That influences positively on screening efficiency and also on amount of produced finest fraction <4 mm and dusts. Resignation of one comminution stage would allow to lower energy consumption even till about 1 kWh/Mg of comminuted aggregate and save costs connected with crusher's working parts consumption being equal from about 0.2-0.5 PLN/Mg. And the costs connected with exploitation of additional screen are not significant and will be equal to about 15-35 PLN/1000Mg of sieved aggregate dependably on sort of screen and applied sieves.

It supposes to be underlined that the advantage of the discussed system, apart from energy savings, is possibility of selective division of any particles fractions as well regular and irregular particles in these fractions. This can be done without their crushing for too long time what unfortunately takes place in traditional multistage systems. That is why more technologically advanced systems are equipped with cubisers or cone granulators on final stages of comminution which purpose is to comminute fine final aggregates by small values of comminution degrees. This is done to avoid their excessive comminution.

4. Summary

Compact rock materials especially of volcanic and metamorphic origin are valuable materials to produce aggregates for road, railway and civil engineering from which gravel, arch blocks, grits (granulated aggregates). Particle size distribution and particles shape decide about aggregate's quality which influence highly on its durability. The contents of irregular particles in mineral aggregates depends mainly on the way of material crushing, so on sort of applied comminuting devices, their constructive and exploitive parameters, comminution degrees and amount of crushing stages. In industrial and laboratory investigations it was noticed that the harder rock material (more compact) is more difficult is to obtain regular aggregates. Besides, in finer particles fraction of comminution products the biggest amount of irregular particles is obtained so the using of cubisers on final comminution stages is advisable. With growth of comminution degree the contents of irregular particles grow too so crushers should work by not too big comminution degrees. However, all of these significant factors influence on necessity of applying multistage systems which increase both investments and exploitive costs.

An alternative in this respect can be the applied inventions of AGH in the form of installations for the production of broken aggregates in a circuit with closed cycle of selective and following process of screening and comminution (P.408045), or installations with multi-deck and multi-fraction screen (PL 231748B1), which occur (depending on the particle size of feed) in a one- or two-stage circuit, eliminating at the same time one crushing stage.

References

[1] Zieliński Z 1983 *Korelacja parametrów technologicznych mechanicznego kruszenia i przesiewania materiałów skalnych stosowanych w budownictwie drogowym*, Wyd. Uczelniane Politechniki Szczecińskiej, zeszyt 228, Szczecin

[2] Neville A M 2000, *Właściwości betonu*, Polski Cement, Krakow

[3] Tumidajski T Naziemiec Z 2004 *Wpływ warunków procesu kruszenia na kształt ziaren kruszyw mineralnych,* IV Konferencja „Kruszywa Mineralne - surowce - rynek - technologie - jakość", Szklarska Poręba, Wyd. Politechnika Wrocławska, Wrocław

[4] Naziemiec Z Gawenda T 2006 *Ocena efektów rozdrabniania surowców mineralnych w różnych urządzeniach kruszących.* VI Konferencja „Kruszywa Mineralne – surowce – rynek – technologie – jakość", Szklarska Poręba, OWPW Wrocław, s. 83-94

[5] Malewski J 2014 *Kształt ziaren w produktach kruszenia*, Wyd. Elamed, Kruszywa 3/2014, s. 52-55

[6] PN-EN 933-3:2012. *Badania geometrycznych właściwości kruszyw - część 3: Oznaczanie kształtu ziaren za pomocą wskaźnika płaskości.*

[7] PN-EN 933-4:2008. *Badania geometrycznych właściwości kruszyw - część 4: Oznaczanie kształtu ziaren – wskaźnik kształtu.*

[8] Naziemiec Z Gawenda T 2007 *Badanie procesu kruszenia z zamkniętym obiegiem*, Kruszywa mineralne: surowce – rynek – technologie – jakość, Szklarska Poręba, OWPW Wrocław, nr. 48, s. 107–116

[9] Nowak A Gawenda T 2006 *Analiza porównawcza kruszarek w wielostadialnych układach rozdrabniania skał bazaltowych,* Uczelniane Wydawnictwa Naukowo-Dydaktyczne, Górnictwo i Geoinżynieria, Zeszyt 3/1, Kraków-Zakopane, s. 267-278

[10] Eloranta J 2006 *Sposoby wpływania na jakość kruszyw*, Prezentacja badań firmy Metso Minerals na nośniku CD, VI Konferencja „Kruszywa Mineralne – surowce – rynek – technologie – jakość", OWPW Wrocław-Szklarska Poręba

[11] Gawenda T 2012 *Analiza efektów rozdrabniania w granulatorze stożkowym w zależności od wielkości uziarnienia nadawy i jego obciążenia*, Górnictwo i geologia XVII, Oficyna Wydawnicza Politechniki Wrocławskiej, Prace Naukowe Instytutu Górnictwa Politechniki Wrocławskiej, s. 71–83

[12] Gawenda T 2014 Projekt wynalazczy pt. *Układ urządzeń do produkcji kruszyw foremnych*, Pismo CTT-owi-1/333/2013/100 z dnia 13.06.2013 AGH w Krakowie, Nr P.408045 z dnia 28.04.2014

[13] Gawenda T 2015 *Zasady doboru kruszarek oraz układów technologicznych w produkcji kruszyw łamanych, Monografia* nr 304, Wyd. AGH Krakow

IOP Conf. Series: Materials Science and Engineering **641** (2019) 012013 doi:10.1088/1757-899X/641/1/012013

[14] Gawenda T 2015 *Badania procesu rozdrabniania dolomitu z kopalni Skała I według innowacyjnej koncepcji układu technologicznego do produkcji kruszyw foremnych.* Praca zrealizowana na zlecenie Semav Stones Sp. z o.o. AGH Krakow
[15] Gawenda T 2019 *Wibracyjny przesiewacz wielopokładowy.* Patent nr PL 231748B1, AGH Krakow

Acknowledgments
The article is the result of the National Center for Research and Development (NCBiR) project: competition No. 1 under Sub-measure 4.1.4 "Application projects" of POIR in 2017, entitled: Opracowanie i budowa zestawu prototypowych urządzeń technologicznych do budowy innowacyjnego układu technologicznego do uszlachetniania kruszyw mineralnych wraz z przeprowadzeniem ich testów w warunkach zbliżonych do rzeczywistych". Project is co-financed by the European Union from the sources of European Regional Development Fund under Measure 4.1 of the Intelligent Development Operational Program 2014-2020.

Fundusze Europejskie Inteligentny Rozwój
Rzeczpospolita Polska
Narodowe Centrum Badań i Rozwoju
Unia Europejska

IOP Conf. Series: Materials Science and Engineering **641** (2019) 012014 doi:10.1088/1757-899X/641/1/012014

Analysis of impact of HPGR device operation on technological effectiveness of downstream operations of raw materials processing

K Leśniak and A Saramak

AGH, University of Science and Technology, Faculty of Mining and Geoengineering, Department of Mineral Processing and Environmental Engineering,Cracow, Poland

E-mail: kasiakarolina95@onet.pl

Abstract. The aim of the paper was to investigate the impact of HPGR operation on the grinding process effectiveness. A series of laboratory crushing tests, together with tests of grinding in a ball mill, were carried out. There were determined comminution degree values for HPGR and ball mill operation. Results of investigation showed that operational pressing force may determine both effectiveness of HPGR crushing process, as well as the grinding effectiveness. The operating pressing force may influence the dust pollution level, while the noise emission level is not correlated with operational pressure.

1. Introduction – HPGR technology

High pressure technology was invented and introduced in the early 70's [11] and initially applied mainly to the limestone and cement clinker comminution. Together with development of high-pressure technology, HPGR devices appeared to be useful also in ore processing circuits (iron, copper, gold) and kimberlite crushing (diamonds) [1,3]. Currently, it is one of the most efficient crushing technology in terms of energy-consumption in hard mineral comminution [2]. HPGR device consists of two cylindrical rolls with the same diameter and length, rotating in opposite directions. Each roll is powered by a separate engine of the same power. The rollers are mounted on a solid frame in such a way that one roll is fixed, while the other has the ability to move horizontally due to the hydraulic system acting.

The feed is crushed in the working chamber between two rolls of HPGR device as a result of the pressing forces action. The layer of material is being compacted to a density of approx. 85% of the material original density. Such compression is achieved by applying a high pressure that exceeds the compressive strength of comminuted material [9]. The HPGR product contains a significant yield of fine particles, sometimes compacted in the form of so-called flakes. Comminution process in HPGR takes place in two stages. At the beginning, the material is gradually compressed and pre-crushed as a result of narrowing the space between the rotating rolls in the chamber. In the next stage, the pre-crushed material is passing into compacting zone, where the high pressure caused by the force of floating roll pressure acts on the material layer. It acts on all particles passing through the crushing zone primarily by many points of contacts between the individual particles in the layer, which causes a disintegration of most particles. During this process micro-cracks are also created in particles, which reduce the required energy of comminution in downstream operations - grinding in mills. The HPGR products undergo faster disintegration during grinding operation, compared to conventional crushers.

The Bond energy index of HPGR product is decreased, which is one of the main energy-saving factors for roller presses [12].

HPGR usually operates in a closed circuit with material recycle. The device is installed at the crushing stage following cone crushers, jaw crushers or SAG and AG mills. The HPGR product usually goes into a ball mills.

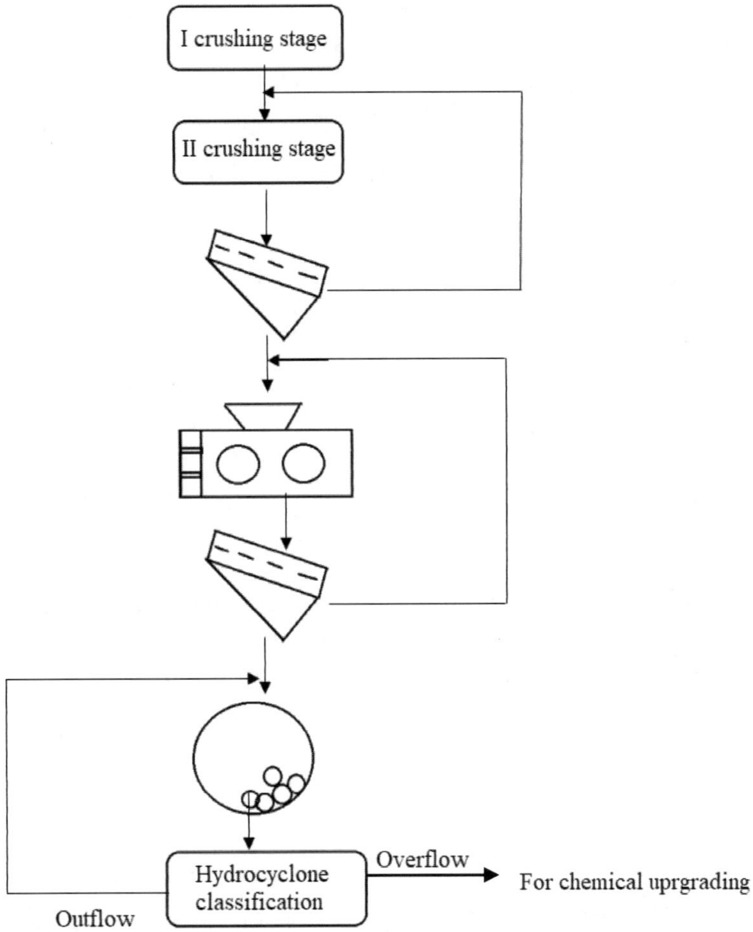

Figure 1. Typical HPGR-based circuit [8]

Generally, the benefits from HPGR application in technological circuits of raw materials processing, can be divided into three groups.

- technological effects – causing increased capacity of entire processing circuit,
- economic benefits – resulting from decreasing the energy consumption of HPGR products. This is caused by micro-cracks and a reduction of the Bond index can be from 10 to 25% [4,5].
- ecological effects – lower noise level, as well as dust and vibrations.

Main aim of the paper was an assessment of economic and ecological effects of HPGR. Economic effects were measured through the course of a downstream grinding process of HPGR products, while ecological effects were investigated through measurements of noise and dust pollution generated by the press device.

2. Materials and methods

Testing programme was carried on a laboratory HPGR device on disposal of AGH University of Science and Technology with the rolls diameter 300 mm, and length 100 mm. Maximum pressing force of the device is 20 kN. HPGR crushing programme included three tests for various operating pressing force: 10, 13 and 16 kN. Each HPGR crushing product was then ground in laboratory ball mill. Three grinding times was used in investigations: 1 minute, 3 minutes and 5 minutes.

The limestone rock was the material used in investigations. This type of limestone was with a rather low resistance for comminution, the Bond's index value W_i = 9.81 kWh/Mg. Scheme of investigative programme was presented in Fig. 2.

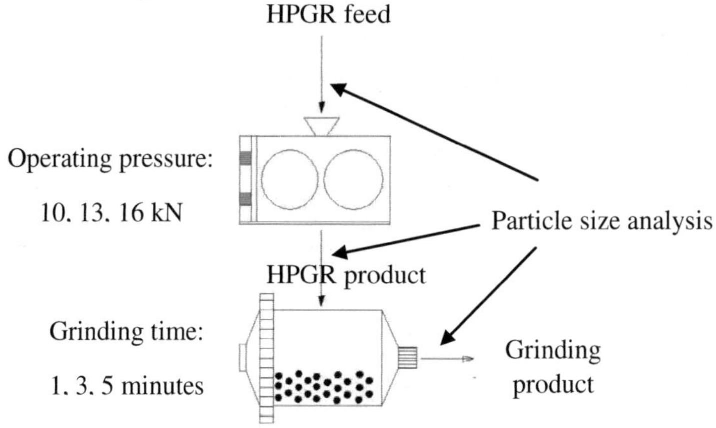

Figure 2. Scheme of investigative programme.

Particle size analyses were performed for the feed material, for each HPGR crushing products, as well as for each grinding test. The nine grinding products were obtained (three grinding products from each HPGR test), what was presented in Table 1.

Table 1. Summary of all crushing and grinding tests.

	HPGR operating pressing force								
HPGR tests	10 kN			13 kN			16 kN		
Number of HPGR crushing products	1			2			3		
Grinding tests	1 min	3 min	5 min	1 min	3 min	5 min	1 min	3 min	5 min
Number of grinding products	1_1	1_2	1_3	2_1	2_2	2_3	3_1	3_2	3_3

There were calculated comminution degrees for HPGR products as well as for grinding products according to the formula:

$$S_x = \frac{D_x}{d_x} \qquad (1)$$

D_x – characteristic particle of feed [mm]
d_x – characteristic particle of crushing (grinding product), [mm].

The x value denotes the type of characteristic particle, i.e. average – 50% (d_{50} and D_{50}), eighty per cent – 80% (d_{80} and D_{80}) or ninety-five – 95% (d_{95} and D_{95}). For the purpose of article there were determined S_{50} and S_{80} values.

During HPGR tests there were also registering dust emissions [10] (in the form of TSP – Total Suspended Particles) and noise generations [7] (L_{eqT} level according to [6]) in order to determine ecological effects of high-pressure grinding. The dust emission level was recorded with using the particle dust analyzer *Casella*.

Procedures of noise registering and calulcations of respective noise indicators are described in the Regulation of the Minister of Environment (2008) [6]. Two main values are calculated most frequently: L_{Aeq} and L_{AeqT}. The Equivalent Sound Level (L_{Aeq}) can be determined according to formula (2):

$$L_{Aeq} = 10 * \log\left(\frac{1}{T}\sum_{i=1}^{n} t_i * 10^{0,1*L_{Ai}}\right)[dB] \tag{2}$$

where:
T – total measuring period, [s];
t_i – time intervals of T, [s];
L_{Ai} – registered sound level during the period t_i [dB].

The value has to be adjusted through suitable corrective filters that adapt the results to the sensitivity range of the human ear. The procedure was described in [6]. For determination the second value, the noise emitted into the environment during the time T (L_{AeqT}), the following formula should be used:

$$\boldsymbol{L_{AeqT} = 10 * \log(10^{0,1*L_{Aeq}} - 10^{0,1*L_{At}})\ [dB]} \tag{3}$$

L_{At} – level of background sound.

3. Analysis of results

The particle size distribution of HPGR feed was presented in Fig.3, together with HPGR crushing products. Feed analysis shows that maximum particle size is finer that 14 mm. About 15% of feed material constitute particles with size below 0.3 mm. Average particle D_{50}=6.2 mm, and D_{80}=11.9. Particle size distributions of HPGR crushing results were also presented in Fig 3.

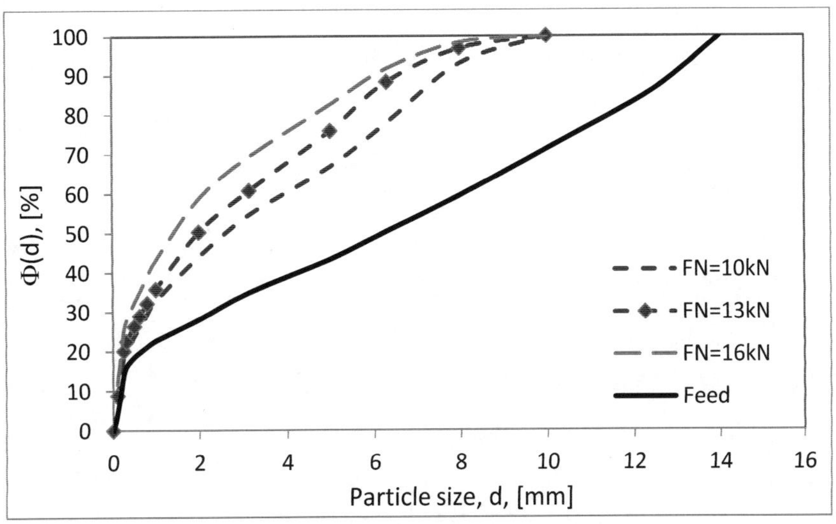

Figure 3. Particle size distribution of HPGR feed and HPGR crushing products.

Analysis of the results shows that all HPGR products were finer than 10 mm. Characteristic particles were calculated and presented in Table 2.

Table 2. Characteristic particles calculated for all HPGR tests.

Characteristic particle	HPGR operating pressing force		
	10 kN	13 kN	16 kN
d_{50} [mm]	2.8	1.9	1.4
d_{80} [mm]	6.7	5.4	4.8

Results of ball mill grinding were presented in Fig. 4 – 6. Figure 4 presents grinding products for HPGR product crushed at operating pressure 10 kN, while Figs 5 and 6 shows the grinding products for HPGR products treated with the pressing forces 13 and 16 kN, respectively.

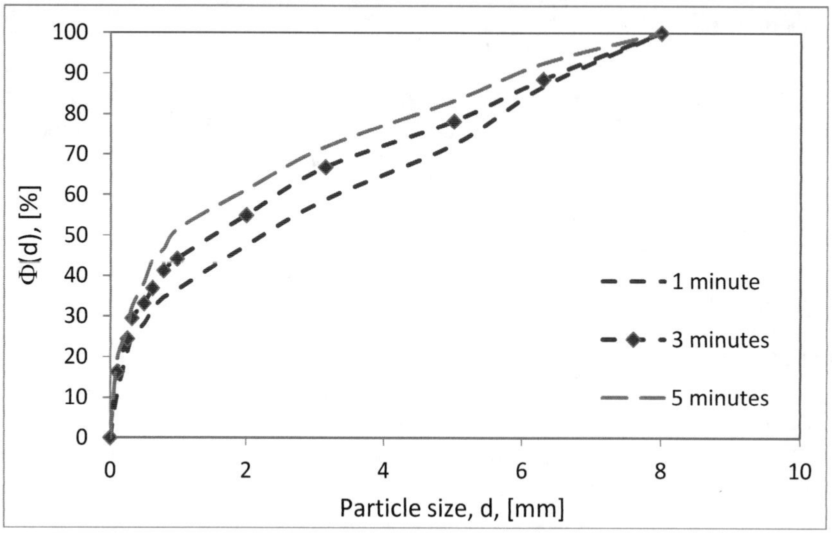

Figure 4. Grinding results for HPGR products comminuted at 10 kN.

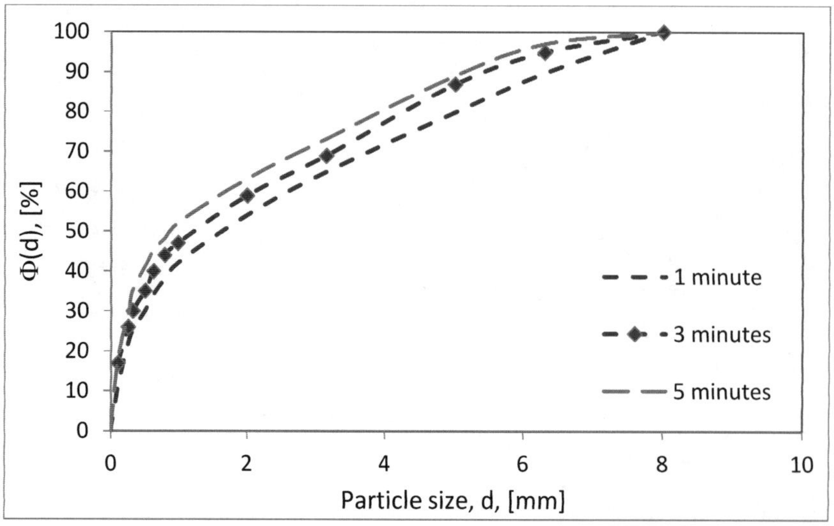

Figure 5. Grinding results for HPGR products comminuted at 13 kN.

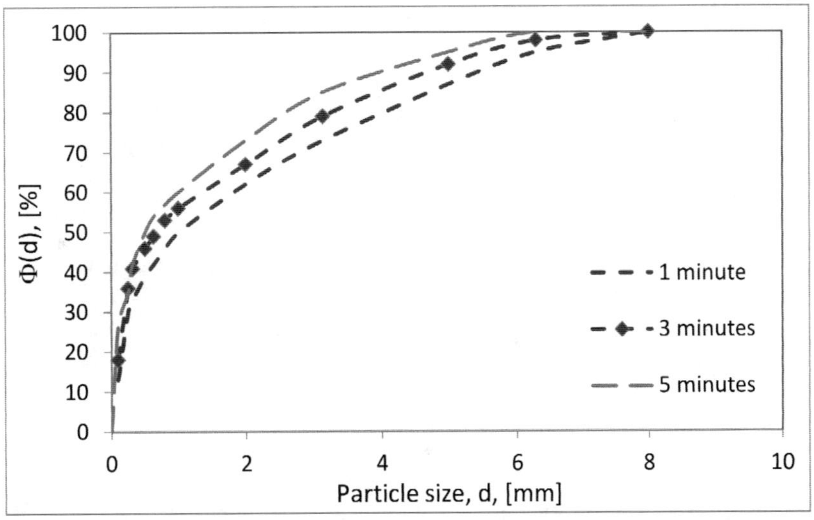

Figure 6. Grinding results for HPGR products comminuted at 16 kN.

3.1. Characteristics particles and comminution degrees

Characteristic particles calculated for all grinding products are presented in Table 3.

Table 3. Characteristic particles for the grinding products.

HPGR operating pressing force 10 kN			
Characteristic particle	Grinding time		
	1 minute	3 minutes	5 minutes
d_{50} [mm]	2.3	1.6	0.9
d_{80} [mm]	5.8	5.3	4.5
HPGR operating pressing force 13 kN			
Characteristic particle	Grinding time		
	1 minute	3 minutes	5 minutes
d_{50} [mm]	1.7	1.3	0.8
d_{80} [mm]	5.1	4.6	4.1
HPGR operating pressing force 16 kN			
Characteristic particle	Grinding time		
	1 minute	3 minutes	5 minutes
d_{50} [mm]	1.1	0.7	0.5
d_{80} [mm]	4.4	3.2	2.9

Table 4. Comminution degree for HPGR products.

Comminution degree	HPGR operating pressing force		
	10 kN	13 kN	16 kN
S_{50} [mm]	2.21	3.26	4.43
S_{80} [mm]	1.78	2.20	2.48

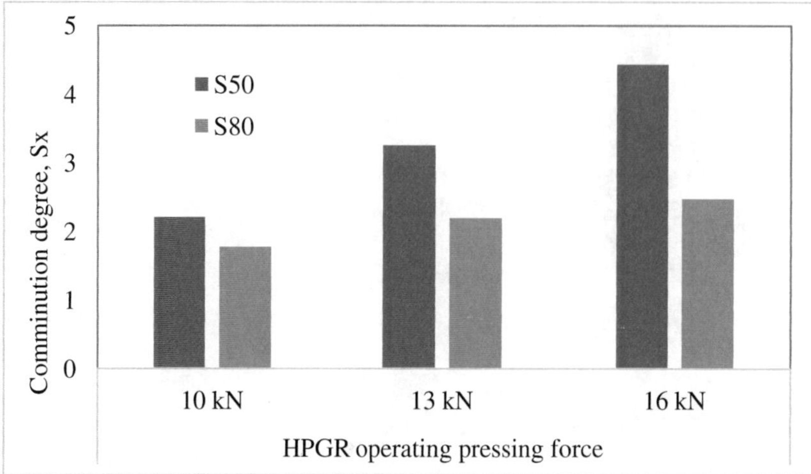

Figure 7. Fifty and eighty percent characteristic particles calculated fo HPGR tests.

3.2. Dust emission analysis

During the experimental programme also an environmental effect of HPGR was investigated. For each single test a dust emission level was recorded with using the particle dust analyzer *Casella*. Prior to measurements it was determined a dust emission in the laboratory, when no equipment was operating (so-called background level). The results are presented in Figure 11. It can be seen that average level of dust emission is around 0.1 – 0.2 mg/m^3. Values of dust emission for each single test, together with standard deviations, are presented in Table 5.

Table. 5. Average values and standard deviations of dust emissions for HPGR tests

HPGR pressing force, [kN]	Average dust emission [mg/m^3]
10	4.8
13	5.3
16	5.2

Results show that it is rather difficult to clearly indicate if the operating pressure significantly affects the dust emission. Values for pressing force 13 and 16 kN are very similar, what may suggest that differences between individual dust emissions can be insignificant (especially for the two higher values of HPGR pressing force). However, further investigations within this matter are necessary to determine some more clear relationships or models.

3.3. Results of noise pollution

Table 6 presents the results of noise emission level (in dB) of the HPGR device, registered during crushing tests. The values defined by formula (3) were determined and calculated for all HPGR crushing tests.

Table 6. Values of noise and dust emissions obtained for laboratory devices.

HPGR pressing force, [kN]	Noise level LeqT [dB]
10	86.70
13	89.04
16	87.23

The results presented in Table 6 are similar, regardless the operational pressing force. Differences are insignificant and one may conclude that the level of noise generation during HPGR operation cannot be directly correlated with the operating pressure.

4. Summary and conclusions

The aim of investigations was to verify potential impact of HPGR on the results and effectiveness of downstream grinding operations. Results of investigations showed that various operational conditions of HPGR are effective in different grinding results. There were generally confirmed relationships that can be found in literature that indicate on different effectiveness of downstream crushing and grinding operations, achieved for different values of operational pressure of HPGR device.

Results of investigations carried out indicate that together with increasing operational pressing force comminution degrees of HPGR and grinding products increases too. The more intense growing of average comminution degree can be observed together with increasing of HPGR pressure value. The S80 values also increase, together with increasing of the HGR pressing force, but this growth is significantly lower, comparing the S50 value.

The HPGR operational pressing force – the main operating parameter – is correlated with the dust emission level. Results of investigations show that for higher values of pressure, an increased dust emission level was observed. On the other hand, noise emission of HPGR is regardless the operational pressure.

Results of investigations also confirmed that application of HPGR technology into raw material processing circuits may be effective in lower energy consumption, more environmental friendly as well as achieve more favorable technological effects. The next stage of investigations should be assessment of HPGR operation in ore comminution and processing circuits together with verification of beneficiation effectiveness.

References

[1] Baum, W., Patzelt, N., Knecht, J. 1997 Metallurgical benefits of high pressure roll grinding for gold and copper recovery. *SME*, Denver, Feb. Conference print 111-116.

[2] Gawenda T. 2013 The influence of rock raw materials comminution in various crushers and crushing stages on the quality of mineral aggregates. *Mineral Resources Management-Gospodarka Surowcami Mineralnymi* **29(1)** 53-65

[3] Hilden M Suthers S 2010 Comparing energy efficiency of multipass high pressure grinding roll (HPGR) circuits *XXV International Mineral Processing Congress (IMPC) 2010, Proceedings* The Australasian Institute of Mining and Metallurgy, Brisbane, 801-811.

[4] Maxton, D., Morley, C., Bearmen, R. 2003 A quantification of the benefits of high pressure rolls crushing in an operating environment. *Minerals Engineering* **16** 827-838

[5] Pahl, M. H. 1993 Praxiswissen Verfahrenstechnik – Zerkleinerungstechnik. *Fachbuchverlag Leipzig/Verlag*, TÜV Rheinland, Köln

[6] Regulation of the Minister of the Environment, 4 November 2008 (2008). *W sprawie wymagań w zakresie prowadzenia pomiarów wielkości emisji oraz pomiarów ilości pobieranej wody.* (Dz.U. Nr 206, poz. 1291)

[7] Saramak A., Naziemiec Z., Saramak D. 2016 Analysis of noise emission for selected crushing devices *Mining Science* **23** 145-154

[8] Saramak D. 2011 Analiza efektywności pracy technologicznych układów rozdrabniania surowców z wysokociśnieniowymi prasami walcowymi. *Górnictwo i Geoinżynieria* **6(2)** 2011

[9] Saramak D. 2011 The influence of chosen ore properties on efficiency of HPGR-based grinding circuits. *Mineral Resources Management-Gospodarka Surowcami Mineralnymi* **27(1)** 33-44

[10] Saramak D., Wasilewski S., Saramak A. 2017 Influence of copper ore comminution in HPGR on downstream minerallurgical processes. *Archives of Metallurgy And Materials* **62(3)** 1689-1694

[11] Schönert, K 1979 Aspects of the physics of breakage relevant to comminution *Fourth Tewksbury Symposium,* University of Melbourne
[12] Smit, I. 2005 Bench scale ore characterization using the High Pressure Grinding Roll. *Workshop 2005,* Perth, August 22, 2005

IOP Conf. Series: Materials Science and Engineering **641** (2019) 012015 doi:10.1088/1757-899X/641/1/012015

The comparison of laboratory and industrial copper ore upgrading indices during introduction of new flotation reagents

W Pawlos[1], M Krzemińska[1] and P Kurzydło[2]
[1] KGHM Polska Miedź S.A.
[2] University of Wroclaw, Faculty of Earth Sciences and Environmental Management

E-mail: pawel.kurzydlo@kghm.com

Abstract. This article draws attention to the need for the introduction of a laboratory testing methodology for new flotation reagents prior to the implementation of them for industrial use which would be more effective than the one currently used. Laboratory and industrial indicators of copper ore beneficiation during the testing of new flotation reagents are compared herein. For this purpose, two-stage laboratory tests and industrial trails were carried out on three types of collector mixtures, the results of which were used to analyse the technological indicators achieved. It has been concluded that the applied laboratory testing methodology requires a new approach that allows for a more precise correlation of variables which will allow the results of industrial trial to be predicted with greater probability than at present.

1. Introduction

The regulation on the manufacture and use of chemicals (REACH) introduced by the European Union has led to certain restrictions on the placing on the market of chemicals which could be used as flotation collectors. For this reason, it is more difficult than ever to apply on an industrial scale collection reagents which have not previously been used. This is mainly due to legal restrictions on the production of reagent in a quantity that would allow for the verification of laboratory test results under industrial conditions. Therefore, it is advisable to develop a laboratory methodology that reflects industrial conditions to a greater extent than it did before, and thus will allow effective implementation of new collecting reagents in industrial practice, eliminating the risk of production losses.

Despite the fact that a variety of work has been carried out so far to develop an effective method for prediction of beneficiation results on an industrial scale on the basis of data from laboratory experiments [1, 2, 3, 4], there is still no effective tool for achieving a higher degree of correlation of industrial research results on the basis of results obtained during laboratory tests.

All the methods, which have been presented in the literature as well as developed for the needs of processing plants, boil down mainly to conduct research in simple and small-scale systems. The results obtained are chemical analyses based on which balances of experiments are prepared in the form of tables, with the determination of upgrading indices (product yields and grades and metal recoveries). Therefore, the analysis of the impact of a reagent on flotation performance is created mainly on numerical chemical analysis data as well as on graphical interpretation. On the basis of the analysis of the obtained results, a decision is made concerning the carrying out of industrial scale trial.

The current actions, based on what has already been achieved by researchers, aim at developing an effective method for testing new reagents under laboratory conditions that will make possible the prediction of industrial results. In order to meet the expectations of technology optimization works have been started towards the development of a methodology that would allow for a decision of launching industrial scale trial on the basis of laboratory tests results with minimizing the risk of production losses. The issue of searching for new reagents for the industrial process is an open question. New chemical compounds whose application may improve the efficiency of the technological process are constantly being sought, which makes it necessary to conduct research in this area.

The number and complexity of different factors present in industrial conditions make the issue of precise and approvable results prediction extremely difficult. In existing plant technology lines the ore beneficiation process is disturbed by natural fluctuation of ore physicochemical properties influencing on process efficiency such as: chemical and mineral composition, degree of minerals liberation, grain size, contains of compounds disturbing process. Moreover the technology regime causes changes in throughput, materials flow rates, flotation reagents distributions, the scale of slurry recirculation and water to solids ratio having impact on slurry density. Additionally, gradually aging of machinery, servicing and maintenance breaks, unplanned shutdowns and processing water chemistry are also significant for process efficiency. All listed factors have independent impact on ore processing results, some of them, but not all, have the numerical values and this is the reason for difficulties in developing an universal formula for results scale-up.

2. The analysis of the influence of feed grade fluctuation on the results of laboratory tests

A comprehensive analysis concerning the existing methodology of laboratory tests of flotation reagents does not allow for defining guidelines for its implementation to forecast of industrial results. Therefore, the factors that may influence the increase in the degree of achievement of industrial results based on laboratory tests were analysed. Several of them were selected, the most important of which are the quality of the output constituting a feed suitable for processing, the content of individual lithological fractions and the quality of mineralization.

First of all, the influence of the variability of ore grade on the results was analysed. The results of laboratory test carried out simultaneously during the industrial trail, compared with previous laboratory test on the basis of which it the decision concerning the carrying out of industrial trail was made, will show whether the variability of feed over time has a significant impact on the prediction of industrial trial results.

Introduction of a new type of reagent for industrial practice at KGHM was an example to research of influence of feed variability on effects resulting from the scale-up of results. In order to verify this relationship, laboratory tests with different mixtures of flotation reagents (named A, B, C) were carried out and then repeated in parallel with ongoing industrial trails.

Laboratory experiments were carried out on material from one of the concentrator plant. Material for the study was collected in two periods: 3 months before the planned industrial test and during the industrial test. In both cases, the methodology of laboratory flotation was identical. The experiments were carried out with a Mechanobr laboratory flotation machine, with a cell of 1 dm^3 capacity. The flotation tests included laboratory flotations with selected mixtures. The flotation time has been set at 30 minutes. Fractional flotations were carried out, three froth products were collected (concentrates K1 = 5 min, K2 = 10 min, K3 = 30 min) and remaining tailing (OK). Collectors were dosed in the amount of 100 g/Mg, whereas frother in the amount of 60 g/Mg. Collectors were dosed in two stages: the first dose (60% of the total reagent) was added during agitation and the next 40% was added after 5 minutes of flotation. The frother was dosed in one step. The flotation products were dried, weighed and prepared to chemical analyses for Cu content. In order to reduce the systematic errors, the flotation experiment was conducted for each mixture twice, determining Cu in each of the products.

The results of flotation experiments are presented in Tables 1 to 6. On the basis of the data obtained, the Fuerstenau curves ($\varepsilon_r = f(\varepsilon)$) were plotted, the magnifications of which are shown in Fig. 1a ÷ 3a and the Halbich curves ($\varepsilon = f(\beta)$), the fragments of which are shown in Fig. 1b ÷ 3b. Figures 1 ÷ 3 also show the point of industrial upgrading, in order to illustrate the differences between the results of laboratory and industrial scale.

IOP Conf. Series: Materials Science and Engineering **641** (2019) 012015 doi:10.1088/1757-899X/641/1/012015

2.1. Results of flotation conducted with mixture A

Table 1. Results of laboratory flotation prior to the industrial trial

Product	Flotation time	Product yield γ[g]	Product yield γ[%]	Cu content λ[%]	Cumulat. yield Σγ[%]	Cumulat. Cu content ΣCu[%]	Cu recovery, [%]
K1	5 min	81.26	17.09	8.69	17.09	8.69	81.21
K2	15 min	75.06	15.79	1.38	32.87	5.18	93.16
K3	30 min	34.58	7.27	0.48	40.15	4.33	95.09
OK		284.6	59.85	0.15	100.00	1.83	100.00
Σ		475.5	100.00	1.83	100	1.83	

Table 2. Results of laboratory flotation carried out during the industrial trail

Product	Flotation time	Product yield γ[g]	Product yield γ[%]	Cu content λ[%]	Cumulat. yield Σγ[%]	Cumulat. Cu content ΣCu[%]	Cu recovery, [%]
K1	5 min	86.04	16.67	8.62	16.67	8.621	83.50
K2	15 min	69.37	13.44	1.14	30.10	5.281	92.40
K3	30 min	30.16	5.84	0.49	35.94	4.502	94.04
OK		330.7	64.06	0.16	100.00	1.721	100.00
Σ		516.27	100.00	1.72	100	1.72	

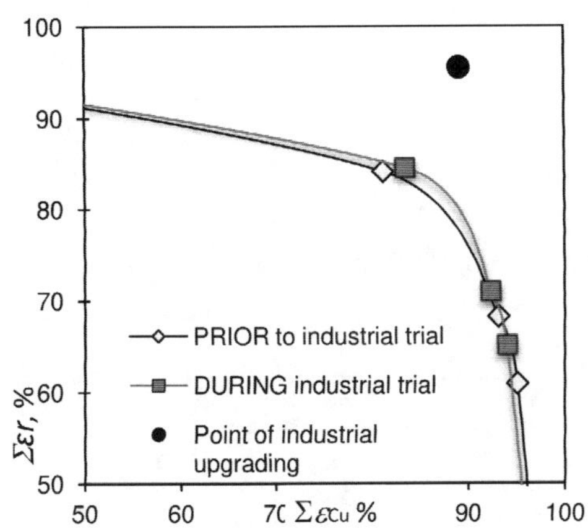

(a)

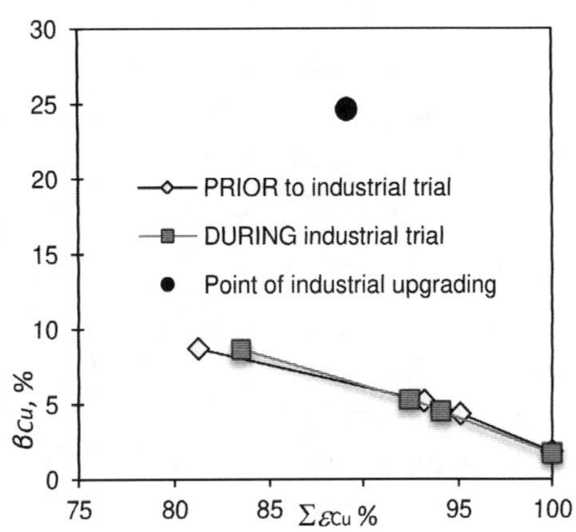

(b)

Figure 1. Laboratory upgrading curves: Fuerstenau (a) and Halbich (b) for flotations conducted in the presence of mixture A

2.2. Results of flotation conducted with mixture B

Table 3. Results of laboratory flotation prior to the industrial trail

Product	Flotation time	Product yield γ[g]	Product yield γ[%]	Cu content λ[%]	Cumulat. yield Σγ[%]	Cumulat. Cu content ΣCu[%]	Cu recovery, [%]
K1	5 min	80.71	16.95	8.85	16.95	8.85	82.77
K2	15 min	74.5	15.64	1.13	32.59	5.15	92.57
K3	30 min	37.34	7.84	0.54	40.43	4.25	94.90
OK		283.69	59.57	0.16	100.00	1.81	100.00
Σ		476.24	100.00	1.81	100	1.81	

Table 4. Results of laboratory flotation carried out during the industrial trail

Product	Flotation time	Product yield γ[g]	Product yield γ[%]	Cu content λ[%]	Cumulat. yield Σγ[%]	Cumulat. Cu content ΣCu[%]	Cu recovery, [%]
K1	5 min	74.45	17.69	8.09	17.69	8.091	84.79
K2	15 min	61.36	14.58	0.83	32.28	4.808	91.91
K3	30 min	34.78	8.27	0.50	40.54	3.930	94.37
OK		250.17	59.46	0.16	100.00	1.689	100.00
Σ		420.76	100.00	1.69	100	1.69	

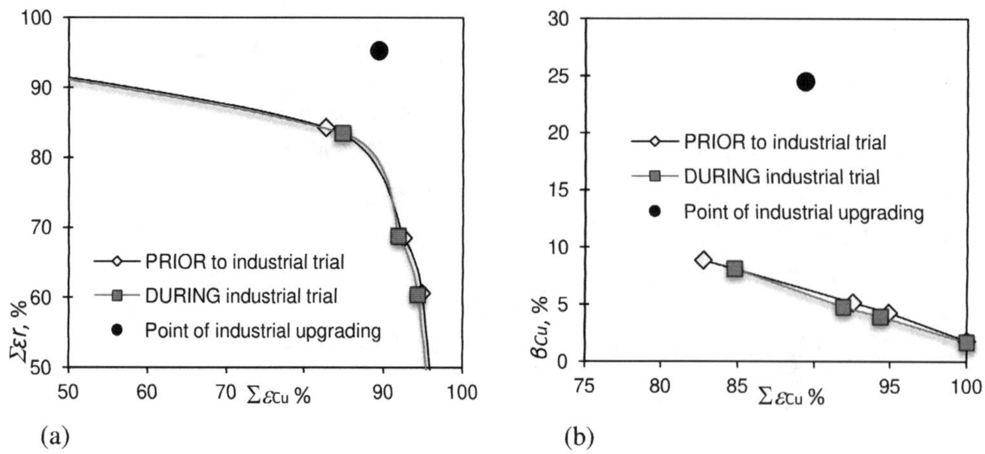

Figure 2. Laboratory upgrading curves: Fuerstenau (a) and Halbich (b) for flotations conducted in the presence of mixture B

2.3. Results of flotation conducted with mixture C

Table 5. Results of laboratory flotation prior to the industrial trail

Product	Flotation time	Product yield γ[g]	Product yield γ[%]	Cu content λ[%]	Cumulat. yield Σγ[%]	Cumulat. Cu content ΣCu[%]	Cu recovery, [%]
K1	5 min	83.56	17.47	8.82	17.47	8.82	84.12
K2	15 min	76.57	16.01	1.02	33.49	5.09	93.08
K3	30 min	34.87	7.29	0.52	40.78	4.27	95.15
OK		283.18	59.22	0.15	100.00	1.83	100.00
Σ		478.18	100.00	1.83	100	1.83	

Table 6. Results of laboratory flotation carried out during the industrial trail

Product	Flotation time	Product yield γ[g]	Product yield γ[%]	Cu content λ[%]	Cumulat. yield Σγ[%]	Cumulat. Cu content ΣCu[%]	Cu recovery, [%]
K1	5 min	78.71	15.70	8.66	15.70	8.664	85.19
K2	15 min	68.02	13.57	0.81	29.27	5.021	92.04
K3	30 min	38.16	7.61	0.51	36.88	4.090	94.47
OK		316.38	63.12	0.14	100.00	1.597	100.00
Σ		501.27	100.00	1.60	100	1.60	

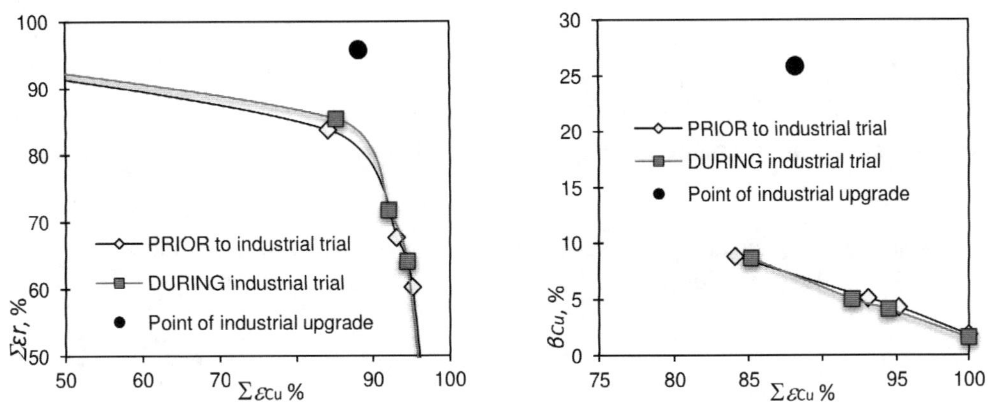

(a) (b)

Figure 3. Laboratory upgrading curves: Fuerstenau (a) and Halbich (b) for flotations conducted in the presence of mixture C

The results of laboratory tests carried out with mixtures of reagents A, B and C before the industrial trial compared with results during industrial trial indicate that the process with a given mixture in a specific period of time was similar, as evidenced by similar upgrading curves. This means that the observed changes in Cu content in the feed have practically no influence on the beneficiation results. In addition, the process efficiency when using different reagent mixtures and specific test periods was characterised by similar indices. The analysis of results obtained in both periods of laboratory tests indicates that the best effects were obtained when using a mixture of reagents A in comparison to other mixtures. On the basis of the conducted research it may be stated that the variability of feed grade as a decisive parameter in the prediction of industrial results does not have a significant impact as long as period of research (3 months).

3. The impact of scaling-up of experiments on results

Differences in upgrading indices between laboratory tests and industrial trials were analysed in next stage of the research. Industrial trials were conducted with the same reagent mixtures (A, B, C) in one of the KGHM production plant according to a regular procedure. During the trial carried out, the dose of the collecting reagent was determined in accordance with the operating instruction specified for this technological circuit. The effect of the applied collector mixtures on the copper recovery was determined. Although all the trial periods were conducted on the same technology line, with a comparable technological regime with the only variable parameter, e.g. the use of different mixtures of collectors, it was impossible to retain the same experimental conditions. Due to process disturbances occurring in industrial conditions, such as fluctuations of throughput and feed grade, each working shift was treated as a separate piece of data. This allowed for the comparison the both the feed parameters and the upgrading results versus time, as well as the determination of the confidence intervals of the selectivity index *a* on the basis of its variability.

The following equation [5, 6] was used to determine the industrial upgrading curves in the $\varepsilon_r=f(\varepsilon)$ coordinates:

$$\varepsilon_r(a') = a'^{\frac{(100-\varepsilon)}{(a'-\varepsilon)}} - 0.07\left(a'^{\frac{(100-\varepsilon)}{(a'-\varepsilon)}} - 95.5\right)^2 \left(100 - a'^{\frac{(100-\varepsilon)}{(a'-\varepsilon)}}\right) \quad (1)$$

where:

- a' - is numerically equal to the value of *a*,
- *0.07* - empirical constant of the equation,
- *95.5* - means the point of maximum curvature of the industrial upgrading curve occurring at ε_r = *95,5%*.

The results of industrial upgrading results during trials together with the results of laboratory experiments (before and during industrial trial) are presented on the Fuerstenau upgrading curves, $\varepsilon_r=f(\varepsilon)$ on Fig. 4 ÷ 6.

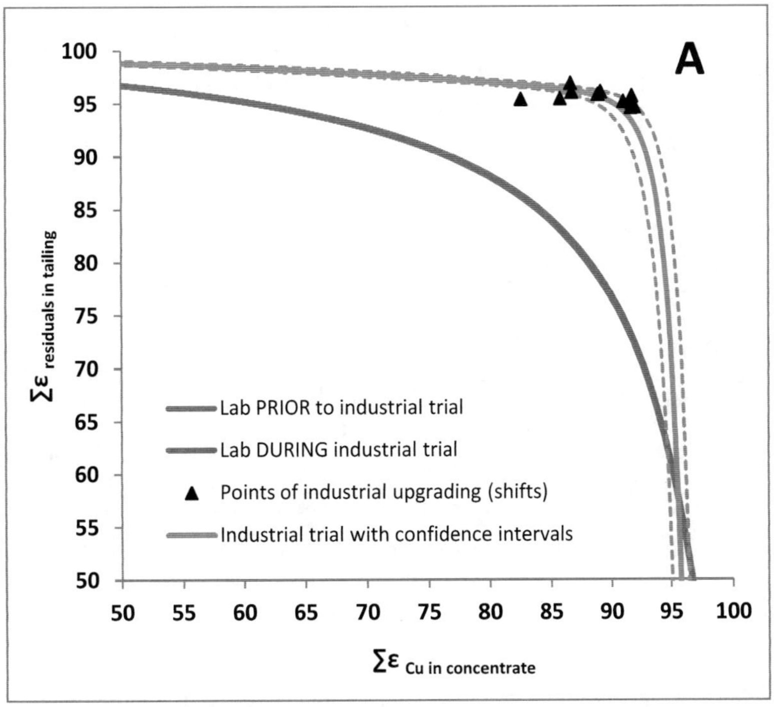

Figure 4. Enlarged part of Fuerstenau curves for flotation with mixture A.

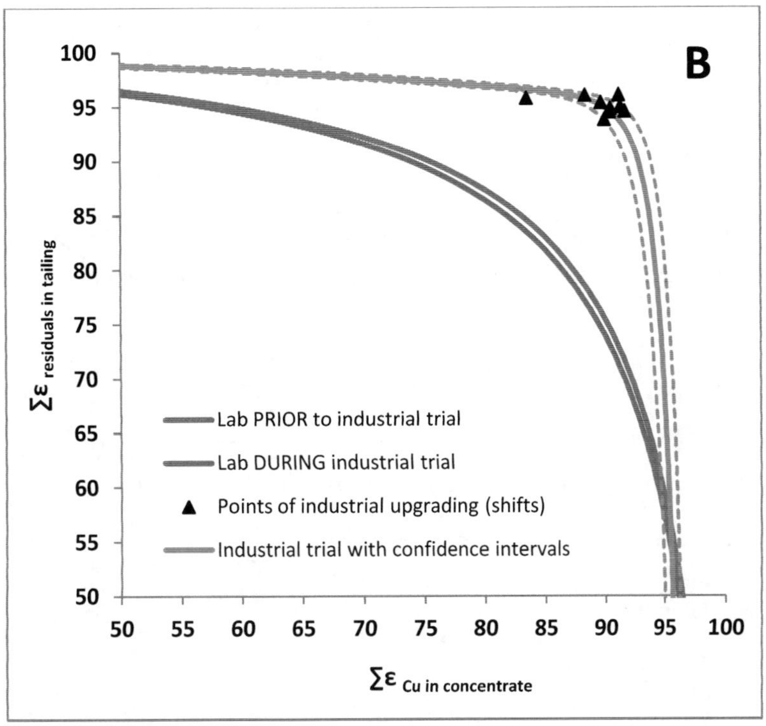

Figure 5. Enlarged part of Fuerstenau curves for flotation with mixture B.

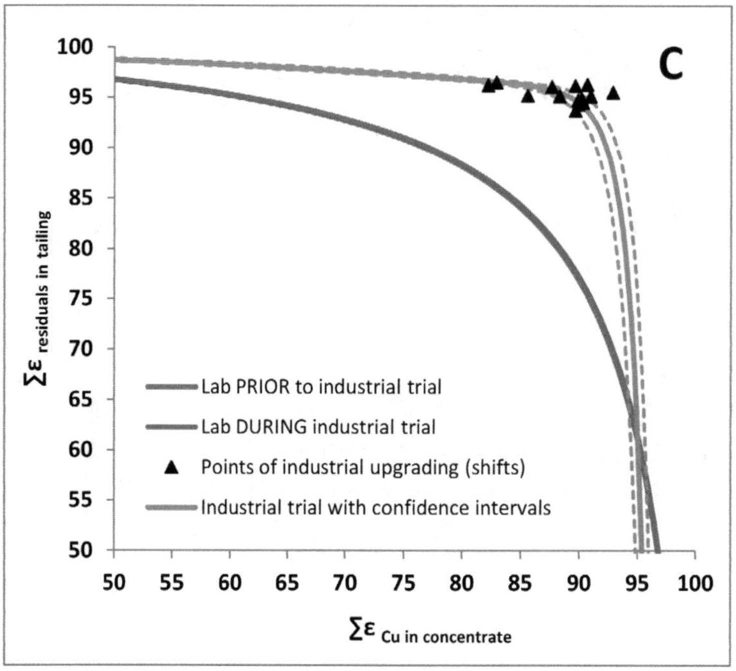

Figure 6. Enlarged part of Fuerstenau curves for flotation with mixture C

The industrial upgrading curves in each of the analysed cases (Fig. 4 ÷ 6) show that the point of the greatest convexity, i.e. the point when more useless than useful components start to get into the concentrate, take similar values. Hence it is reasonable to claim that the feed had similar enrichment properties and that the differences between the laboratory curves of the two research periods and the industrial curve for all three mixtures are similar. The swarms of industrial upgrading points indicate some regularities of industrial enrichment in each of the mixtures discussed. The evidence for this is the oscillation their positions around a constant value at approximately ε_r=95.5%.

It should be noticed that the variability of enrichment results under industrial conditions is significantly greater than the differences determined in laboratory tests. Moreover, the effects obtained in laboratory conditions were not confirmed in the industrial conditions. In order to analyse the reasons for this phenomenon, Table 7 summarizes the Cu content in the feed and the values of selectivity index *a*, which describes the efficiency of the enrichment process regardless of the content of the useful component in the feed.

Table 7. Summary of selectivity indices of *Cu* for laboratory flotation and industrial trail.

	Laboratory flotations		Industrial trails	
	Cu content in the feed; α [%]	selectivity index *a*	*Cu* content in the feed; α [%]	selectivity index *a*
Mixture A	1.83	103.43	1.60	100.57
Coefficient of variation; ν [%]			4.05	0.17
Confidence interval, 1-α = 0.95				±0.10
Mixture B	1.81	103.74	1.67	100.58
Coefficient of variation; ν [%]			4.61	0.14

Confidence interval, 1-α = 0.95				±0.09
Mixture C	1.83	103.48	1.63	100.63
Coefficient of variation; ν [%]			5.31	0.15
Confidence interval, 1-α = 0.95				±0.08

The analysis shows that the differences in enrichment results are poorly correlated with the variability of *Cu* content in the feed. Additionally, it is confirmed that the variance of shift *Cu* content in the feed, measured by the coefficient of variation, is at a low and constant level of about 5%. There are no clear correlations and influence of individual parameters on each other. The factors determining the differences in the curves (Fig. 4 ÷ 6) should result from the tested reagent mixtures. The relations between the parameters obtained under industrial and laboratory conditions should be the same for all three cases. This would make it easier to determine the scale-up factors and thus to predict the industrial enrichment parameters.

It was expected that the determined laboratory and industrial enrichment indices, while eliminating feed variability, would allow the determination of the scale-up factor. The lack of correlation between laboratory and industrial parameters indicates that the determination of a simple dependence, enabling the prediction of industrial enrichment parameters, requires more comprehensive approach than the one which has been applied so far. Therefore, the number and variability of enrichment parameters indicate the necessary of searching for the influence on the scaling-up such parameters as: the variability of process with related variability of throughput and grinding times, flotation time as well as differences in mineralogical properties of ore and degree of mineral liberation, pH, Eh and other important process variables [6]. All of these factors and the influence of parameters related to the operation of the processing plant (density of pulp, reagent dosing accuracy, wear aging of machine working parts) may be the reason why the effect of introducing new reagents is very often unnoticeable or even negative in industrial conditions.

Therefore, the problem of the absence of correlation between the results of laboratory tests and industrial research should be seen in the current methodology of laboratory tests. Such conclusions were also reached by Łuszczkiewicz and others [5]. In their report, they pointed out that the currently practised methodology of laboratory scale research differs significantly from the flotation conditions present in processing plants (backflows, accumulation of disturbing components, continuity of the process, the recycling of industrial water with some impurities, etc.). It appears necessary to develop a methodology for laboratory testing of new flotation reagents taking into account these factors. Therefore, the issue of so-called "scaling-up of laboratory research" requires thorough research and analyses.

The new attitude to prediction of industrial plant upgrading results based on previously executed laboratory experiments should also contain an implementation of gradually scaling up process from laboratory, pilot plant, semi-industrial and finally existing plant technology line. Each step should be observed in order to formulate algorithms of prediction results from obtained results. Such approach should point critical factors having the most significant influence on correctness and precision of scaled-up results. Moreover some attempts should be undertaken to modify laboratory and pilot scale methodology to develop optimised procedure and practise enabling to predict results with satisfactory quality and with approvable costs.

4. Summary

The presented results of both laboratory and industrial scale studies on new mixtures of collecting reagents (A, B, C) indicate that the positive results obtained in laboratory tests are not sufficient to make a decision regarding the introduction of a new reagent for use without unnecessary risk. The reasons for this phenomenon are probably due to the simplification of the current laboratory testing practices, which do not take into account the complexity of the industrial conditions. Taking into account a limited amount of data from laboratory flotations carried out in an open system (yields with concentrate and tailing grade) as well as Cu content in the feed are the most common data, it should be assumed that the applied methodology is also susceptible to measurement errors of analysis, i.e. determination of masses and contents. Even the execution of multiple flotations with the same parameters does not significantly increase the accuracy of the results.

Further work on finding correlations between laboratory and industrial scale results should be based on a more extensive scheme of laboratory flotation. In addition, it is necessary to take into account previous studies in which the authors suggest that the result of copper enrichment in concentrate may be influenced by other ore minerals (galena, sphalerite, pyrite) as well as base rock minerals [7, 8]. Therefore, when scaling-up the results, it is advisable to investigate the relationship between the main sulphide minerals of copper, associated metals and base rock minerals. The introduction of mineralogical studies may provide a number of information on the interactions between scale-up of individual minerals and process performance after the introduction of new flotation reagents. This methodology should provide a number of necessary information to enable the decision to introduce a new reagent with minimal risk of loses. It should be emphasized that the direction of research may contribute to the increase of production effects and to the reduction of irreversible losses of copper and other useful metals in tailing.

References

[1] Yianatos J.B., Bergh L.G., Aguilera J., Flotation scale up: use of separability curves, *Minerals Engineering*, **16**, 2003, 347-352

[2] Bourassa M., Barbery G., Broussaud A., Conil P., Flotation kinetics scale up: comparison laboratory batch test to pilot plant, *XVI Int. Min. Proc. Congress*, 1988, Elsevier, Amsterdam, p. 579

[3] Yianatos J.B. et al., 2010, A novel scale-up approach for mechanical flotation cells, *Minerals Engineering*, **23**, 2010, 877–884

[4] Łuszczkiewicz A., Duchnowska M., Drzymała J., Konopacka Ż., Henc T., Laskowski J., Karwowski P., Określenie granicznej wzbogacalności urobku przerabianego w O/ZWR Rejon Lubin, *Instytut Górnictwa Politechniki Wrocławskiej*, Wrocław, grudzień 2012

[5] Łuszczkiewicz A., Foszcz D., Drzymała J., Duchnowska M., Bakalarz A., Szyszka D., Tumidajski T., Konopacka Ż., Niedoba T., Kowalczuk P., Hupka J., Niewiadomski M., Karwowski P., Księżniak K., Rogala A., 2013. Opracowanie metodyki badania odczynników flotacyjnych pod kątem ich własności użytkowych, *Raport Instytutu Górnictwa Politechniki Wrocławskiej*, No. I-11/2013/S-30, Wrocław.

[6] Foszcz D., Łuszczkiewicz A., Drzymała J., Tumidajski T., Trybalski K., Muszer A., Niedoba T., Henc T., 2009, Określenie wpływu wzbogacalności przerabianych rud na jakość koncentratów miedziowych dla potrzeba optymalizacji górniczo-hutniczego procesu wytwarzania miedzi. *Sprawozdanie z pracy AGH*, grudzień 2009

[7] Krzemińska M. Wpływ mieszaniny kolektorów flotacyjnych na efektywność wzbogacania rud miedzi, *Praca doktorska*, Wrocław 2017

[8] Krzemińska M., Kurzydło P., 2018, Preliminary assessment of new approach to scale-up the laboratory results of flotation reagents tests based on mineralogical analysis, *Mineral Engineering Conference, IOP Conf. Series: Materials Science and Engineering* **427** (2018)

Influence of reagent dose on the flotation selectivity of copper ore from LGOM area (SW Poland)

M Duchnowska, A Bakalarz and A Luszczkiewicz

Wrocław University of Science and Technology, Faculty of Geoengineering, Mining and Geology, Wybrzeże Wyspiańskiego Street 27, 50-370 Wrocław

E-mail: alicja.bakalarz@pwr.edu.pl

Abstract. The influence of amount of flotation reagents on the efficiency of copper ore flotation in standard laboratory experiments was investigated. The aim of the study was to evaluate the effect of collector and frother amount on the selectivity of copper upgrading during flotation process of dolomite-shale ore from Fore-Sudetic Monocline area (Legnica-Glogow Copper Basin). The amount of collectors added in industrial conditions was the starting point for the process assessment. Since the dose of flotation reagents influences on the quality and quantity parameters of obtained concentrates, a decrease or increase of reagent dosage can have a major impact on the overall metal production costs at the mining-metallurgical complex.

1. Introduction

One of the main factors which determine the efficiency and upgrading selectivity is amount, type and dosage of flotation reagents. Usually flotation reagents are divided into: collectors, frothers and modifying reagents (regulators). The role of collectors is to form a hydrophobic layer on a given mineral surface in the flotation suspension while the frother creates conditions for froth formation. The role of regulators is controlling the interaction of collectors between individual minerals [1].

For flotation of sulphide minerals, xanthates as well as dithiophosphates and dithiocarbamates from the anionic collectors group are most commonly used. The basic collecting reagents in industrial systems of non-ferrous ores enrichment are xanthates, characterized by great selectivity of sulphide minerals and native metals flotation, good solubility in water and stability in alkaline environment.

In recent years, interest has increased for the use of mixtures of different type of collectors for enhancing the selectivity and recovery. First research on application of mixed collector can be found during the 1950's [2]. The interactions between differently structured collectors, for example strong and weak collectors like xanthate and non-ionic, and the synergism of them are described in many papers [3,4,5,6,7,8]. The main advantages of using such mixtures include: reducing the costs of the whole process by reducing the dose of the main and usually more expensive collector, improving the flotation kinetics, increasing the useful minerals recovery, improving the selectivity of the process and increasing the size range of the floatable particles (e.g. increased the recovery of coarse particles). The combination of xanthates and dithiophosphates has a positive influence on the sulphide minerals flotation efficiency [9].

The technological properties of Polish copper ore from Fore–Sudetic Monocline are specific and unique in the global copper resource base [10]. The presence of three various lithological with different properties types of rocks: sandstone, dolomitic and shale, make some difficulties in processing of mined copper ore. The lithological and mineralogical composition of the ore requires creation and use of complex technological flowsheets. Moreover, the complexity of copper ore is the main reason of difficulties in keeping of high upgrading efficiency, despite the relatively high contents of precious metals in the feed.

In the case of the processing of Polish copper ores an important factor is the properties of technological waters used in flotation. At processing plants, circulating technological (flotation) waters are strongly saline, and all dissolved salts act as additional portion of the frother reagent in the flotation process [11].

In the case of copper ore flotation, the effectiveness of the process is measured by the loss of copper in waste, which in the technological system is a non-linear function of froth depth and, above all, the amount of flotation reagents dosed into the system [12]. An insufficient amount of the flotation reagent may reduce the yield of the final concentrate, while too high dose of reagents may reduce the selectivity of the separation of useful and useless components. It is extremely important that the dose of the collecting reagent should be appropriate to the parameters of ore being processed and technological system.

At present, a mixture of sodium ethyl and isobutyl xanthates alone or their mixture with the addition of dithiophosphates as collectors are used in flotation process of Polish copper ore. The amount of collector and frother at concentrator plants is between 70–100 and 10–20 grams per ton, respectively. The doses of flotation reagents at each concentrator plant depend on feed density, technological system, content of useless components in the feed and floatability of ore being processed [13]. Wherefore, the aim of this paper is to evaluate the effect of collector and frother amount on the selectivity of copper upgrading during flotation process of sulphide ore from Fore-Sudetic Monocline area (SW Poland).

2. Experimental

The examined material was the sample of dolomite-shale ore with chalcocite mineralization predominance which was collected from Legnica-Glogow Copper Basin (LGOM) area. The mineral composition of studied copper ore is presented in Table 1. The sample was dry-crushed in a jaw crusher below 1 mm. Directly before the flotation test, the ore sample was wet-ground in a laboratory ball mill to obtain about 80% of the mass passing 0.040 mm. Particle size distribution of the feed is presented in Table 2.

Table 1. Mineral composition of flotation feed.

Mineral/minerals	Content (%)
Chalcocite/digenite/djurleite	1.52
Bornite	0.27
Chalcopyrite	0.12
Covellite	0.10
Pyrite/marcasite	0.14
Galena	0.05
Sphalerite	0.02
Quartz	23.94
Ca, Mg carbonates	56.97
Clay minerals + micas	13.26
Others	3.61

Table 2. Particle size distribution of flotation feed.

Particle size (mm)	Yield, γ (%)	
	before wet milling	after wet milling
>0.10	66.1	0. 4
0.07–0.10	3.5	1.7
0.04–0.07	4.8	8.9
<0.04	25.6	89.0

2.1. Materials and methods

All flotation experiments were conducted in a laboratory mechanical flotation machine of Denver D12 type equipped with 2.5 and 1.5 L flotation cells. Each experiment was carried out according to the standard method of multi-stage operation which consist of rougher and cleaning flotation. The last cleaning stage was kinetic flotation test in which the feed was the concentrate obtained from the first stage of cleaning flotation.

In Figure 1 the scheme of flotation methodology is presented. The density of the flotation suspension was 300 g/L. The industrial water and reagents were used in flotation experiments. As a frother an aqueous solution of polyethylene glycols was used. The mixture of sodium ethyl and isobutyl xanthate (in ratio 7:3) was applied as a collector. Both reagents were prepared directly before flotation test. After the experimental part, all the products were dried in a laboratory dryer at 70 °C, and next weighed. The chemical analysis of copper content was conducted.

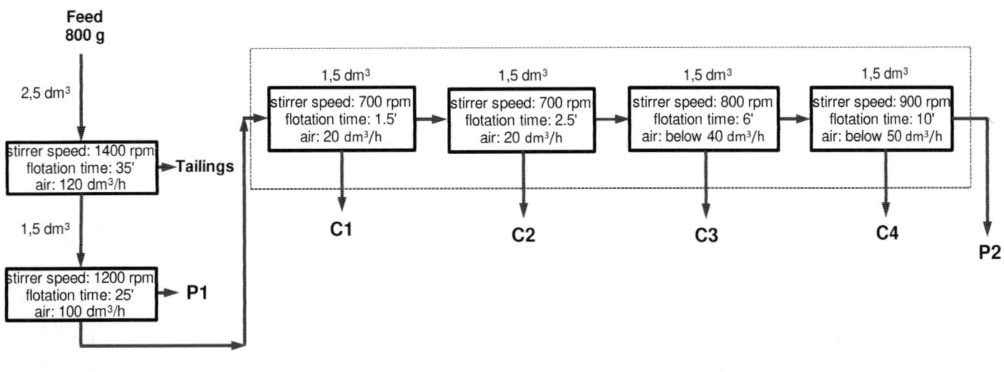

Figure 1. The scheme of flotation methodology.

Tests were conducted in two series. In the first series an influence of collector dose on the upgrading selectivity of copper in concentrates was analysed. The collector was added in three various doses: 60, 80 and 120 g/Mg while the frother amount was constant 20 g/Mg. In second series the impact of amount of frother on the process selectivity was studied. The frother was dosed in range of 10 to 40 g/Mg while the amount of collector was constant and equal 80 g/Mg.

2.2. Results and discussion

The results of flotation were evaluated by the mass balance of components and products of separation (Table 3) as well as by plotting recovery-recovery (the Fuerstenau upgrading curve) and grade-recovery separation curves (Figures 2-3).

As it can be seen in Figure 2 quite similar flotation selectivities of copper upgrading were obtained in the first series. It should be noted that for the test with the usage of medium collector dose

(80 g/Mg) the recovery-recovery curve in the range of the maximum curvature of the curve (the point characterizing the industrial system) was characterized by the highest selectivity of upgrading (Figure 2a). In this experiment, the lowest content and the loss of copper in tailings were observed. It has been seen in Figure 2a, the curve for this test is close to the ideal upgrading curve (the higher process selectivity) for higher recoveries values.

Table 3. The mass balance of components and products of separation.

	Influence of collector dose on flotation								
collector (g/Mg)	60			80			120		
frother (g/Mg)	20								
Product	γ, %	β, %	ε %	γ, %	β, %	ε %	γ, %	β, %	ε %
concentrate 1	1.2	34.3	24.5	2.8	28.5	45.4	1.8	32.1	32.6
concentrate 2	0.7	29.3	8.8	2.8	21.3	22.8	2.0	26.2	24.1
concentrate 3	5.1	18.1	40.0	5.6	13.0	14.2	4.2	16.8	20.2
concentrate 4	3.4	13.5	7.6	4.8	9.5	3.8	3.0	13.0	4.9
product 2	11.2	7.0	5.7	14.0	5.3	4.0	7.9	7.9	3.6
product 1	23.0	3.6	5.8	38.6	2.5	6.8	25.9	3.6	6.6
tailing	55.3	1.7	7.5	31.4	1.8	3.0	55.3	1.8	7.9
feed	1.7			1.8			1.8		

	Influence of frother dose on flotation											
collector (g/Mg)	80											
frother (g/Mg)	10			20			30			40		
Product	γ, %	β, %	ε %	γ, %	β, %	ε %	γ, %	β, %	ε %	γ, %	β, %	ε %
concentrate 1	3.4	24.5	49.5	2.8	28.5	45.4	1.4	30.9	25.7	1.7	23.8	23.4
concentrate 2	3.3	17.2	18.3	2.8	21.3	22.8	2.7	22.8	29.4	2.7	19.4	26.1
concentrate 3	4.9	11.6	11.5	5.6	13.0	14.2	4.8	14.4	20.4	11.0	9.1	31.8
concentrate 4	6.1	8.2	5.7	4.8	9.5	3.8	5.7	9.8	7.8	9.7	6.0	6.8
product 2	15.2	4.7	4.9	14.0	5.3	4.0	13.3	5.4	5.2	17.5	3.7	4.7
product 1	27.8	2.7	5.5	38.6	2.5	6.8	27.8	2.9	6.0	29.9	2.3	4.7
tailing	39.3	1.7	4.6	31.4	1.8	3.0	44.2	1.7	5.4	27.6	1.7	2.6
feed	1.7			1.8			1.7			1.7		

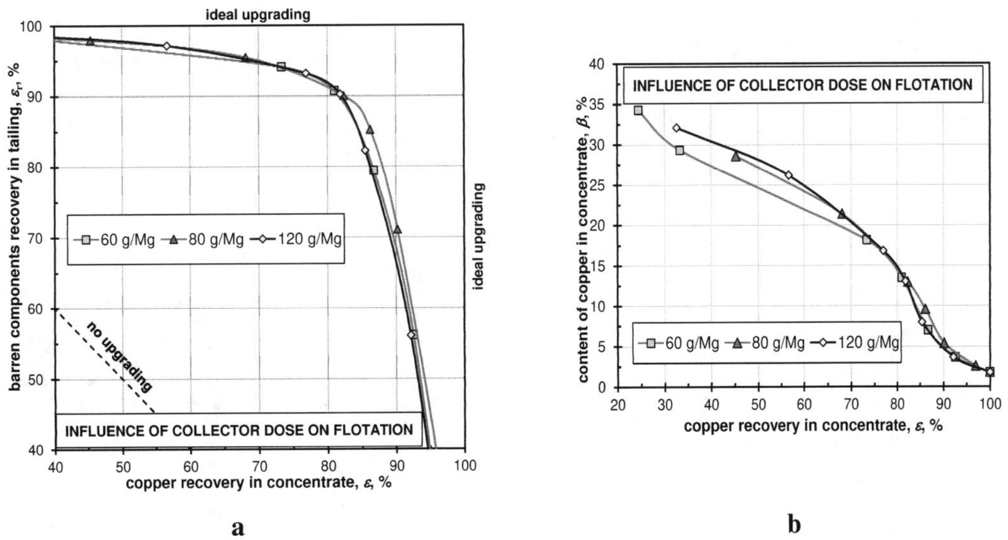

Figure 2. The recovery-recovery and grade recovery separation curves for the flotation of dolomite-shale copper ore in the presence of various doses of collecting agent

The analysis of separation curves in Figure 2b has been shown that in flotation test in the presence of lower dose of collector, the concentrates are characterized by lower contents of copper at the similar recovery of this metal in concentrate. It was noted that the increase of collector dose more than 80 g/Mg causes the poorer upgrading parameters at rougher flotation stage. It results in higher losses of metal in final tail despite the higher selectivity of copper upgrading at cleaning stages.

At the next step of experiments the impact of frother dosage on the copper upgrading selectivity in concentrate was examined. It has been shown in Figure 3a that the increase of frother dose above 20 g/Mg has negative effect on process efficiency, particularly at cleaning stages. The concentrates collected in cleaning flotations are characterized by lower contents of copper compared to experiment with the medium dose of frother. Too high dose of frother can result in increased mechanical entrainment of useless components particles into concentrate. It can reduce the quality of concentrates from cleaning stages. Moreover, the poorer yield of tailings and the lower content of copper in tailings from rougher flotation in the test in the presence of lower dose of frother were observed (Figure 3b).

In the tests with the lowest and higher amounts of frother, the concentrates have a lower yield and contain less copper compared to dose of 20 g/Mg. Final tailings are characterized by higher losses of copper and higher contents of this metal in these products (Figure 3). Reducing the dose of frother below 20 g/Mg has a negative influence on upgrading selectivity of copper at cleaning stages which is related to the small amount of arising froth – too small dose of reagent.

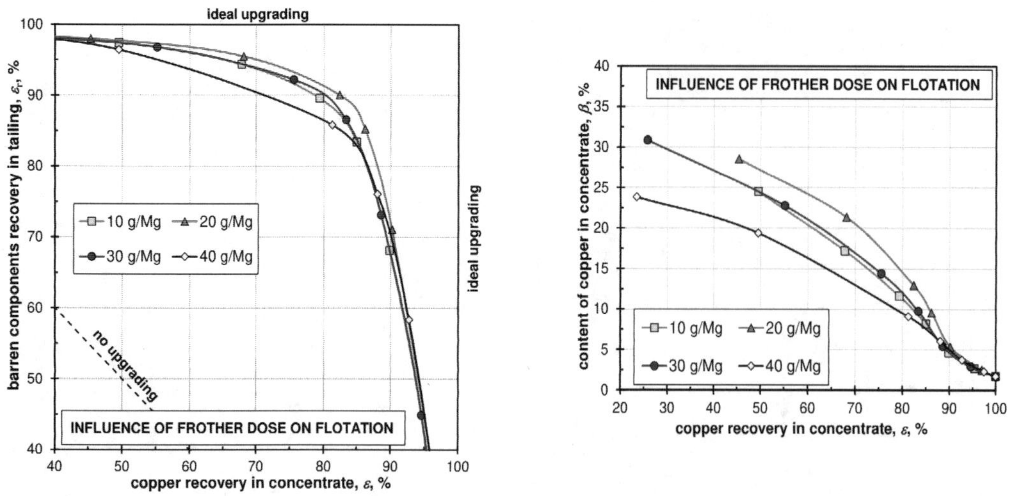

a **b**

Figure 3. The recovery-recovery and grade recovery separation curves for the flotation of dolomite-shale copper ore in the presence of various doses of frothing agent

A statistical analysis of the obtained results was carried out by determining the selectivity indicator ***c*** which allows for one-parameter evaluation of the upgrading process (Table 4). The indicator was determined on the basis of approximation of enrichment results on the Fuerstenau plots using the equation for asymmetric curve in regard to the diagonal curve. This curve is characterized by noticeable convexity for lower recovery values and flattened course for higher recoveries [14]. The higher ***c*** selectivity indicator the greater upgrading efficiency and close to the ideal upgrading process.

Table 4. Statistical analysis of obtained upgrading results

	Influence of collector dose on flotation		
collector (g/Mg)	60	80	120
frother (g/Mg)		20	
selectivity indicator, c^a	10.82	12.29	10.64
standard error of estimation, *SEE*	1.23	1.72	1.66

	Influence of frother dose on flotation			
collector (g/Mg)		80		
frother (g/Mg)	10	20	30	40
selectivity indicator, c^a	10.59	12.29	10.68	10.55
standard error of estimation, *SEE*	2.01	1.72	1.67	2.34

[a] $\varepsilon_r = (100^c - \varepsilon^c)/100^{(c-1)}$

The highest upgrading selectivity was obtained for flotation test with the collector and frother dose of 80 g/Mg and 20 g/Mg, respectively. It was observed that the influence of collector amount on upgrading results is not such significant as the impact of frother dosage. The increase of frother amount noticeably reduces the efficiency of upgrading (lower selectivity indicator ***c***) which is probably result of mechanical entrainment of useless components. Decreasing of frother dosage below 20 g/Mg causes higher losses of copper in tailings and poorer quality of final concentrates.

3. Conclusions

The analysis and evaluation of separation curves for flotation tests using various doses of collector have been shown that regardless of reagent dosage the process selectivity is quite similar. The highest upgrading selectivity of concentrates in copper in test in the presence of collector and frother in doses of 80 and 20 g/Mg respectively was observed. The increase of frother dosage above 20 g/Mg clearly reduces the upgrading selectivity of concentrates in copper. It is related to the mechanical entrainment of gangue particles. The reducing the dose of frother below 20 g/Mg causes an increase of content and loss of copper in tailings with poorer quality of final concentrates.

It has been noted that a change of collector dose has only a slight impact on upgrading selectivity of concentrates in copper. As it can be seen that the flotation process of examined material is much more responsive on the dosage changes of frother than the collector. In the presence of too low frother dose the copper concentrates are characterized by poor content of copper while higher amount of copper accumulates in tailings. In the process when the amount of frother is too high, the concentrates are diluted by useless components that results in decreasing of upgrading selectivity.

It is advisable both for the collecting and frothing reagents to perform technological tests to determine the optimum dosages of flotation reagents which are used in current flotation process. As it has been shown in the paper, the collector amount should be reduced to 80 g/Mg while the dose of frother should be about 20 g/Mg. These changes of flotation reagents dosages affect the quality and quantity parameters of final products. Moreover, it has a major impact on the total costs of purchase of these chemicals and the overall metal production costs at the mining-metallurgical complex.

4. References

[1] Bulatovic S M 2007 *Handbook of Flotation Reagents* Vol. 1 Elsevier Science & Technology Books pp 5–40
[2] Plaksin I N, Glembockii V A, and Okolovich A M 1954 *Tr. Inst. Gorn. Akad. Nauk SSSR* **1** pp 213–214
[3] Hanumantha K and Forssberg K S E, 1997 *J. Miner. Process.* **51** pp 67–79
[4] Rao K H and Forssberg K S E 1997 *J. Miner. Process.* **51** pp 67–79
[5] Bradshaw D J, Harris P J and O'Connor C T 1998 *J. S. Afr. I. Min. Metall.* **98** pp 189–194
[6] Hangone G, Bradshaw D and Ekmekci Z 2005 *J. S. Afr. I. Min. Metall.* **105** pp 199–206
[7] Zhu Shu-quan, Bai Ya-na, Xie Wei-wei, Guo Mei-ling, Yuan Hui and Liu Gui-hua 2009 *The 6th International Conference on Mining Science & Technology* (Procedia Earth and Planetary Science 1) pp 724–730
[8] Ignatkina V A, Bocharov V A and Tubdenova B T 2010 *J. Mining Sci.* **46(1)** pp 82–88
[9] Wills B A and Finch J A 2016 *Wills' Mineral Processing Technology, An Introduction to the Practical Aspects of Ore Treatment and Mineral Recovery* (Eight Edition, Elsevier Ltd.)
[10] Preidl M and Rydzewski A 2007 *Monografia KGHM Polska Miedz S.A., Cześć II-Geologia* ed A Piestrzynski, A Banaszak and M Zaleska-Kuczmierczyk (CBPM „Cuprum" Sp. z o.o. Wroclaw) pp 102–104
[11] Luszczkiewicz A, Konieczny A, Kasinska-Pilut E and Drzymala J 2015 *Mineralurgia i wykorzystanie surowcow mineralnych* Materialy III Polskiego Kongresu Gorniczego Wroclaw pp 28–34
[12] Konieczny A, Pawlos W, Jach M, Pepkowski R, Krzeminska M and Kaleta R 2011 *Gornictwo i Geoinżynieria* **2** pp 61–71
[13] Wieniewski A, Pluskota B, Steczkowski J and Skorupska B 2007 *Monografia KGHM Polska Miedz S.A., Cześć IV-Przerobka* ed A Piestrzynski, A Banaszak and M Zaleska-Kuczmierczyk (CBPM „Cuprum" Sp. z o.o. Wroclaw) pp 498–541
[14] Drzymala J and Ahmed H A M 2005 *Int. J. Miner. Process.* **76 (1–2)** pp 55–65

Acknowledgments

Financial support by the Polish Statutory Research Grants (0402/0044/18 and 049U/0098/19) is greatly acknowledged.

Electrostatic and magnetic separations for the recovery of metals from electronic waste

T Suponik[1], D Franke[1] and P Nuckowski[2]

[1]Silesian University of Technology, Faculty of Mining, Safety Engineering and Industrial Automation, Akademicka 2, 44-100 Gliwice, Poland
[2]Silesian University of Technology, Faculty of Mechanical Engineering, Konarskiego 18A, 44-100 Gliwice, Poland

E-mail: tomasz.suponik@polsl.pl

Abstract. The aim of the study was to recover metals from e-scrap using electrostatic and magnetic separation successively. The type of phases in the four magnetic separation products was determined by X-ray diffraction (XRD). Three grain classes were tested: 2.00 - 0.56, 0.56 - 0.32 and 0.32 - 0.10 mm. Based on the tests, it turned out that the separations were the most efficient for grain class in the range from 0.32 to 0.10 mm. The yields of the products obtained from electrostatic and magnetic separations were as follows: in the case of electrostatic separation, 13.12% metals and 86.88% plastics and glass; and for magnetic separation 1.51% of ferromagnetics, 1.56% of paramagnetics and 10.05 % of diamagnetics. In the diamagnetics Cu was dominant, while in the paramagnetics and ferromagnetics CuSn, γ-Fe and Ni, Fe_3O_4, respectively. Pb, Sn were identified in average amounts in all products of magnetic separation.

1. Introduction

Due to the exhausting deposits of metals, including precious metals and rare earth elements, alternative sources of their acquisition should be sought, among other things by using a closed-circuit economy. In the era of dynamic development of technology (Industry 4.0), there is a need for systematic replacement of electronic equipment components, which results in the creation of a significant amount of electronic waste containing precious and critical metals listed on the European Commission list. Metal recovery is therefore a very important aspect for economic, political and environmental reasons.

Large amounts of valuable metals are needed for production of electric and electronic equipment that are used in many areas of our lives. The amount of metals in these wastes is 60.6%, of which 47.9% is iron and steel, 7.0% copper, 4.7% aluminum, 1.0 non-ferrous [1]. Printed circuit boards (PCBs) are used in many electronic devices, such as personal computers, televisions, mobile phones, hard disks, graphic cards, RAMs, etc. Due to the high content of metals in them, they are particularly interesting in the context of metal recovery [2, 3]. PCBs contain copper 11-14%, iron 4.5-8%, tin 2-4%, aluminum 1.5-3%, lead 1.5-2%, nickel 1-2.5%, zinc 0.5-1% and small amounts of precious metals such as: 0.005% gold, 0.008% silver, 0.002% palladium, 0.004% platinum [4, 5].

The type of metals and their amount in PCBs change each year, depending on the development of technology and current market standards assigned by producers. The metals content is about 20% to 45%, depending on the technology used and the year of production. In 1993, metals such as: Cu, Al,

Pb, Zn, Ni, Fe, Sn, Ag and Au were used for PCB production. Next, other metals were systematically used for the production, such as: Pd, Mg, Sb, Cr, In, Mn, Mg, Co, Ti, Cd, K, Se, and As. The content of metals also varies depending on the purpose of the PCB, eg. PCBs from mobile phones, household appliances, monitors, or stationary computers. It can be seen that the largest contents of expensive metals have cell phones. The reason is the small size of the PCBs of mobile phones, on which elements of electronic components similar to computers must be integrated [6, 7].

As provided by Tuncuk et al. [8] electrostatic and magnetic processes can be used to recover metals from PCBs. These methods have been extensively described in many works [9-14].

The aim of the study was to recover metals from e-scrap using electrostatic and magnetic separation. To assess the type of recovered metals XRD spectroscopy was applied.

2. Methods and materials

2.1. Preparation for electrostatic and magnetic separation

In the study the printed circuit boards (PCBs) from: personal computers (PC), hard disks, graphic cards and RAMs were applied. To separate metals from plastic and glass, the method shown in Figure 1 was used. Before grinding, some parts of PCB i.e. batteries, capacitor, inductors, quartz crystals etc. were removed using basic tools such as screwdrivers, pliers and others. Such prepared PCBs were cut into 4x4 cm pieces. The way of preparing and grinding electronic waste was presented in the paper written by Franke and Suponik [15]. The knife mill manufactured by TESTCHEM [16] was used to grind PCBs. The rotation speed of mill was 2815 rpm. Hardened steel blades and perforated sieve with 2 mm mesh size were used. Four grain classes were separated from the grinded material: 2.00 - 0.56 mm, 0.56 - 0.32 mm, 0.32 - 0.10 mm and <0.10 mm. The last, smallest grain class was not subjected to separation processes. Leaching methods for metals recovery are to be analyzed for this class in subsequent studies.

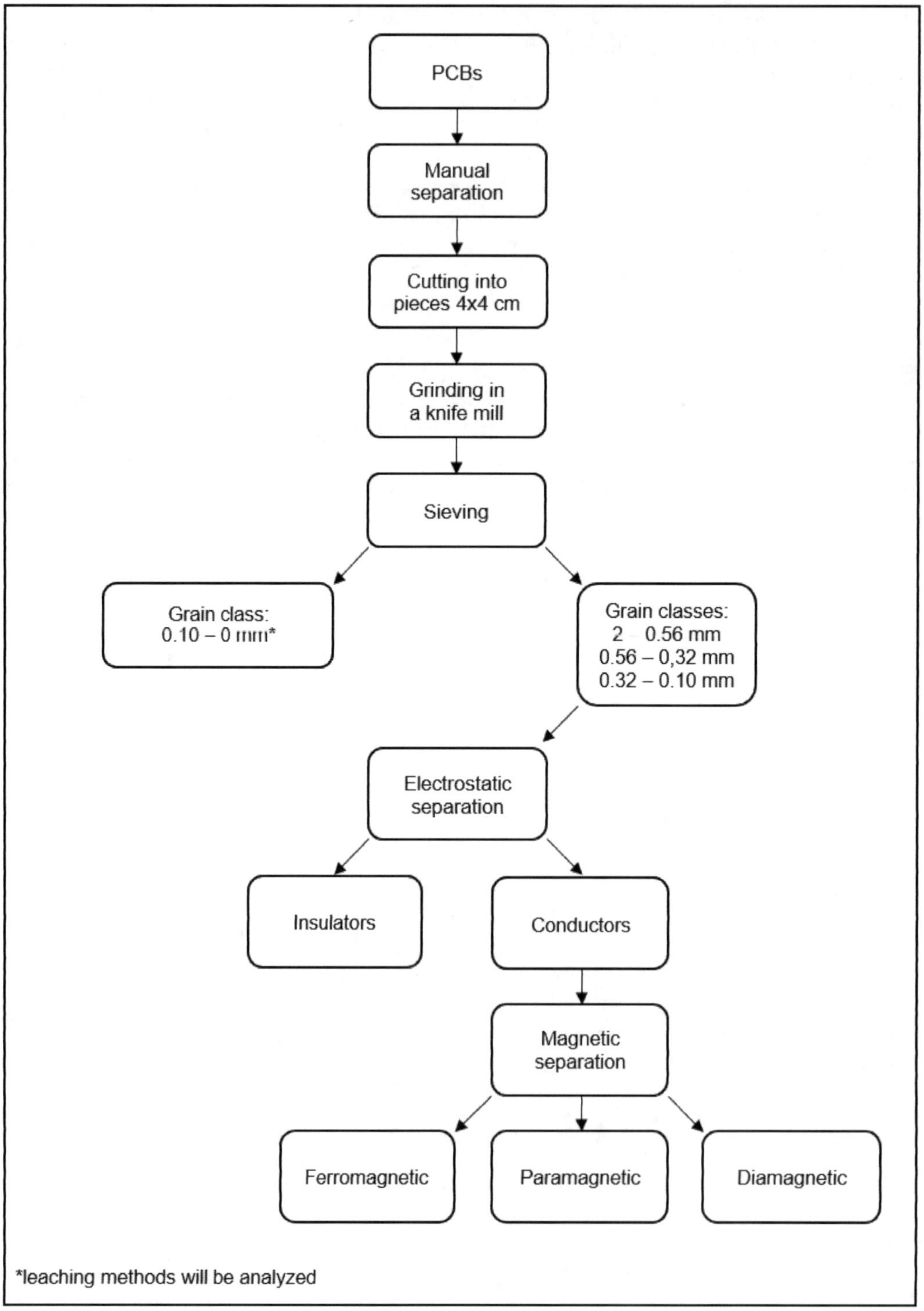

Figure 1. Research method.

2.2. Electrostatic separation

Boxmag-rapid Ltc separator was applied for electrostatic separation. The main parameters of this separation are: rotational speed of the shaft, voltage flowing through the electrode and its distance from the shaft, and the size of the material and feeding speed [17].

In the separator, the feed was directed to the belt of rotating shaft. The rotational speed of the shaft was 50 rpm. 5 cm from the shaft there was an electrode wire through which high voltage flowed. The voltage flowing through the electrode was 20 kV. As a result of air ionization, the grains of material on the shaft were charged. These with high conductivity quickly lost their charge and were ejected from the rotating shaft by centrifugal forces. The remaining grains that had not lost their charge were removed by a brush at the rear of the shaft.

2.3. Magnetic separation

A disks separator, that ensures heterogeneity of the magnetic field, was used for magnetic separation. In this type of separator, the difference in the magnetic susceptibility of various materials was used. The separator allowed to separate the material by means of two different magnetic forces produced by two electromagnets [18]. The currents supplying two electromagnets were 2 and 2.7 A, respectively. Thus, the magnitude of the magnetic forces in the separator was a parameter that improves the separation of materials. Additionally, at the beginning of the separator there was a permanent magnet that captured the ferromagnetic material.

The grains of material on the moving belt were affected by a magnetic field of varying intensity. Subsequently, the grains from the highest to the lowest magnetic susceptibility were removed from the belt to the four containers. These were successively: ferromagnetics, strong and weak paramagnetics and finally diamagnetics.

2.4. Assessment of products

The qualitative phase analysis of the magnetic separation products was based on X-ray diffraction measurements, performed with the use of a Panalytical X'Pert Pro MPD diffractometer, utilizing filtered radiation of a copper-anode lamp ($\lambda_{K\alpha} = 0.154$ nm), and a PIXcell 3D detector on the diffracted beam axis. Diffraction lines were recorded in the angular range of 5-120° (2θ), at step = 0.05° and count time per step = 100 s. Panalytical High Score Plus software with dedicated PAN-ICSD database was used for the identification of phases.

The content of ferromagnetic materials in the samples was carried out using the Satmagan 135 meter by Rapiscan Systems. The density of products was specified using pycnometer method in line with the PN-88/B-04481 standard.

3. Results and discussion

Table 1 shows the granulometric composition of grinded printed circuit boards. Two grain classes represented over 80% of the sample. They are 0.56 - 0.32 mm and 0.32 - 0.10.

Table 1. The results of the screening tests of comminuted PCBs.

Grain class, mm	Yield of grain class, (in % by mass)
2.00 - 0.56	8.4
0.56 - 0.32	42.1
0.32 - 0.10	39.1
< 0.10	10.4

The results of electrostatic and magnetic separation for tested grain classes are presented in table 2. In the grain classes 2.00-0.56 and 0.56-0.32 the yields of conductors (metals) after electrostatic separation were ca. 30%, while in the class of 0.32-0.10 it decreased to 13%. For a smaller grain class, metals were probably much less connected with insulators and thus the separation efficiency was greater. In addition, for larger classes of grains, the force of gravity, on electrostatic separator, acting on larger particles of insulators was probably greater than electrostatic forces, and therefore these particles fell into metallic products. This is evidenced by the higher density of insulators for larger grain classes and much higher yield of diamagnetics for these classes in magnetic separation products (see table 2). In general, the high content of diamagnetics indicates the imperfection of the electrostatic separation process.

Analysis of the content of ferromagnetic materials in the magnetic separation products (table 2) confirmed the correctness of magnetic separation in relation to metals with ferromagnetic properties. The yields of paramagnetics in all analyzed grain classes were the smallest.

Table 2. Results of electrostatic and magnetic separations.

The grain classes of the feed on the electrostatic and magnetic separators	2.00-0.56 mm				0.56-0.32 mm				0.32-0.10 mm			
Electrostatic separation												
Type of product after electrostatic separation	Conductors		Insulators		Conductors		Insulators		Conductors		Insulators	
The yield of the products in grain class, in % by mass	33,79		66,21%		28,47		71,53		13,12		86,88	
Density of product, g/cc	10.71		3.57		10.50		3.86		11.32		2.49	
Magnetic separation												
Type of product after magnetic separation	F^*	P_{str}^*	P_{wea}^*	D^*	F^*	P_{str}^*	P_{wea}^*	D^*	F^*	P_{str}^*	P_{wea}^*	D^*
The yield of the products in grain class, in % by mass	2.75	3.57	1.63	25.84	3.37	2.83	1.00	21.27	1.51	1.11	0.45	10.05

Content of ferromagnetics in product, in % by mass	94.1 %	0.4	<0.1	<0.1	82.3 %	0.4	<0.1	<0.1	92.4	0.2	<0.1	<0.1

*F - ferromagnetics; P_{str} - strong paramagnetics; P_{wea} - weak paramagnetics; D - diamagnetics

Based on the diffraction patterns shown in figure 2, the phases presented in table 3 were identified in magnetic separation products. The magnetic properties of these metals are presented in table 4. This table contains information on the use of presented metals in the production of PCBs.

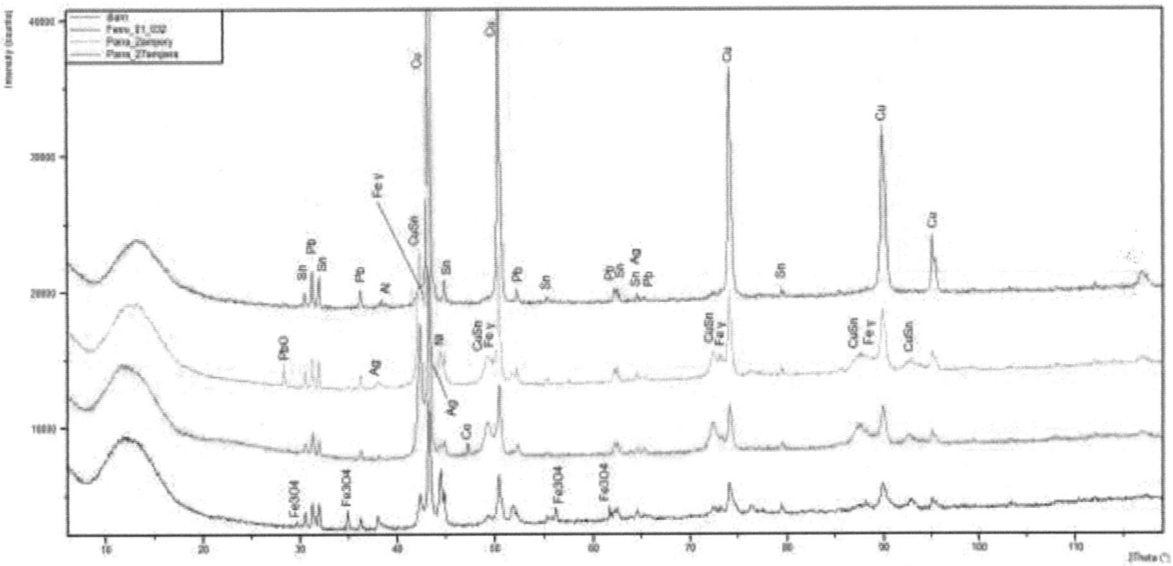

Figure 2. Diffractograms for magnetic separation products for: ferromagnetics (blue), strong paramagnetic (green), weak paramagnetics (pink), diamagnetics (red).

Table 3. Share of identified phases in the separation products.

Sample	Identified phases									
	Cu	Sn	Pb	CuSn	Fe γ	Fe_3O_4	PbO	Ag	Ni	Co
Ferromagnetics	+	+	+	+	+	+		+	+	
Strong paramagnetics	+	+	+	+	+		+	+	+	
Weak paramagnetics	+	+	+	+	+			+	+	+
Diamagnetics	+	+	+	+				+		

Table 4. Magnetic properties of identified metals (metallic compounds) and examples of their applications in PCB production [5, 8].

Metal or metallic compounds	Magnetic properties	Application examples
Fe_3O_4 [19]	Ferromagnetic	Data storage
Ni	Ferromagnetic	Relays, connectors and transformers

CuSn		Contact base material
γ-Fe	Paramagnetic	
Sn	Paramagnetic	Capacitors
PbO	Diamagnetic	Paint
Pb	Diamagnetic	Capacitors, inductors, batteries
Cu	Diamagnetic	Leadframe, cables and wires, capacitors, indicators, inductors, relays, connectors, transformers
Ag	Diamagnetic	Leadframe, connectors, capacitors, relays, indicators,

The intensity of basic diffraction lines indicated a clear quantitative differentiation of minerals in the samples:

- in diamagnetics Cu dominated, while Pb, Sn were identified in medium and Ag and Al in small quantities,
- in a weak and strong paramagnetics CuSn, Cu and γ-Fe dominated, while Sn and Pb were identified in smaller quantities,
- in ferromagnetics there were Ni, Fe_3O_4, Sn, Pb and CuSn in average amounts.

A relatively large amount of Cu, both in paramagnets and ferromagnetics, indicates that copper as a diamagnetic was probably mechanically bound to other elements or penetrated into paramagnetic and ferromagnetic products as a result of imperfections in the separation process. Also, in this case some fragments of metals may be soldered or covered by others (e.g. Cu or Sn) to increase conductivity.

4. Conclusions

Based on the research, the following conclusions were drawn:

- the yield of grain classes 0.56 - 0.32 and 0.32 - 0.10 mm obtained after grinding PCBs in the knife mill was over 80 %;
- electrostatic separation, and thus also magnetic, is much more efficient for a smaller grain class, in the range of 0.32-0.10 mm. The quantity of metallic products is smaller, but they are much less contaminated with plastics. The yields of the products obtained from electrostatic and magnetic separation were as follows: in the case of electrostatic separation, 13.12% metals and 86.88% plastics and glass; and for magnetic separation 1.51% of ferromagnetics, 1.56% of paramagnetics and 10.05 % of diamagnetics. High content of diamagnetics indicates the imperfection of the electrostatic separation process;
- The yield of magnetic products for the grain class of 0.32-0.10 mm was twice lower than in the case of larger classes. The feed on the magnetic separator for this grain class, i.e. for the conductors of grain class 0.32-0.10 mm, was also twice as small than for larger grains. This proves that magnetic separation worked with similar efficiency for all grain classes;
- In the diamagnetics Cu was dominant, while in paramagnetics and in ferromagnetics CuSn and γ-Fe and Ni, Fe_3O_4, respectively. Pb, Sn were identified in average amounts in all products of magnetic separation. In all magnetic separation products, the most was copper. It appeared even in paramagnets and ferromagnetics. Copper was probably mechanically bound to other chemical substances or penetrated into paramagnetic and ferromagnetic products as a result of imperfections in the magnetic separation process.

References

[1] Widmer R, Oswald-Krapf H, Sinha-Khetriwal D, Schnellmann M and Böni H 2005 Global perspectives on e-waste *Environmental impact assessment review* 25(**5**) pp 436-458

[2] Hagelüken C 2006 Recycling of electronic scrap at Umicore precious metals refining *Acta Metallurgica Slovaca* **12** pp 111-120

[3] Yazıcı E, Deveci H, Alp I, Akcil A and Yazıcı R 2010 Characterisation of computer printed circuit boards for hazardous properties and beneficiation studies

[4] Oh CJ, Lee SO, Yang HS, Ha TJ, and Kim MJ 2003 Selective Leaching of Valuable Metals from Waste Printed Circuit Boards *Journal of the Air & Waste Management Association* 53(7) pp 897-902

[5] Menad N and Van Houwelingen J 2011 Identification and recovery of rare metals in electric and electronic scrap: a review. *Tirtheenth International Waste Management and Landfill Symposium*pp 10 p

[6] Bizzo W, Figueiredo R and de Andrade V 2014 Characterization of printed circuit boards for metal and energy recovery after milling and mechanical separation *Materials* **7(6)** pp 4555-4566

[7] Akcil A, Erust C, Gahan CS, Ozgun M, Sahin M and Tuncuk A 2015 Precious metal recovery from waste printed circuit boards using cyanide and non-cyanide lixiviants–a review *Waste Management* **45** pp 258-271

[8] Tuncuk A, Stazi V, Akcil A, Yazici EY and Deveci H 2012 Aqueous metal recovery techniques from e-scrap: hydrometallurgy in recycling *Minerals engineering* 25(**1**) pp 28-37

[9] Svoboda J 1987 *Magnetic methods for the treatment of minrals* Amsterdam Elsevier

[10] Drzymała J 2007 *Mineral processing* Ofic Wyd PWr

[11] Cui J and Forssberg E 2003 Mechanical recycling of waste electric and electronic equipment: a review *Journal of hazardous materials* 99(**3**) pp 243-263

[12] Zhang S and Forssberg E 1998 Mechanical recycling of electronics strap-the current status and prospects *Waste Management & Research* 16(**2**) pp 119-128

[13] Laskowski JS and Łuszczkiewicz A 1989 *Przeróbka kopalin wzbogacanie surowców mineralnych* Dział Wydawnictw Politechniki Wrocławskiej

[14] Kelly E G and Spottiswood D J 1982 *Introduction to mineral processing*

[15] Franke D and Suponik T 2019 Metals recovery from e-scrap using gravity, electrostatic and magnetic separations *IOP Conf. Series: Materials Science and Engineering* 545(012016)

[16] www.testchem.pl

[17] Bedeković G, Salopek B and Sobota I 2011 Electrostatic separation of PET/PVC mixture *Technicki vjesnik* 18(**2**) pp 261-266

[18] Blaschke S 1972 *Przeróbka mechaniczna kopalin* Wydawnictwo Śląsk

[19] Wang M, Liu P, Wang Y, Zhou D, Ma C, Zhang D and Zhan J 2015 Core–shell superparamagnetic Fe3O4@β-CD composites for host–guest adsorption of polychlorinated biphenyls (PCBs) *Journal of Colloid and Interface Scienc* **447** pp 1-7

IOP Conf. Series: Materials Science and Engineering **641** (2019) 012018 doi:10.1088/1757-899X/641/1/012018

Influence of grinding media movement on the throughput of dry grinding circuit with electromagnetic mill

D Foszcz[1], M Wołosiewicz-Głąb[3], O Krauze[2], S Ogonowski[2] and T Gawenda[1]

[1]AGH University of Science and Technology, Faculty of Mining and Geoengineering, Department of Environmental Engineering and Mineral Processing, Mickiewicza 30 Av., 30-059 Krakow, Poland
[2]Institute of Automatic Control, Silesian University of Technology, Akademicka 16, 44-100 Gliwice, Poland
[3]The Mineral and Energy Economy Research Institute of the Polish Academy of Sciences, Krakow, Poland

E-mail: foszcz@agh.edu.pl

Abstract. The paper investigates how the movement of grinding media affects the throughput of dry grinding circuit with the innovative electromagnetic mill. General structure of the grinding circuit, control system and its advantages are presented. Three air flows are critical for determining material throughput and providing proper operating conditions of the installation: flow through the working chamber of the mill, through the main classifier and in the recycle stream. They are affected by the moving grinding media. To assess this influence, air speed measurements were taken for different positions of dampers in air streams, for several masses of grinding media and frequencies of the rotating electromagnetic field. For each air stream, a set of polynomial models was identified. Control scheme for the air flows was proposed, including compensation for grinding media movement. Introduction of hierarchical control and distribution of particular control tasks on different layers was necessary.

1. Introduction

In order to produce fine particles, it is necessary to use technological installations equipped with comminution machines (crushers and mills) and classifiers (pneumatic, hydraulic, mechanical) that are able to produce various types of mineral powders, filling aggregates or fine aggregates used in many industries[1-6]. The usefulness of products is determined by physical and chemical properties of raw materials as well as features newly created as a result of mechanical, thermal, chemical or even biological processing. Development is based on searching for faster, cheaper, energy-efficient, more accurate and multifunctional comminution methods [7]. The electromagnetic mill meets all of the specified requirements. It is an innovative solution in the field [8-10]. Its main application is grinding of loose materials. The process can be carried out in dry or wet conditions, ie. transport medium may be gas or liquid [11]. Working in a closed circuit allows to overcome the disadvantages of conventional devices.

2. Dry grinding circuit with electromagnetic mill

Figure 1 presents the electromagnetic mill system in the version for dry grinding [12]. The electromagnetic mill is a grinding device in which a rotary electromagnetic field is used to move ferromagnetic grinding media in a working chamber. The fixed, vertical position of the working chamber means that there are energy savings since there is no need to move the chamber, which is the case in conventional mills. The working chamber is filled at around 20% to 25% of its capacity with grinding media, the shape and size of which depends on the type of material and final product particle size distribution [13]. Thanks to the rotary electromagnetic field, the grinding media circulate at a certain speed in the working chamber – depending on the frequency of the field.

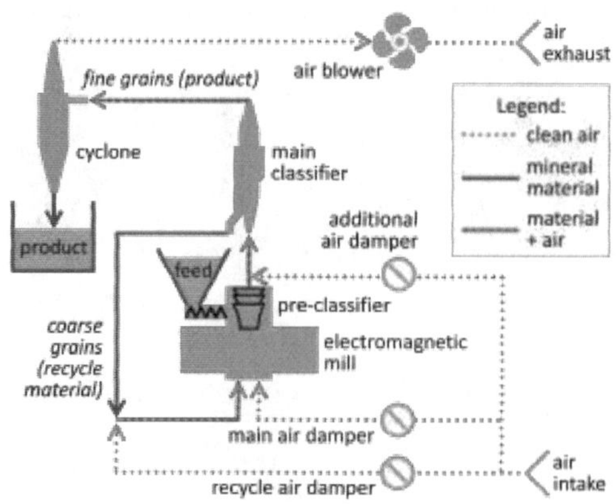

Figure 1. Diagram of the grinding system with the electromagnetic mill.

The material is comminuted due to collisions between grinding media and the material. The grinding efficiency is also raised thanks to the heat generated in the process, whose main task is to dry the material. The material movement in the system is caused by an air blower. The feed is supplied directly to the working chamber with a screw feeder – due to this solution we gain control over the loading speed of the feed. The air flow allows the ground material to move up, where the pre-classifier (directly above the working chamber) returns the unground particles back to the working chamber, while particles of smaller size pass through [14]. Then the material goes to the main classifier (much more accurate) – which separates the grains into the product stream (particles of the desired size) and the recycle stream (where particles of coarse size get). The material in the recycle stream returns to the working chamber, where it is subjected to grinding again. The material in the product stream goes to the cyclone, where the material is separated from the air and goes into the final product container. Thanks to the use of many technologies that make up the system with the electromagnetic mill, we get a huge advantage over conventional solutions. Faster grinding time results in a decrease in energy demand and in increased process efficiency. Other advantages include a reduction in the cost of replaceable parts of the mill, the ability to control the product (eg. size, shape, humidity) or finally the possibility of grinding various materials [15].

3. Model identification

From a technological point of view, three air flows play the major roles in ensuring proper operating conditions of the milling installation: flow through the working chamber F_W, through the main classifier F_C and in the recycle stream F_R. They are controlled by setting desired openings (0–100%) of three air dampers installed at air inlets (see Fig. 1). Due to cross-couplings, the positions of all air dampers: main P_M, recycle P_R and additional P_A nonlinearly affect air streams in inlets: main F_M, recycle F_R and additional F_A [16-18]; thus,

$$F_x = f_x(P_M, P_R, P_A), \quad x = \{M, R, A\}. \tag{1}$$

These streams in turn influence the remaining two key air flows:

$$\begin{aligned} F_W &= w_M F_M + w_R F_R = f_W(P_M, P_R, P_A), \\ F_C &= c_M F_M + c_R F_R + c_A F_A = f_C(P_M, P_R, P_A), \end{aligned} \tag{2}$$

where $w_M = w_R = 1.12, c_M = c_R = c_A = 0.2$ are constants related to pipe diameters [16]. As it has already been stated, only flows F_W, F_C, F_R will be further considered as they are the targets of control algorithms during the milling process.

Relationships (1, 2) were investigated e.g. by Ogonowski et al. [16] for test conditions with the mill turned off; however, when moving grinding media are present in the working chamber, they introduce extra pneumatic resistance to the system and modify the air flows. This means that models (1, 2) need to be extended.

To simplify model structure and improve goodness of fit of model outputs to measured data, modelling procedure was decomposed with respect to position of additional damper P_A [16]. Decomposition with respect to f and m was also done, to make the models consistent with the ones already used by air flow control algorithms. (For operating conditions when f or m do not fall into the tested set of values, interpolation of model coefficients or model outputs may be used.) Moreover, the models were transformed to incremental form, to enable design of compensators suitable for the existing control scheme (see next section of the paper). Consequently, for each output signal a set of models was identified, one model per each tested triple of P_A, f and m values:

$$\Delta F_x \overset{\text{def}}{=} F_x - F_{x0} = f_x(P_M, P_R), \tag{3}$$

where $x = \{W, C, R\}$, and F_{x0} is flow F_x measured for no milling case ($f = 0,\ m = 0$).

To identify relationships (3), polynomial approximation was used:

$$\Delta F_x = \sum_{i=0}^{N_i} \sum_{j=0}^{N_j} a_{ij} \cdot P_M^i \cdot P_R^j, \tag{4}$$

where: a_{ij} – polynomial coefficients to be identified; N_i, N_j – maximum degrees of individual variables, selected as 4; also, only terms up to degree 4 were allowed ($\forall_i \forall_j, i + j \leq 4$), to minimize the risk of overfitting the model to noisy data. Prior to estimation, input and output signals were scaled by 0.01 and 100, respectively, to have the same order of magnitude equal to 1, which provides better numerical properties of matrix equations to be solved. Then, coefficients a_{ij} of the full model (with 15 terms) and of simpler structures (that exclude some of the terms) were estimated with least squares method. Finally, adjusted coefficient of determination AR^2 was calculated for each model (18-23):

$$AR^2 = 1 - (1 - R^2)\frac{N - 1}{N - p - 1}, \tag{5}$$

where: N – number of observations in the data set; p – number of model coefficients (excluding the free coefficient, if present); R^2 – coefficient of determination, that is [28-30]:

$$R^2 = 1 - \quad \sum_{i=1}^{N}(y_i - \bar{y})^2 , \tag{6}$$

with: y_i – measured output signal (ΔF_x); $\hat{y}_i$ – output signal calculated from the model; $\bar{y}$ – mean value of the measured output. High values of AR^2 (close to 1) indicate a well fitted model. Selection of best model structure was performed according to the following criteria:

the model has high value of AR^2 (good fit);

the model does not have many terms (low complexity);

for one air stream, model structure is the same for all decomposed models, i.e. for all values of P_A, f and m (needed for compensator design).

As a result, the following seven-parameter model was chosen:

$$\Delta F_x = a_{00} + a_{10}P_M + a_{20}{P_M}^2 + \\ +a_{01}P_R + a_{02}{P_R}^2 + a_{03}{P_R}^3 + a_{04}{P_R}^4. \tag{7}$$

This structure turned out the best for all air flows (ΔF_W, ΔF_C, ΔF_R); identical model structure for all outputs was not an assumption during model creation, but it followed from satisfying the above selection criteria a)–c) individually for each output signal. Exemplary model response is shown in Figure 2.

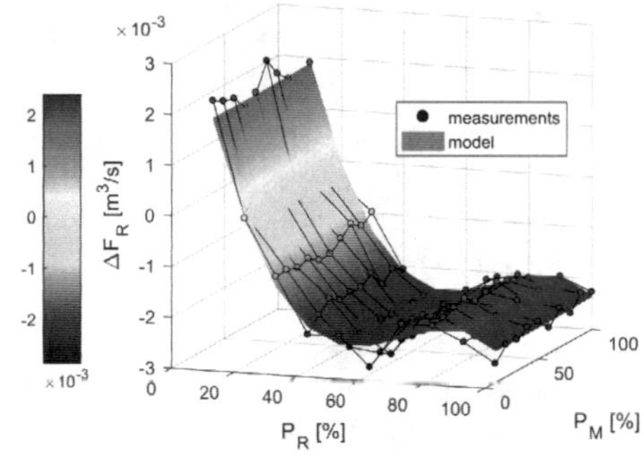

Figure 2. Output of the identified model compared to measured data: recycle air stream, $P_A = 30\%, f = 60$ Hz, $m = 500$ g.

4. Control system design

The control system of the electromagnetic mill is designed as layered, as shown in Figure 3. Its individual components are controlled by a SCADA system [13]. The task of the optimization layer is to determine the operating points of the electromagnetic mill. The most important point of the mill's operation is its load, i.e. mass stream of the feed. For the supervisory and direct control layers, the feed stream is the leading value, which is the basis for design of the functional structure of control systems in these layers.

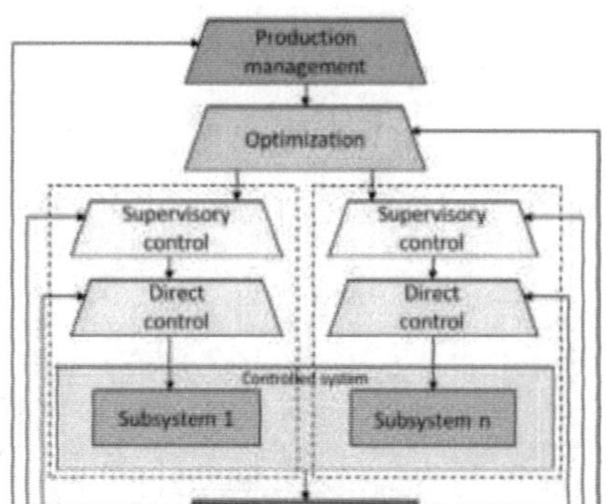

Figure 3. Layered control system of the electromagnetic mill.

In general, the task of the optimization layer is to determine mill operation parameters that minimize energy consumption with constraints resulting from the required quality of the product, expressed through its particle size. The optimization task can also take into account other limitations: product temperature and humidity as well as particles' geometric properties. If the mill is powered by a frequency converter, its output frequency and base frequency can be changed. In addition, the mass of grinding media inside the working chamber may change. The tests confirmed that the output frequency, base frequency and mass of grinding media have the greatest influence on the active power of the mill [27, 28].

To manage all the control tasks on different layers, an HMI/SCADA control system was created. It consists of two controllers – the main one is SIMATIC S7-300 with analogue input/output and the other is SIMATIC S7-1200, responsible for inverter control (operating in the MODBUS network). Intra-system communication between S7-300, S7-1200 and SIMATIC Industrial PC (IPC) is possible thanks to the PROFINET network, and displayed thanks to the IFIX SCADA. There is a large number of sensors and actuators in the system [24]. As a result, the measurement of the following parameters can be obtained in the system: air velocity, temperature and underpressure in streams; air humidity at intake and exhaust; temperature of various sections of the system; position of air dampers; feed moisture; the loading speed of the feed; fill level of the working chamber; mass of the product; quality of the product.

From the technological point of view, the most important task for the control system is to stabilize the air flows in each part of the circuit. These air flows are changed on purpose or are disturbed with different time horizons, based on the production requirements changes, dynamics and cross-coupling of different direct control loops and safety loops, and other factors. This fact requires hierarchical control and distribution of particular control tasks on different layers [25]. As described by Ogonowski et al. [24], the hierarchical structure of the control system determines certain flow of the control decisions. Optimisation layer calculates required set points of air flows in particular parts of the circuit and passes them to the supervisory layer. Then, dedicated algorithm (see Figure 4) calculates the set point for the particular dampers positions. Since not all possible values of F_{Sref}, F_{Cref} and F_{Rref} (required by optimisation layer) may be simultaneously set in the system, the first task of the supervisory control algorithm is to check whether the required values are reachable. The task is achieved by solving the models of working chamber and separator for empty, not working mill [16]. If the required parameters are not reachable, the algorithm terminates with the response: operating points are not reachable. Otherwise the first step is completed with the set of the solutions (P_M, P_R, P_A). Then the constraint for F_{Rmin} is verified and if there is more than one solution, the one with minimum F_{Rref} is chosen. If no solution satisfies the F_{Rmin} constraint, then the restriction on P_A interval is performed and the whole algorithm is repeated.

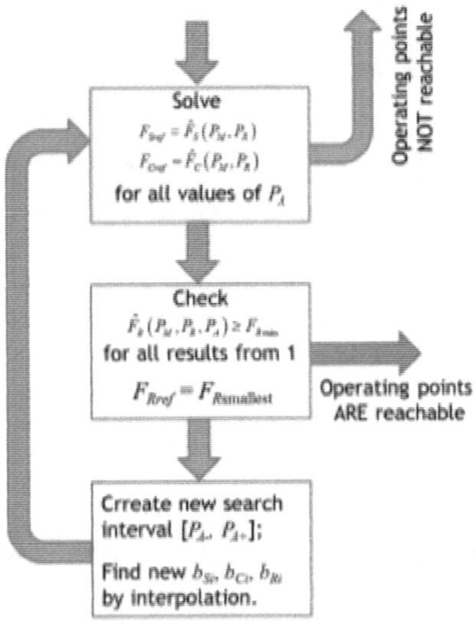

Figure 4. Scheme of the supervisory layer algorithm for air flow control.

The above steps completely neglect the influence of the grinding media mass and rotation frequency on the transport air flow, that was pointed out in Section 3. Since this influence changes more frequently than the decisions of optimization layer, instead of model modification in supervisory layer, one of the solutions would be to introduce non-linear static compensation in the direct control layer. If one assumes the structure as in Fig. 5, then $\boldsymbol{y}$ represents the steady state of the controlled air flow and $\boldsymbol{d}$ represents the set point of frequency or grinding media mass.

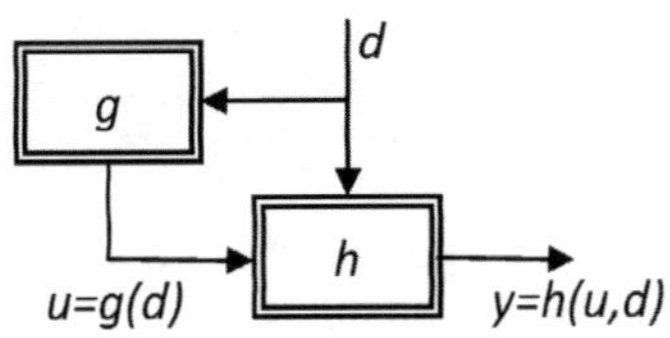

Figure 5. General idea of non-linear static compensator.

Since models (4) are incremental, the compensator formula can be obtained by proper choice of the function $\boldsymbol{g}(\boldsymbol{d})$ that will satisfy the following equation:

$$h(\,g(d), d\,) = 0\,. \tag{8}$$

Two separate compensators should be used: one to correct for the effect of varying field frequency and the other to react to changing mass of grinding media. Such choice is due to different time horizons for these compensators' operation. The output of the frequency compensator needs to be recalculated each time when setpoint for $\boldsymbol{f}$ changes, which may happen quite often, as $\boldsymbol{f}$ is the control variable for minimizing energy consumption. On the other hand, setpoint for $\boldsymbol{m}$ is constant for normal operating conditions of the milling circuit and is equal to $\boldsymbol{m} = \mathbf{500}$ g. This setpoint is maintained by a separate direct control loop and its change is rather unlikely; it could be caused only by some special technological requirements or an emergency situation (e.g. lack of grinders in the supply tank or hardware damage in this control subsystem). So, it is reasonable to design separate compensators for the influence of mass and frequency; moreover, it is justifiable to base the latter on models for constant $\boldsymbol{m} = \mathbf{500}$ g.

5. Summary

Grinding circuit with electromagnetic mill is characterized by multiple good features among the systems for fine milling, but it requires compound control system to work efficiently. Because of numerous input and output signals in the milling process, and many interactions (in different time horizons) between them, control must be hierarchical. This also applies to control of flow of transport air, which determines maximum throughput, target particle size, grinding efficiency and other parameters of the process. The paper suggests a layered control strategy for the key air flows, that takes into account the openings of dampers at air inlets and the influence of mass and frequency of grinders rotating in the mill chamber. The control algorithm is based on polynomial models of air flows estimated from experimental data.

References

[1] Chau, K. T. and Wu, S. 'Impact breakage of single particles: double impact test', in Salman, A. D.; Ghadiri, M. and Hounslow, M. J. (eds.) *Handbook of powder technology. Volume 12: Particle breakage*, Amsterdam: Elsevier Science B.V., **2007**, pp. 69–85.

[2] Napier-Munn, T.; WILLS, B.A., *Wills' Mineral Processing Technology, 7th ed.;* Elsevier Science Ltd.: New York, NY, USA, **2006**, pp.90–108.

[3] M. Cooke, C. F. Poole, I. D. Wilson, *Encyclopedia of Separation Science*, Academic Press, **2000**.

[4] Shapiro, M. and V. Galperin, *Air classification of solid particles: a review.* Chemical Engineering and Processing, **2005**, 44(2): p. 279-285.

[5] Rousseau R. W., *Handbook of Separation Process Technology,* John Wiley & Sons, **1987**.

[6] King, R.P., *Modeling and simulation of mineral processing systems*. **2001**, Elsevier.

[7] CEEC 2012 *The CEEC roadmap for eco-efficient comminution*, Coalition for Energy Efficient Comminution. Accessed 1 May 2019. URL https://www.ceecthefuture.org/about/roadmap.

[8] Sosiński, R., *Opracowanie metodyki projektowania trójfazowych wzbudników z biegunami jawnymi pola wirującego do młynów elektromagnetycznych (Development of design methodology for three-phase salient-pole exciters of rotating field for electromagnetic mills* – in Polish). PhD thesis. Czestochowa University of Technology, **2006**. [in polish]

[9] Styła, S. and Pietrzyk, W., *Młyn elektromagnetyczny z trójfazowym wzbudnikiem pola wirującego* (*Electromagnetic mill with the three-phase rotating field exciter* – in Polish). Polish patent no. PL 221027 B1, **2011**.

[10] Łokieć, H. and Łokieć, T. *Wzbudnik młyna elektromagnetycznego* (*Inductor of electromagnetic mill*, in Polish). Polish patent no. PL 226554 B1, **2015**.

[11] Ogonowski, S.; Wołosiewicz-Głąb, M.; Ogonowski, Z.; Foszcz, D. and Pawełczyk, M. Comparison of wet and dry grinding in electromagnetic mill. *Minerals*, **2018 b**, *8*, 138.

[12] Pawełczyk, M.; Ogonowski, Z.; Ogonowski, S.; Foszcz, D.; Saramak, D.; Gawenda, T. and Krawczykowski, D. *Sposób mielenia na sucho w młynie elektromagnetycznym* (*Method for dry grinding in the electromagnetic mill* – in Polish). Polish patent no. PL 228350 B1, **2015**.

[13] Wołosiewicz-Głąb, M.; Ogonowski, S. and Foszcz, D., Construction of the electromagnetic mill with the grinding system, classification of crushed minerals and the control system. *IFAC-PapersOnLine*, **2016**, *49*, pp. 67–71.

[14] Wołosiewicz-Głąb, M.; Ogonowski, S.; Foszcz, D. and Gawenda, T. Assessment of classification with variable air flow for inertial classifier in dry grinding circuit with electromagnetic mill using partition curves. *Physicochemical Problems of Mineral Processing*, *54*, **2018**, pp. 440–447.

[15] Ogonowski, S.; Ogonowski, Z.; Swierzy, M. and Pawełczyk, M.,Control system of electromagnetic mill load. *Proceedings of the 2017 25th International Conference on Systems Engineering (ICSEng)*, Las Vegas, NV, USA, 22–24 August 2017, **2017 b**, pp. 69–76.
[16] Ogonowski, S.; Ogonowski, Z. and Pawełczyk, M., Model of the air stream ratio for an electromagnetic mill control system. *Proceedings of the 2016 21st International Conference on Methods and Models in Automation and Robotics (MMAR)*, Miedzyzdroje, Poland, **2016**, pp. 901–906.
[17] Krauze, O. and Pawełczyk, M., Modelling dynamics of strongly coupled air paths in pneumatic transport system for milling product. *Proceedings of the 2017 22nd International Conference on Methods and Models in Automation and Robotics (MMAR)*, Miedzyzdroje, Poland, 28–31 August 2017, **2017**, pp. 843–848.
[18] Chatterjee S., Hadi Ali S., Regression Analysis by Example, Wiley, **2015**.
[19] R. Durrett, *Probability: Theory and Examples*, 2nd edition, Duxbury Press, **1996**.
[20] G. Casella and R. Berger, *Statistical Inference*, 2nd edition, Duxbury Advanced Series, Pacific Grove, CA, **2002**.
[21] R. Larson and B. Farber, *Elementary Statistics: Picturing the World*, Prentice-Hall, Englewood Cliffs, NJ, **2003**.
[22] D. Moore and G. McCabe, *Introduction to the Practice of Statistics*, W. H. Freeman and Co., London, **2003**.
[23] Vercellis, C.,*Business intelligence: data mining and optimization for decision making*, ch. 8: Regression. Chichester, UK: John Wiley & Sons Ltd., **2009**.
[24] Ogonowski, S.; Ogonowski, Z. and Pawełczyk, M., Multi-objective and multi-rate control of the grinding and classification circuit with electromagnetic mill. *Applied Sciences*, **2018**, *8*, 506.
[25] Brdyś, M. A. and Tatjewski, P., *Iterative algorithms for multilayer optimizing control*. London, UK: Imperial College Press, **2005**.
[26] Delta OHM, 2012. *HD 2903T..., HD 29V3T..., HD 2937T..., HD 29V37T...HD 29371T..., HD 29V371T... Temperature, relative humidity and air speed transmitters* (manual). Available at: http://www.deltaohm.com/ver2012/download/HD2903T_uk.pdf.[Accessed 13.08.2019]
[27] Ogonowski, S.; Ogonowski, Z. and Swierzy, M., Power optimizing control of grinding process in electromagnetic mill. *Proceedings of 2017 21st International Conference on Process Control (PC)*, Strbske Pleso, Slovakia, 6–9 June 2017, 2017 a, pp. 370–375.
[28] Kvålseth, T.,Cautionary note about R^2. *The American Statistician*, 39(4), **1985**, pp. 279–285.
[29] Box, G. E. P., Hunter, W. G. and Hunter, J. S. *Statistics for Experimenters*, New York: John Wiley, **1978**.
[30] Draper, N.R. and Smith, H., *Applied Regression Analysis,* , 2nd ed., New York: John Wiley, **1981**.

Acknowledgments

The research reported in this paper co-financed by statutory activities of AGH No. 11.11.100.276 and grant of Institute of Automatic Control, Silesian University of Technology, BK RAU1 2018.
The open access charge was financed by statutory activities AGH no. 11.11.100.276.
The authors would like to thank Bartosz Kordala, MSc. Eng. from Silesian University of Technology, Gliwice, Poland, for gathering experimental data.
The dry grinding circuit used for experiments was partially financed by the National Centre for Research and Development, Poland, under Applied Research Programme, project no. PBS3/B3/28/2015.

The Study Of Influence Of Fine Coal Fraction Addition To Coking Blend And Its Partial Briquetting On Coke Quality Parameters

M Rejdak[1], P Pawłowski[1], A Rodź[1], K Ignasiak[1] and I Helt[2]

[1] Institute for Chemical Processing of Coal, 1 Zamkowa Street, 41-803 Zabrze, Poland
[2] JSW Innowacje S.A., 41 Paderewskiego Street, 40-282 Katowice, Poland

E-mail: mrejdak@ichpw.pl

Abstract. Paper presents the results of study of influence of fine coal fraction addition to coking blend and its partial briquetting on coke quality parameters CRI and CSR. CRI and CSR are currently the key quality parameters of coke commonly used to assess its technological suitability for blast furnace coke. The raw materials used for the research were coals and fine coal fractions (flotation concentrates) from one of the domestic producers of coking coals. These coals are the basic components of blends used in the domestic coke industry. Studies have shown that increase in the content of flotation concentrates (FC) in the coal blend results in a significant reduction of the bulk density of the coal charge. As a consequence of the decrease in the density of the coal charge, coke reactivity CRI increased and coke strength after reaction CSR decreased. To minimize the adverse impact of FC addition, partial batch briquetting was implemented. Briquetting of the coal charge made it possible to produce coke with qualitative parameters similar to the same blend without the addition of a flotation concentrate and allows to improve the quality of coke produced or to produce coke of the same quality but with a higher share of semi-soft coals

1. Introduction

The dynamic technological development of the metallurgical industry observed during the last decade (operation of blast furnaces with an increasing volume, use of substitute fuels) has led to a significant increase in the requirements for the quality of coke, including in particular its strength parameters [1]. Achieving quality parameters with the values demanded by its customers requires a high share of the highest quality coking coals in the charge mixture, which significantly translates into the increase in unit production costs (approx. 75% of the production cost is the cost of the charge mixture) [2]. This is particularly important for the Polish coke industry which has been the world's leading coke exporter in recent years, targeting its product to demanding Western European consumers.

The problem of domestic coke producers is the lack of coking coals with the best quality parameters in the domestic mining structure and considerable variations in the quality of domestic coking coals. Over the last several years, there has also been an unfavorable upward trend, in coal concentrates sent to coking plants, of the finest fraction (<0.5 mm), which results in a reduction in the bulk density of the charge mixture and, consequently the quality of the coke obtained. Currently, domestic producers take advantage of the import of high quality overseas coals (mainly Australia, the USA) and introduce them as additional components of the blends which enables the production of coke of the appropriate quality. The volume of share of imported coals in the coke production increases year by year and the share of domestic coals decreases.

In addition, there is a problem (on the part of the coal producers) of the use of fine coal fractions (FCF) from the production of coking coals which, in accordance with the applicable legal acts (Regulation of the Minister of Energy regarding quality requirements for solid fuels, resolution of provincial assemblies under the so-called anti-smog law [3]) have been virtually eliminated from the fuel market. FCF, in particular from the coking coal flotation, has proper coking parameters, however, its very fine graining and relatively high moisture content, virtually prevent its use in top (gravity) charging batteries, due to its unfavorable impact on the density of the coal charge (as a consequence on the quality of coke) and the economics of the coking process (energy for evaporation of additional moisture). A solution that allows for significant reduction of the above problems, is the use of appropriate technology to increase the density of coal charge, directly affecting not only the quality of the obtained coke but also the productivity of coke oven batteries [4][5][6]. The introduction of such technology makes it possible to improve the quality of coke when using a high-quality coal-blend or to maintain the quality of coke with partial replacement of these coals with domestic coals of worse coking parameters. Briquetting of a part of the coal charge is one of the most effective methods of compacting it, possible to be implemented with coke oven batteries for top (gravity) charging system, designed for continuous operation. It gives an option of compacting FCF and introducing it into a charge blend in the form of a compacted component (briquette or pellet). The response to the aforementioned problems is to develop and implement into practice a technology for the production of compacted component of FCF mixtures in the batteries for top charging. Briquette / pellet component thus produced will be a component of the coke mixture intended for the coking process.

The aim of study was to assess the influence of fine coal fraction addition to the coking blend on crucial coke quality parameters i.e. coke reactivity index CRI and coke strength after reaction CSR. Fine coal fractions were implemented to the coking blend in loose and compacted form.

2. Materials and methods

2.1. Raw materials

The raw materials used for the research were coals and fine coal fractions (flotation concentrates) from one of the domestic producers of coking coals. These coals are the basic components of blends used in the domestic coke industry. The basic physicochemical parameters of coal raw materials are presented in Table 1.

The analyses of single coals were performed according to proper standards procedures. Ash content A^d was determined according to PN-ISO 1171:2002. Carbon (C^d), hydrogen (H^d) and nitrogen (N^d) contents were determined according to procedure ISO 29541:2010 and sulfur content according ISO 19579:2006. Alkalinity index (AI) were calculated based on ash chemical composition (determined according to ICHPW procedure Q/LP/55/B:2016) with use of following formula:

$$AI = A^d \times \frac{Na_2O + K_2O + Fe_2O_3 + MgO + CaO}{Al_2O_3 + SiO_2} \quad (1)$$

where:

A^d – ash content (dry basis), %

Na_2O, K_2O, Fe_2O_3, Al_2O_3, SiO_2, MgO, CaO – content of individual components, %

For coking tests, coking blends with a composition similar to those used in industrial practice for coke top (gravity) charged coke oven batteries. Coals (C1-C3) and flotation concentrates (F1-F1) correspond to type 35 (hard) (according to PN-G-97002: 1982P), while the other coals and flotation concentrates correspond to type 34 (semi-soft). The compositions of coking blends were agreed with the industrial partner of the project – JSW KOKS S.A. The B20 blend is a reference blend with 20% type 34 (semi-soft) coal content. B30 and B40 blends contain 30 and 40% of type 34 coals, respectively. The shares of the remaining coals were reduced proportionally.

Table 1. Properties of raw materials used.

Parameter	Coals				
	C1	C2	C3	C4	C5
A^d, %	6.0	9.2	6.4	6.3	4.3
C^{daf}, %	89.6	86.9	89.3	86.9	86.8
H^{daf}, %	4.7	5.1	4,6	5.1	5.0
N^{daf}, %	1.3	1.2	1,0	1.1	1.0
S_t^{daf}, %	0.52	0.69	0.48	0.46	0.68
AI, –	1.84	2.11	2.81	1.87	3.82
	Flotation concentrates				
	F1	F2	F3	F4	F5
A^d, %	6.0	9.2	6.4	6.3	4.3
C^{daf}, %	89.20	87.36	89.80	86.50	85.99
H^{daf}, %	4.70	4.,92	4.71	4.98	5.01
N^{daf}, %	1.38	1.35	1.10	1.21	1.28
S_t^{daf}, %	0.60	0.76	0.43	0.60	1.15
AI, –	1.60	1.21	1.46	3.60	4.51

Table 2. Composition of coal blends for coking tests.

Share of coals, %	Coking blend		
	B20	B30	B40
C1/F1	30.0	26.3	22.4
C2/F2	35.0	30.6	26.3
C3/F3	15.0	13.1	11.3
C4/F4	15.0	20.0	25.0
C5/F5	5.0	10.0	15.0

2.2. Research methodology

The assessment of the possibility of increasing the use of fine coal fractions (in the form of flotation concentrates) and increasing the share of type 34 (semi-soft) Polish coals was carried out on the basis of laboratory coking tests in the Karbotest® installation (4 kg of coal charge). Generally, in coal concentrates sent to domestic coking plants, there are some quantities of flotation concentrates, however their participation is limited.

The first series of tests assessed the impact of flotation concentrates share in the coking blend on the coal blend bulk density and crucial coke quality indicators, i.e. CRI (coke reactivity index) and CSR (coke strength after reaction). The B20 blend without a flotation concentrate addition (an ideal case) is a reference blend – composition similar to blends used in domestic coke making industry (top charged batteries). To the aforementioned blend, 15, 30, 40 and 50% of flotation concentrates (blended) were added. The composition of a part of the blend composed of flotation concentrates corresponded to a coal blend composition without the addition of flotation concentrates (Table 2).

In the second series of tests, the optimum share (proportion) of briquettes in the coal charge was determined (in the aspect of maximum coal blend bulk density). The possibility of introducing of flotation concentrates into the reference blend was also investigated using the method of partial briquetting of the charge – for an optimal share of briquettes.

The third series of coking tests was carried out using blends B20, B30 and B40 (semi-soft coal content respectively: 20, 30 and 40%) with 30% flotation concentrates content and optimal share of the briquettes. Two coking tests were performed for each of the blends: the first test included briquetting a mixture of coals and flotation concentrates, the second test included briquetting only a part consisting of flotation concentrates. For the briquetting process, coal tar was used as a binder in the amount of 5% m/m. Dimensions of the produced briquettes were: approx. 24 x 24 x 13 mm. Device for briquetting (roller press) and the general appearance of the briquettes are presented in Fig. 1. As in the previous test series, the impact of aforementioned technological operations on the bulk density of the coal blend and the quality of the produced coke was carried out.

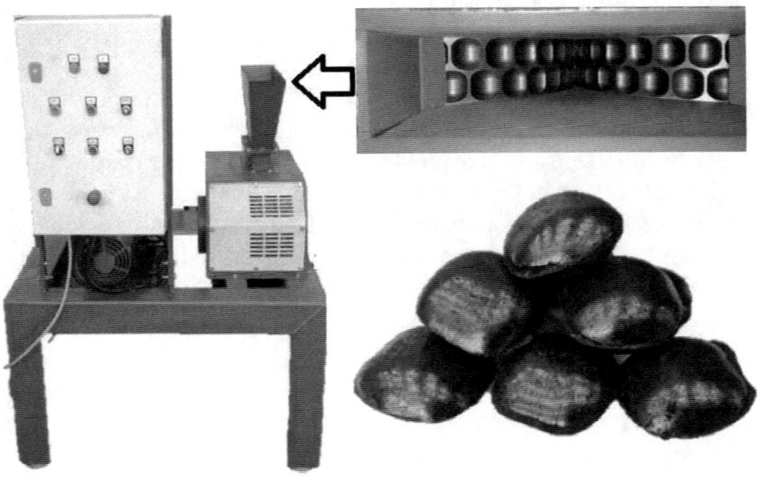

Figure 1. General view of briquetting press, forming elements and produced briquettes.

3. Results and discussion

Density of coal charge influences the quality of the obtained coke and coke oven chambers production capacity [1][2]. As results from the research presented in Figure 2, the increase in the content of flotation concentrates (FC) in the coal blend results in a significant reduction of the bulk density of the coal charge. The value of the coal charge density decreased from 746.5 kg/m^3 (for a blend with no flotation concentrate) to 716.8 kg/m^3 for a blend with the addition of 50% flotation concentrate. This is mainly due to the very fine graining of the flotation concentrates i.e. d(0.1) 17.0 µm, d(0.5) 224.5 µm and d(0,9) 737,9 µm. Fine graining and hence the higher surface area of the coal grains hinders their rearrangement during the gravitational loading of the coal charge. This is the result of the increase in the adhesion associated with the higher grain surface.

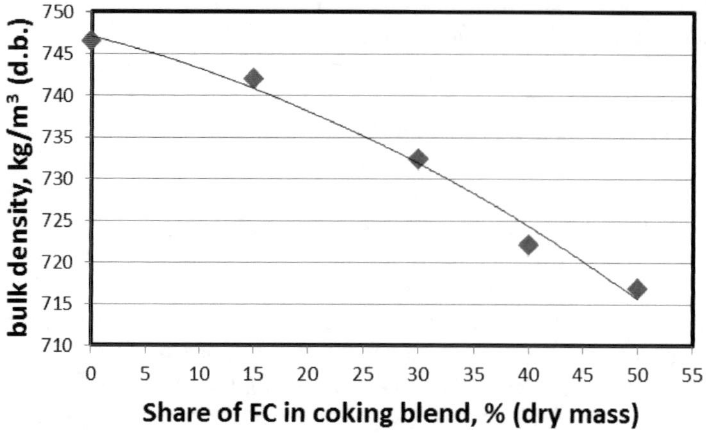

Figure 2. Influence of flotation concentrate share on bulk density of coking blend.

CRI and CSR are currently the key quality parameters of coke commonly used to assess its technological suitability for blast furnace coke, used all over the world. As a consequence of the decrease in the density of the coal charge, an adverse increase in the reactivity of the produced coke was noted (Fig. 3). The value of coke reactivity index CRI increased from 31.7 to 36.9%. At the same time, the CSR value of coke decreased (from 56,8 to 47,0%) which is clearly visible in Fig. 4. The test results clearly indicate that the addition to the coal charge of flotation concentrates in a loose form negatively affects the efficiency of the coking process. Both the density of the charge (which determines the productivity of coke oven batteries) and the key quality parameters of the coke obtained have decreased. In the case study, both the coal blend and the blend of flotation concentrates were characterized by a fixed moisture content of 9%. In industrial practice, the flotation concentrates are characterized by a higher content of moisture reaching even more than 25%. In that case their influence could be even more visible.

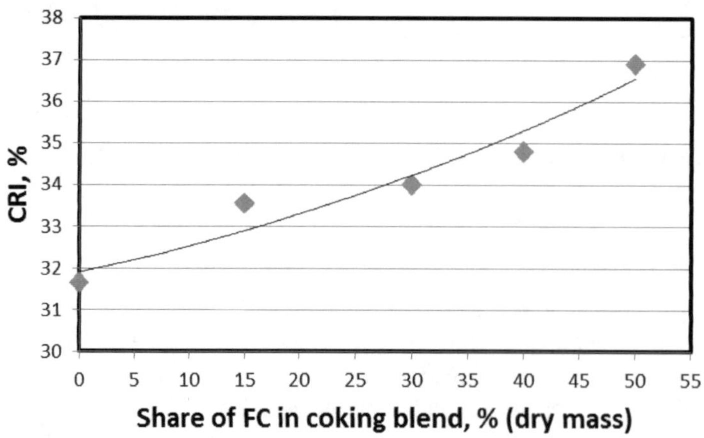

Figure 3. Influence of flotation concentrate share in coking blend on coke reactivity index CRI.

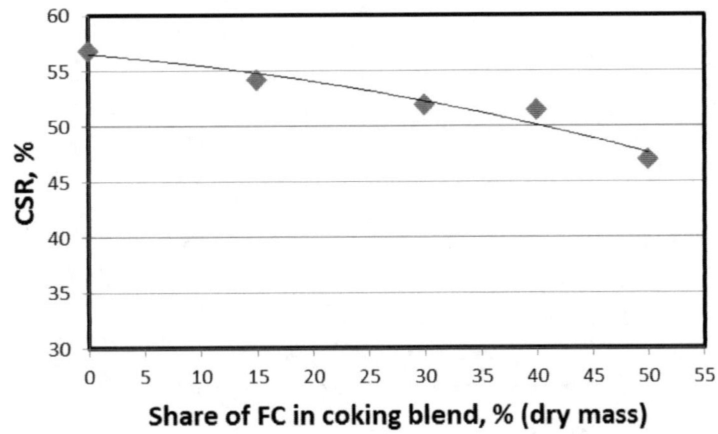

Figure 4. Influence of flotation concentrate share in coking blend on coke strength after reaction CSR.

In order to counteract the adverse effect of the flotation concentrate additive, it is necessary to simultaneously limit the main effect that this concentrate causes, i.e. the decrease in bulk density of the charge. This can be achieved by implementing an effective method of increasing the density of the coal charge. I that case, there is the technological possibility to use a certain amount of flotation concentrates in the coal charge and/or to increase the share of cheaper components in the coal charge. There are a few possibilities to increase the coal charge bulk density [2][4][5][6]: adjusting the grain size distribution, moisture content (drying), oil addition and mechanical treatment (e.g. partial briquetting or stamping). For coke oven batteries with gravity charging, the use of stamping of the charge is impossible and the most effective technology (in the aspect of density increase) from the above mentioned is partial briquetting. The mentioned technology consists in separating and briquetting a part of the coal charge, and then mixing the briquetted and loose parts and subjecting them to the coking process. The key point in the application of this technology is the proper selection of the share of briquettes in the coal charge in order to maximize the density of the charge. The research shows that the highest density is obtained for 30% briquettes content in the coal charge (Fig. 5). The increase in density in relation to the coal charge without briquettes amounted to approx. 6.7%. Therefore, the value of 30% of briquettes was considered to be the optimal value – used in further tests.

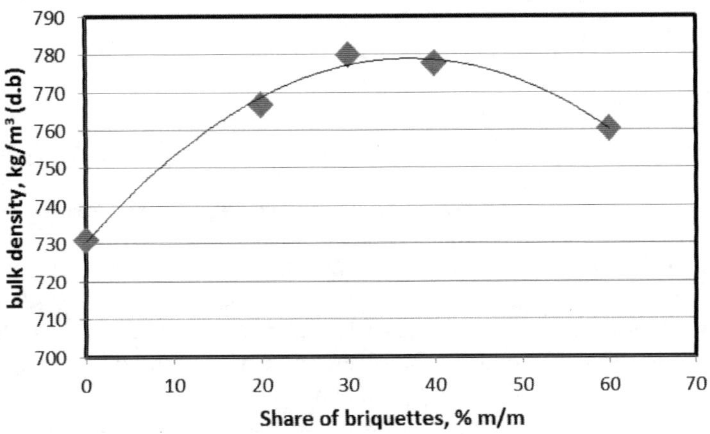

Figure 5. Influence of briquettes share on coal charge bulk density (assessed for B30 blend containing 30% flotation concentrates).

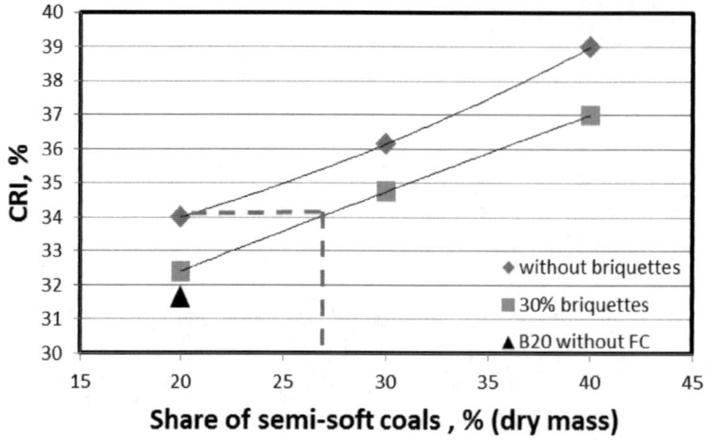

Figure 6. Influence of semi-soft coals share and partial briquetting on coke CRI.

In Figure 6 the influence of semi-soft coals share and partial briquetting implementation on coke CRI was presented. Red dots represent coal blend with 30% content of flotation concentrates in a loose form. The black dots represents a blend without flotation concentrate, while the green dots refer to partially briquetted coal blends containing 30% flotation concentrates. It is clearly visible that the increase in the share of semi-soft coals caused a decrease in the quality of coke – an increase in coke reactivity index CRI. At the same time, with the use of partial briquetting technology, beneficial results in the form of reduced CRI were observed. The value of the reactivity index decreased by 1.7 percentage points on average. Consequently, the CSR improvement was also noted (Fig. 7). The value of post-reaction strength increased on average by 4.2 percentage points.

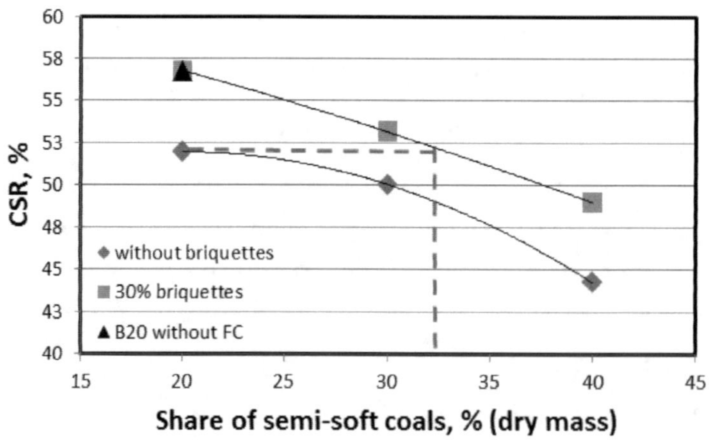

Figure 7. Influence of semi-soft coals share and partial briquetting on coke CSR.

According to the presented data, the use of partial briquetting technology allows to improve the quality of coke produced or to produce coke of the same quality but with a higher share of semi-soft coals. Moreover, in the case of B20 blend with 30% flotation concentrate content, briquetting of the coal charge made it possible to produce coke with qualitative parameters similar to the same mixture without the addition of a flotation concentrate. Blue dotted lines in Figure 7 show the possibility of increasing the share of semi-soft coals, maintaining the quality of the coke corresponding to the reference coal blend B20. In the case of the CRI index, the quality of coke can be maintained with the introduction of 6.8% more semi-soft coals, while in the case of CSR – even 12.9% more. In industrial practice, this would allow for a significant reduction in the costs of preparing a coking coal blend. Obtained test results, however, require confirmation in industrial conditions, which will be implemented in the further stages of the project.

4. Conclusion

Based on the conducted research, the following conclusions can be formulated:

- the increase in the content of flotation concentrates (FC) in the coal blend results in a significant reduction of the bulk density of the coal charge
- as a consequence of the decrease in the density of the coal charge, an adverse increase in the reactivity CRI and decrease of post-reactive strength CSR of the produced coke was noted
- briquetting of the coal charge made it possible to produce coke with qualitative parameters similar to the same blend without the addition of a flotation concentrate
- the use of partial briquetting technology allows to improve the quality of coke produced or to produce coke of the same quality but with a higher share of semi-soft coals.

5. References

[1] Vander T, Alvarez R, Ferraro M, Fohl J, Hofherr K, Huart J M, Mattila E, Propson R, Willmers R and Vdvelden B 1996 Coke Quality Improvement Possibilities and Limitations *3-rd International Cokemak. Congr. Proc.* Gent pp 28–37

[2] Karcz A and Strugala A 2008 Increasing chances of utilizing the domestic coking coal resources through technological operations in coal blend preparation *Miner. Resour. Manag.* **24** pp 5–18

[3] Journal of Laws of 2018, item 1890

[4] Czaplicki A and Janusz M 2012 Preparation of Coal Batch for Top Loading: Experimental Research *Coke and Chem.* **55** pp 366–371

[5] Rejdak M and Wasielewski R 2015 Mechanical Compaction Of Coking Coals For Carbonization In Stamp-Charging Coke Oven Batteries *Physicochem. Probl. Miner. Process.* **51(1)** pp 151−161

[6] Sobolewski A, Rejdak M, Czaplicki A, Janusz M and Mianowski A 2014 The effect of coal charge preparation on coke quality *Przem. Chem.* **93(12)** pp 2103–2110

Acknowledgments

Work carried out as part of the project by the acronym DensiCoal by the consortium JSW Innowacje S.A / JSW Koks S.A / JSW S.A. The executor of the presented research part of Project is the Institute for Chemical Processing of Coal, Zabrze (ICHPW, Poland).

The presented results are part of the research carried out as part of the project POIR.01.02.00-00-0203/17 pt. "Technology for production of densified component of coal blends with use of fine coal fraction (FCF) for top charged coke oven batteries", co-financed from the European Regional Development Fund.

Fundusze Europejskie Inteligentny Rozwój | Rzeczpospolita Polska | Narodowe Centrum Badań i Rozwoju | Unia Europejska Europejski Fundusz Rozwoju Regionalnego

Fundusze Europejskie Inteligentny Rozwój | Narodowe Centrum Badań i Rozwoju | Unia Europejska Europejski Fundusz Rozwoju Regionalnego

Polish experiences in fine coal processing

B Tora[1], S Budzyń[2] and T Olkuski[2]

[1]Faculty of Mining and Geoengineering,
[2]Faculty of Energy and Fuels
AGH University of Science and Technology, Al. Mickiewicza 30, PL-30059 Cracow, Poland

E-mail: tora@agh.edu.pl

Abstract. The amount of fine-grain waste containing grains of coal, coke, coke breeze, etc. is significant and it is not being visibly reduced. Particularly significant are quantities of coal slurries generated from the current operations of hard coal mines and settlers previously handed over to local authorities as reclaimed land. The available reported quantities of coal slurries vary widely and range from 0.5 (current production) to over 20 million tonnes (mainly collected in operational and reclaimed settlers).

The group of fine-grain fuel sources include, inter alia, coal slurries, including sediments, flotation tailings from coal beneficiation, brown coal waste dust, coke breeze from the processes of gasification of residues from crude oil processing and fluidized bed gasification of solid fuels, coke breeze from decarburization of fly ash, coke dust, waste from production and processing of carbon and graphite products. The use of these fine-grain materials and waste often encounters serious difficulties, inter alia due to the high water content, heterogeneity, fragmentation, low and variable energy characteristics. With the aim to rationalizing their use in recent years technologies have been extensively developed and implemented for recovery of fine-grain materials and waste to produce commercial fuels.

1. Systematics of coal mining waste

Wastes from hard coal mining, also called coal tailings, are among the so-called mineral waste materials generated in the processes of extraction, beneficiation and processing of minerals. Traditionally, mineral waste materials are divided into four groups, taking into account the technical characteristics of these wastes and the operating processes and technology, from which they are generated [1, 2]:

- accompanying minerals - potential mineral resources found in the main mineral deposit, which generally can be selectively extracted;

- mining waste, also known as extraction waste - rocks from the mining and preparation works opening up the main mineral deposit in underground and open pit mines;
- tailings - rock material extracted along with the mineral and separated in the main mineral beneficiation processes;
- secondary processing waste - remnants of the main mineral processing, generated in the production processes of commercial products (e.g. energy waste).

The mineral composition of these waste materials broken down into the dominant petrographic groups is given in table 1.

Table 1. Brief petrographic description of rock spoil [3].

Rock	Description	Comments
Slate	sedimentary, detrital rock of black colour, less frequently dark grey colour, with a layered (slated) siltstone and pelite texture,	different thickness of layers relatively low mechanical strength, slate separateness
Mudstone	sedimentary, detrital rock of dark grey to black colour, solid, with non-directional, compact, massive, siltstone texture, occasionally the rock contains siderite nodules (spherosiderite – sedimentary carbonate rock, of grey-brown to brownish-yellow colour with high-density, compact, massive, non-directional texture	rocks of varying mechanical strength, depending on the content of coal
Sandstone	sedimentary, detrital rock of light to dark grey, solid, with non-directional texture, less frequently slightly layered, compact, massive, psammitic sometimes mixed with psephitic fractions	rock with a fairly high mechanical strength, depending largely on sandstone binder (the more clayey, the less resistance)

Waste from the coal mining industry is generally divided into three groups: mining wastes, tailings and secondary processing wastes, taking into account their technical characteristics, the operational and technological processes.

Mining wastes, also known as extraction wastes, are rocks from the mining and preparation works opening up the main mineral deposit, mainly cap and interlayer rocks. They represent an average of about 20% of the total mass of waste [4].

Tailings include rock material extracted along with the mineral and separated in the mineral beneficiation processes (e.g. sorting, crushing, washing, flotation), and their share in the total mass of waste is on average 78%).

The third group includes secondary processing wastes, i.e. the remnants of the main mineral processing, generated in the production processes of commercial products.

The coal beneficiation process in mechanical preparation plants of hard coal mines generates coal slurries. These are the finest-grain grades of grain size below 1 mm, where grades below 0.035 mm make up to 60% share in the slurry composition. Depending on the quality parameters (ash and sulphur content, calorific value), such slurries can be transferred as an ingredient to energy mixtures or are dumped in earth settlers of individual mines[5, 6]. Most of slurries have been collected in settlers, as there were no customers interested in buying them. Dumped slurries were treated as waste of coal preparation processes. Most of this waste was actually energy fuel. For this reason, in recent years, the interest in combustion options has increased.

Coal tailings are also used in the manufacture of building's construction products - as an essential raw material for obtaining slate aggregate, i.e. a lightweight building construction aggregate used in the manufacture of lightweight concrete, as well as an essential raw material or component for the production of various building construction elements, such as bricks or roofing tiles [7].

Currently about 0.5% of generated waste is utilized in this way. The waste is also added to the charge in the production of cement, in order to adjust the main module of cement clinkers. Coal tailings may also be useful for the production of refractory materials, but only if they have a high content of Al_2O_3. Part of coal tailings is transferred to preparation plants for recovery of coal contained in the waste. Currently about 9% of generated waste is utilized in this way. The residue after the recovery of coal (secondary waste) is re-dumped or used in hydraulic backfilling or building's construction materials industry. Attempts have been made to recover metal concentrates from coal tailings, including aluminium, iron, titanium, germanium and gallium. Fine coal waste can also, after mixing with a compound fertilizer and peat, be used for biological reclamation and restoration of the fertility of devastated land, or reclamation of soil.

Flotation wastes due to a significant thixotropy, high humidity and difficulties in transport have not yet found an industrial application [8, 9]. These wastes can be used as a material for filling abandoned workings in mines or to seal the surface stockpiles, while post-flotation wastes from beneficiation of coking coals with calorific value more than 5000 kJ/kg (coal slurries) can be used as fuel for the production of building construction ceramics, and after beneficiation as an additive to energy fuel.

Some directions of use of recyclable coal-accompanying materials

The qualitative research conducted in various research centres shows that these materials have the quality features appropriate for many applications [10, 11]:

- Hydro construction and engineering,
- Manufacture of construction products and refractories,
- In agriculture as fertilizer or substrate,
- For recovery of coal, as well as low-energy material (slurries) for combustion in power plants,
- As a filling and sealing material in engineering works.

Coal wastes may be used in hydro construction for building river dams and embankments of settlers and to strengthen the shipping channels, as well as in the road construction industry for building road and railway embankments. Applications in marine building construction include the construction of embankments, coastal protection and of wharves.

2. Directions to optimize the management of fine-grain materials and coal tailings

The most common model for the management of coal slurries is their supply to coal-fired power plants and, to a lesser extent, to industrial energy generation plants. Such a solution, though very simple and practical, is not optimal for environmental as well as economic reasons. In this way, approximately 30% of water is transported, often with a heavy contamination of transport routes and user sites. In the case of fluidized bed combustion, water-slurry pulp is used, having a water content well above 30%.

Undertaken studies, research and trials for optimizing the management of fine-grain materials and waste for fuel production include [12]:

1) qualitative assessment of fine-grain materials as a source of heat energy,

2) technologies for beneficiation of fine-grain materials for the purposes of energy processes.

While the qualitative assessment processes enable identification of the possibilities and conditions for direct management, beneficiation technologies indicate the possibilities and conditions for their use to generate high-quality stand-alone fuels or components for their production.

Technological processes generally provide conditions to influence the quality of fine-grain materials. An example might be the generation of coal slurries from water suspensions; for instance only by replacing the belt presses with chamber filter presses a higher drainage of slurry is achieved together with an improved energy performance of slurries – figure 1. Poor quality of coal slurries is also due to the lack of selective separation of water and slurry suspensions in mines, and also often unoptimized operation and emptying of slurry settlers.

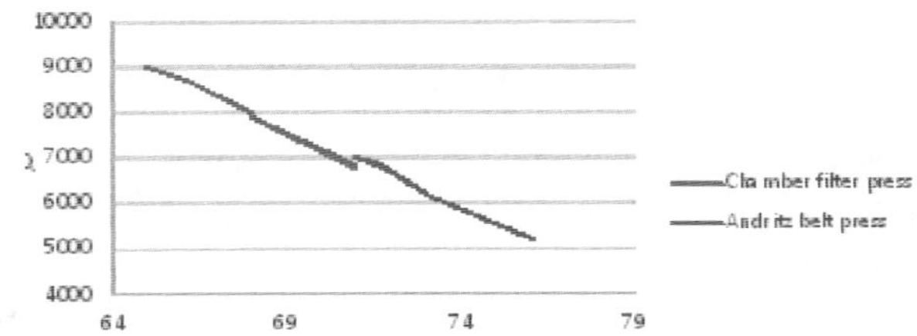

Figure 1. Impact of dewatering method of water-slurry suspension on coal slurry properties.

The caking processes of fine-grain materials and coal tailings for energy purposes.

In recent years, a considerable progress has been achieved in the caking of coal slurries, coke dust, coal and biomass blends and alternative fuels in the processes of briquetting.

Regardless of the direction and method of processing, in some cases significant problems are caused by the loosened structure of coal slurries, which determines the performance of coal blending and biomass blends, achieved durability of granulated materials and effectiveness of slurry drying processes. This problem has not been fully resolved and it requires further testing and trials.

The process for caking fine-grain materials and coal tailings should be selected mainly based on market requirements [13].

The most durable and geometrically adjustable caking of fine-grain materials is guaranteed by the **briquetting process.** It is important to properly prepare the feed and adjust the type and amount of binder added. As a result of blending coal slurries, sediment and flotation concentrate and addition of a specific binder, production process has been established for coal briquettes of calorific value of 16 to 24 MJ/kg. The size of briquettes is adjusted to the requirements of customers.

Figure 2. Caking types of coal slurries granulation and agglomeration [4].

A similar work has been performed for the briquetting of brown coal, biomass, selected municipal waste with and without binders. The quality of briquettes obtained was affected most by the pressures applied, this also should explain the highest mechanical strength of briquettes obtained from briquetting stamp presses. Particularly interesting results were obtained by pressing chopped straw; as a result of friction and release of heat from the feed, water evaporates and the concentrated feed is subject to a strong curing with released resin substances.

Granulation process was applied to graphite dust caking [14]. Due to the hydrophobicity of graphite grains it was necessary to choose the appropriate binder. Granules with the highest mechanical strengths were obtained as a result of additional thermal treatment. Depending on the binder used, hardening of granules can occur within 180-240°C and at higher temperatures.

Granulation of coal slurries and their blends with coal and/or sawdust is a simple process; however, the granulation installations are characterized by relatively low yields.

In recent years there has been a huge interest in caking coal slurries; the simplest solution appeared to be the **agglomeration process.** In cases where a high mechanical strength of grain agglomerates or their specific shape is not required, it is sufficient to intensely mix the feed to cause creation, merging and cross-sticking of grains to form an agglomerate. Mechanical stability of the agglomerate can be raised through the proper preparation of the feed and the addition of selected binders and additional granulation. The effect of different binders on the grain size of agglomerates, after ageing, is illustrated by the results in table 1. With strongly damp clayey coal slurries there is no full relaxation of their structure and proper mixing with a binder, due to which the resulting agglomerate is characterized by larger grains and lower compressive strength.

Agglomerate subjected to ageing by weathering, in most cases is subject to further curing. The year-round experience from heaping agglomerate in the stock yard showed that under the influence of rain and snow and the impact of the sun and changing temperatures the surface of the agglomerate heap developed a shell (2 to 8 cm thick) that insulated the agglomerate (figure. 3).

Figure 3. Dumping ground surface after one year of agglomerate storage (source: [8]

3. Dewatering and drying of fine-grain materials and coal tailings

Energy properties of fine-grain materials and coal tailings depend to a large extent on their moisture; for these reasons, it is sought to minimize the water content in the fuels or fuel additives produced from them [15]. As previously mentioned, the processes most frequently used for this purpose are the processes of filtration, gravity and evaporation under normal weather conditions. In these cases, depending on the type of material, moisture content can vary in a wide range from 20 to 60%.

While until recently coal slurry drying seemed to be not economically viable, now taking into account the access to sources of waste heat this issue should be seriously considered and worked around. The technical progress made in the design of driers of flotation concentrates and coals points to the possibility of rapid deployment of drying processes for coal slurries and their mixtures with additions of biomass. In a number of cases there is an interest and need to use installations for a periodic drying of biomass.

The viability of using combustion engines fired with coal bed methane used in mines was pointed out even earlier. Exhaust gases from the combustion of methane are characterized by a relatively high temperature of 400°C. Mines implementing the program for coal bed methane management are increasingly turning to gas engines as a source of electricity. So far, the exhaust heat has not been utilized. Also system power plants increasingly often consider additional sources of electricity based on internal combustion engines fuelled by natural gas. In all these cases, the exhaust heat can be used for the drying of fine-grain materials and coal tailings.

The traditional source of heat in the drying of flotation concentrates, slurries and their concentrates are exhaust gases from the combustion of coal dust, coke oven gas and coal bed methane. Drying of coal slurries, so far, is not very common. In Germany, for example, there was used a tumble dryer with a fluidized bed combustion for drying coal concentrate obtained from flotation beneficiation of coal slurry and flotation tailings; obtained pulverized coal with a moisture content below 3% was supplied as fuel for cement plants and as a reducing agent for blast furnaces. For the selection of the type of drying kiln, taking into account sources of heat and the possibilities to dry coal slurries, flotation tailings and biomass and their mixtures, tumble dryers, air (tubular) and fluidized bed kilns are taken into consideration, inter alia. Selection of a solution depends on the local conditions and preferences of the entity concerned.

A number of fine-grain materials and coal tailings encounter considerable difficulties in their rational use as fuels or sources of heat, due to their high fragmentation, heterogeneity and water content. The solution to these problems is offered by the processes of caking and drying of fine-grain materials and coal tailings.

The research and testing carried out have led to the development of technology for caking coke and coal dust, graphite, biomass etc. Briquetting processes have been implemented, inter alia, for the production of coal fuel briquettes and eco-pea coal. For the purpose of smelting and foundry, granulated graphite is produced. Based on the assumptions developed in technological and technical terms, an installation for coal slurry agglomeration is being made, with a capacity of 80 tonnes/h.
The properties of coal slurry agglomerate are significantly influenced by addition of binders. Out of the various binders tested the best results are guaranteed by the addition of quicklime, which on the one hand binds the water contained in the product and on the other hand, by reaction with carbon dioxide, preserves the structure of the agglomerate. The conducted economic analyses show that the payback period may be achieved within a period of several months to two years.

Previous works on optimizing the management of fine-grain materials and coal tailings will be extended to include viability of their drying. This, in particular, using sources of waste heat, such as from internal combustion engines or a dried material.

The designed and developed technologies to optimize the management of fine-grain materials and coal tailings are intended for use not only by mining companies and coal fuel distributors but also by power plants, power and heating plants and heating plants.

4. Waste storage

The materials deposited on the heaps originated during coal mining and are much varied. The basic types of materials have markedly different physical-mechanical properties and petrographic or chemical composition [16]. In the heap bodies there are rocks with included coal, low grade coal substance, coal dust from cleaning cross cuts, washery refuse, slag and often also rubble and municipal waste. Especially old heaps contain high percentages of organic mass. Organic mass is found there along with greyish, crumbling coal claystones and siltites. Clay minerals and clastic quartz prevail in the groundmass and there is eaglestone in places. Accessory pyrite is common, which weathers quite rapidly into limonite and sulphates that are fast washed away with rain usually. The waste rock is not mechanically sorted and it contains boulders to clayey-silty particles. Dominant are stone fractions with fragments of different sizes, from first centimetres to decimetres. Erosion factors cause further fragmentation (disintegration of sandstone into sand, laminated disintegration of aleuropelites along the cleavage plane).

The calorific effect of coal substance alteration leads to a considerable heating of the surrounding sedimentary rocks and their gradual natural firing. Clay sediments, during heating of which the temperature of 600 °C was not exceeded, are not much different in their mineral composition from grey sediments before alteration. The most prominent changes occur in the association of clay minerals, kaolinite and illite. Red colouring of the thermally altered sediments is characteristic and is caused by finely dispersed hematite. Clay-silty rocks exposed to higher temperatures (900 - 1200 °C) show more distinct variations in the mineral composition and their alteration is connected with the formation of porcelanite and vitreous phase. The overall character and colour of porcelanite vary. The fired porcelanites in the reducing manner are black or grey; the oxidically fired porcelanites are red. The structure of such rocks may be significantly porous. At running out of reddish-brown vitreous mass on the base of fired porcelanites, irregular cohesive and solid laminar bodies, which are placed on relatively loose material, form in the burnt-out waste rock (the so-called porcelanite sinters).

References

[1] Baic I., Blaschke W., 2017 – *Coal Preparation in Poland – Development Trends for Increasing Production Efficiency*, Inżynieria Mineralna – Journal of the Polish Mineral Engineering Society, No 2(40) pp.7-14

[2] J. J. Hycnar, K. Honysch, B. Tora, S. Budzyń, 2017 – *Charakterystyka fizyko-chemiczna wybranych paliw alternatywnych i ich mieszanin z paliwami węglowymi*, Inżynieria Mineralna 2(40), Wyd. Polskiego Towarzystwa Przeróbki Kopalin, Kraków pp. 201–206

[3] A. Manowska, M. Mazurek, 2018 – *Analysis of Influence of Different Types of Separators on Fine Grain Coal Class Enrichment Process in Respect with Qualitative and Quantitative Analysis of Separation Products*, Inżynieria Mineralna – Journal of the Polish Mineral Engineering Society, No 1(41) pp. 235–243, DOI: 10.29227/IM-2018-01-36

[4] M. Osoba, 2017 – *Polish-Type Water Pulsated Jigs*, Inżynieria Mineralna – Journal of the Polish Mineral Engineering Society, No 1(39) pp.111–117

[5] Giemza H., Gruszka G., Hycnar J.J., Józefiak T., Kiermaszek K., 2007 Optymalizacja zagospodarowania sedymentu węglowego. Technologia brykietowania sedymentu. Polityka Energetyczna vol 10, z. 2.

[6] Giemza H., Gruszka G., Hycnar J.J., Józefiak T., Kiermaszek K., Pyc A., 2008 Innowacyjne kierunki optymalizacji obiegów wodnych dla wydzielenia i wykorzystania „sedymentów" w ZPMW Jastrzębskiej Spółki Węglowej S.A. Innowacyjne i przyjazne dla środowiska systemy przeróbcze surowców mineralnych - KOMEKO.

[7] W. Kępys, E. Wisła-Walsh, J. Matusik, 2018 – *Chemical Examination of Fly Ash and Bottom Ash Derived from Incineration of Hazardous Waste*, Inżynieria Mineralna – Journal of the Polish Mineral Engineering Society, No 1(41) pp. 221–233, DOI: 10.29227/IM-2018-01-35

[8] A. Szymkiewicz A., A. Fraś, Przystaś R., 2009 - Kierunki zagospodarowania odpadów wydobywczych w Południowym Koncernie Węglowym S.A. Wiadomości Górnicze, no 8.

[9] Jelinek J., Malis J., Danek T., Thomas J., Slivka V.: Old coal refuse heaps – possible sources of opening materials for the ceramic industry, Inżynieria Mineralna, Journal of the Polish Mineral Engineering Society, Vol. XII, 1(27) 2011, ISSN 1640-4920

[10] P. Pasiowiec, B. Tora, J. Wajs, K. Bańczyk, L. Strączyński, 2018 – *Sieves as a Basic Element of Processing Processes,* Inżynieria Mineralna – Journal of the Polish Mineral Engineering Society, No 1(41) pp. 13–34, DOI: 10.29227/IM-2018-01-02

[11] Giemza H., Gruszka G., Hycnar J.J., Józefiak T., Kiermaszek K. Technologie odzysku drobnoziarnistych materiałów i odpadów węglowych na potrzeby produkcji paliw i energetyki, XXIII Conference Materials *Issues of energy resources and energy in the domestic economy* Zakopane, 2009, ISBN 978-83-60195-57-4

[12] J. J. Hycnar, 2017 – *Nowa technologia wydzielania koncentratów węglowych z odcieków z wirówek odwadniających flotokoncentraty*, Inżynieria Mineralna 2(40), Wyd. Polskiego Towarzystwa Przeróbki Kopalin, Kraków pp. 251–264

[13] T. SzczygielskI, B. Tora, A. Kornacki, J.J. Hycnar, 2017 – *Fluidal ashes – properties and application,* Inżynieria Mineralna – Journal of the Polish Mineral Engineering Society, No 1(39) pp.207–216.

[14] Patent 2012 *Układ do odzyskania węgla zawartego w odsączu wirówek sedymentacyjno-sitowych.* PL 212053.

[15] Wróbel, A. Fraś, R. Przystaś, J. J. Hycnar, B. Tora, 2017 – *By-products of Coal Enrichment as a Source of Fuel and Aggregates. Management of Post-Production Waste in the Mines of the Southern Concern Coal Company*, Inżynieria Mineralna – Journal of the Polish Mineral Engineering Society, No 2(40). pp 39-46

[16] Patent 2011 Sposób odwadniania koncentratów flotacyjnych węgli kamiennych". PL 390663

Acknowledgments
Work financed from AGH research subsidy No. 16.16.100 215 and 16.16.210.476

IOP Conf. Series: Materials Science and Engineering **641** (2019) 012021 doi:10.1088/1757-899X/641/1/012021

Technical, technological and environmental aspects of the management of technological waters in mines and concentrators owned by KGHM Polska Miedź S.A.

K Witecki and A Grotowski

KGHM Cuprum Ltd. Research and Development Center, Gen. W. Sikorskiego 2-8, 53-659 Wrocław, Poland

E-mail: kwitecki@cuprum.wroc.pl

Abstract. Water and Tailing Management System (WTMS) plays a key role in mining and processing technological chain. In general, two separate but dependent systems can be separated: a network of technological waters and tailings. They constitute a system of connected vessels, a perfect example of which is the WTMS owned by KGHM Polska Miedź S.A. and managed by Hydro technical Department (O/ZH). The mining, technological and flotation water transport systems included in the system together with the accompanying facilities and installations cover the area of approx. 15 x 26 km. They combine 3 mines, 3 concentrators (ZWRs), Żelazny Most Tailing Management Facility (TMF) and the Głogów discharge station. This system makes it possible to conduct mining and processing operations by collecting water from mine workings (drainage), supplying concentrators and other installations (filling) with process water, flotation tailing management and discharge of excess water to the environment. The necessity of excess water discharge is associated with a positive balance of the system. This state results from the specific hydrogeological conditions and applied technological solutions, while providing the opportunity to work without the need to extract fresh water from the environment. Working in closed circuit, the technological water network fits in with the principle of the "circular economy", while meeting the quality requirements of the water both for the sake of issued permits and the flotation process. The global trend in the management of flotation tailings is being observed towards deposition them in thickened form in order to increase the safety of TMF and the best sign in to the BAT requirements. Positive examples obtained in this field by KGHM were possible due to many years of research conducted not only in this direction but also on the reuse of flotation tailings.

1. Introduction

The production of basic metal concentrates - including copper concentrates - requires significant volumes of water to carry out grinding and flotation processes as well as to managing huge waste stream with a size practically equivalent to the tonnage of the processed ore [1]. Economic conditions force everybody to constantly increase the ore throughput, and this entails the need to build the necessary Water & (flotation) Tailing Management System (WTMS) or to adequately develop it [2]. WTMS must ensure safe storage of tailings generated during concentration process, retention of the necessary water volume and its continuous supply according to the needs of processing, as well as, periodic, environmentally safe discharge of water to the nearby watercourses or reservoirs.

Water management in individual mines can vary considerably, depending on specific hydrological, hydrogeological, technological and environmental conditions, wherein, the majority of mines with the negative water balance – in contrast to KGHM Polska Miedź S.A. -, bases on supplementing a technological water system with waters from reservoirs (seas, oceans, lakes) and watercourses [3-5]. This is a serious obstacle especially when conducting concentration processes in dry regions, e.g. Chile, Australia [6, 7], because it forces to carry out additional investments, including construction of water intakes, treatment stations, pumping stations and water transport networks, of a length often exceeding 100 km [3]. If the water balance is positive, i.e. the inflow of water from mine dewatering is greater than their consumption in concentration processes, then periodic discharge of excess water into environment is necessary [8]. In line with global trends, the aim of any water management system is to ensure that water once introduced into the system is used as long as possible, while maintaining their parameters on the required level, to establish both an efficient concentration process and safe water discharge [3, 4].

Process water circling in WTMS is a mix of water from the flotation taillings and concentrate dewatering processes, other various types of water entering the system and make-up water. Maintaining the required water parameters in the global mining industry is becoming more and more difficult due to the widespread use of closed water circuits and the need to supplement the system with low quality waters and/or return water with an increased content of dissolved and/or solids, which results in a continuous deterioration of technological water quality [9]. In critical cases, the quality of used waters is being improved by the addition of low-mineralization waters, obtained by usage, among others, desalination installations [10]. It should be noted, however, that in most cases, highly saline waters are successfully used for flotation [4, 11-13]. Conducting flotation in such conditions requires adjusting the technological parameters of the process to the properties of the concentrated ore and the chemical composition of the water used. Numerous literature reports shows that parameters such as, among others, pH, heavy metals and salt concentration affect the selectivity of the flotation process [14-16], and that the salinity improves the foaming properties of the solution [17-22].

The tasks of water & flotation tailing management systems and their technical solutions are closely related not only to the water balance and local conditions but also to the method of tailing deposition. In the most of cases tailings are deposited in the same form as they leave the last cells of flotation machines. However, flotation tailings are more and more subjected to dewatering before dumping them, in order to obtain the possibly dense slurry [23-26]. This second solution has become a standard wherever there is a shortage of natural waters with quality suitable for supplementing industrial water circuits [27-30]. In order to accelerate the sedimentation of solids, different types of thickeners are used - especially high-rate thickeners, hydrocyclones, and the settling process is usually supported by the addition of flocculants/coagulants [4, 29, 31]. For a long time an increase trend of dense tailings storage is observed in flotation tailings management. Different slurries are used: from simply thick, through paste-like slurry, on dry (almost) tailings ending. [28, 30-32]. This trend results both from the attachment of more and more attention to the safety of Tailing Management Facilities (TMF), as well as from growing amount of information on the failures of various TMFs in recent years [23, 33, 34], and is also caused by the increasingly wider introduction of circular economy principles [35-37].

Water and flotation tailing management in KGHM Polska Miedź S.A. is an example of a system using water exclusively from own resources, which consists of waters from mine drainage, waste water, water from refreshing cooling circuits and - above all - return waters from the concentration process. This is a typical system with a positive water balance, which requires periodic discharge of excess water to the environment. In the currently exploited Tailing Management Facility (Żelazny Most OUOW), tailings are stored in the form of a slurry discharged on so called tailing beaches. In the planned extension of the current TMF with the so-called The Southern Quarter, the dams will be constructed using the tailing segregation and thickening technology.

2. Water and Tailing Management system in KGHM Polska Miedź S.A.

Initially, in the currently exploited LGOM copper basin, the water balance was negative, which resulted mainly from inadequate - in relation to the needs - inflow of water from mine drainage. Therefore, it was necessary to supply WTMS with water coming from the Odra River. The changes caused by the development of the extraction and the associated significant increase in the inflow of water caused that for a long time the water balance is positive and a periodic discharge of excess water is necessary. The Odra I water intake, located at the current discharging node, was finally excluded from use in the mid-1980s [38].

The detailed tasks of WTMS, including mines and concentrators of KGHM Polska Miedź S.A., are as follows:

- collection of mine water and treated rainwater-technological waters and treated sanitary sewage from all 3 mines and 3 concentrators and their safe retention in the Żelazny Most Tailing Management Facility,
- collection of flotation tailings from all 3 concentrators plants and their safe storage (disposal) at Żelazny Most TMF,
- continuous delivery of water to all 3 concentrators, with the quality required for the processing operations, in a quantity appropriate to the processing volume of a given plant,
- periodical discharge of excess waters from the WTMS to the Odra River, in accordance with the ruling water permit.

In WTMS, the management of various types of water is carried out and the waters are sometimes called - depending on the place of origin - in various ways. These are mainly mine water (underground), water introduced by Energetyka sp. z o.o. and mine-technological water. The meaning of the individual terms is explained below.

- **Underground water**, also called mine water, comes from draining of the underground part of the mine. They are captured at the bottom of the mine and using the system of pipelines, settlers and departmental and regional pumping stations are transported to the main dewatering pump station, from where they are pumped on the surface. The underground water intake and transport network is organized in such a way as to make maximum use of gravitational flow. After pumping on the surface, mine water is supplied to surface water transport and distribution systems.
- **Energetyka Ltd. waters** are a mixture of pre-treated rainwater and technological waters from shaft sites, sewage and water from refurbishing cooling systems. They are fed into water transport and distribution systems.
- **Process waters** (also known as industrial, mine-technological, mine-industrial waters), are a mixture of mine waters from individual mines, supernatant and infiltration waters from Żelazny Most TMF and used waters of Energetyka Ltd. All these waters are returned to concentrators plants, where they are used for the processing of copper ores.

There are other names for the technological waters coming from specific parts of the WTMS network.

- **Supernatant water** is a clear, free of suspension water, accumulating over settled down flotation tailings at Żelazny Most TMF. It is collected using the so-called overflow towers and returned to concentrators or discharged to the Odra River.
- **Return water**. This is the name used for this part of the supernatant water that is returned to a concentrator. It is the most important component of waters used for the flotation process.
- **Discharge water**. This is the name used for this part of overflow waters that are directed to the Odra River through the control and discharge node in Głogów. Due to the fact that more water comes from the mines than it is consumed in the concentration process) and lost as the humidity of stored waste, evaporation of water, infiltration and as a concentrate moisture), the excess water must be - and is - systematically discharged to the Odra river.

The WTMS is composed of the transport networks for mining and technological waters as well as flotation tailings with the accompanying facilities and installations, located in the area between Lubin and Głogów, with an surface area of approx. 15 x 26 km. This system is characterized by the following functionalities:

- underground transport of mine water to the surface - to the frame of the shaft,
- surface transport of mine water - from the shaft framework to the concentrators (ZWR),
- (hydro) transport of flotation tailings and technological waters from ZWRs to Żelazny Most TMF,
- transportation of technological waters from Żelazny Most TMF to individual ZWRs and/or to the discharge node,
- collection of water from the Gilów TMF,
- the discharge of excess technological waters to the Odra River,
- the discharge of excess technological waters to the Odra River,
- the discharge of excess technological waters to the Odra River in controlled way, in terms of quantity and quality.

The volume of water discharged to the Odra river depends on the current river flowrate and quality parameters of the river and discharge water and is calculated taking into account the amount of permissible pollution load that can be introduced to the river, while maintaining the parameters specified in the integrated permit.

Water can be discharged to the Odra river in two ways:

- Gravitational - without the use of pumping sets,
- Pressure - using pump sets.

A simplified scheme for the circulation of waters and tailings in WTMS is presented in Figure 1.

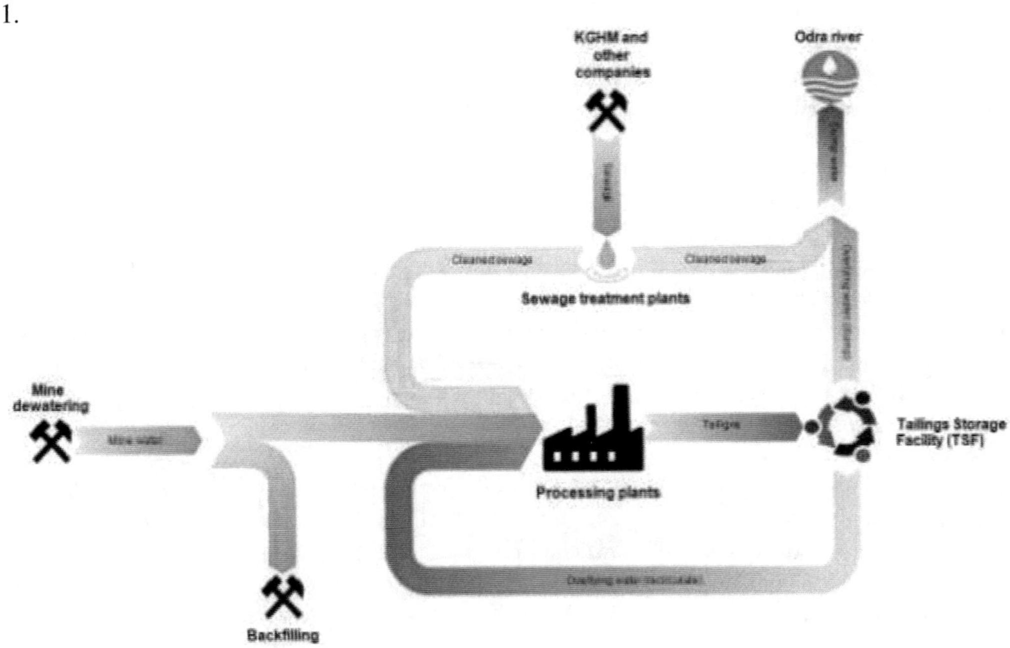

Figure 1. Simplified flowsheet of Water and Tailings Management System (WTMS) of KGHM Polska Miedź S.A.

As part of the WTMS operating at KGHM Polska Miedź S.A. two types of networks can be distinguished, basically differing in the type of medium flowing through, applied technical and technological solutions and tasks assigned to them. These are:

1) Technological waters network.
2) Hydro transport network of flotation tailings

2.1. Technological waters network

The hydro transportation network of water (also known as mine-industrial water), managed by Hydro technical Department (O/ZH), is the longest pipeline network used by KGHM Polska Miedź S.A. The tasks of the technological water network are:

- collection of waters from mines,
- collection of treated sanitary sewage and treated rainwater-industrial waters from ZG Lubin West and Rudna West,
- transport of technological waters to the discharge node in Głogów, with the necessary assistance from Żelazny Most TMF,
- receiving of the clarified return water from Żelazny Most TMF and its delivery to ZWR, in the required quantity and quality,
- collection of excess water from the Gilów TMF reservoir,
- transport of excess water from Żelazny Most TMF to the control and discharge node,
- in necessary cases, purification of the supernatant waters stored in the Żelazny Most TMF from the suspension in the treatment plant next to the facility.

The most important task of the technological water network is to supply the concentrators. In addition, one of the backfill plants is also fed.

The technological water pipeline network is predominantly autonomous in relation to the waste water transport network. Only on the section, concentrators - Żelazny Most TMF, process water is sent along with flotation tailings in the form of an aqueous slurry. The network consists of:

- pipelines for water intakes A, B (closed), D and E in Żelazny Most TMF,
- return water return pipes from water intakes A, B (inactive), D and E,
- Kalinówka and Tarnówek pumping stations,
- infiltration water reservoirs at above mentioned pumping stations,
- return water pressure pipelines,
- distribution station of technological and mine water,
- Polanka retention reservoir,
- treatment plant of water discharged to the Oder River,
- pipelines for discharging supernatant water to the Odra River.

Supernatant water, accumulated in the central reservoir of Żelazny Most TMF, is collected by siphons placed in towers of overflow intakes and pipelines arranged in the bottom of the reservoir, and is supplied to the pumping station (Tarnówek and Kalinówka). From here it is pumped back to the concentrators for flotation, and its excess is discharged to the Odra River, according to the conditions of the integrated permit granted.

The collection of supernatant waters from Żelazny Most TMF takes place by means of tower intakes, located in the reservoir. W-3 and W-6 overflow tower intakes are inactive, W-10 and W-11 intakes feed, respectively, A, B (inactive), D and E inflow lines, which are then connected to the technological water pipeline network. The inflow of supernatant overflow waters to the system is permanent.

The technological water pipeline network is diverse and includes sections of underground, ground, surface and overhead pipelines, made of steel, cast iron, polyethylene and polyester resins, with diameters from 400 to 1,400 mm, with a total length of approx. 150 km. The final element of the technological waters network is the control and discharge node in Głogów.

The pressures and flows sizes in individual pipelines depend on the current concentrators needs and fluctuate. The working pressure at the Tarnówek pumping station varies between 10-13 atm, and at small demand it drops below 11 atm. The Kalinówka pumping station runs between 11 and 14 atm. The pressure value decreases with distance, depending on the terrain. For example, the RW-4 pipeline supplying the Rudna concentrator, at the Tarnówek pumping station, has a working pressure of 12 atm, whereas at the concentrator the pressure drops to 2.7atm. Flowrates occurring in pipelines supplying water to individual concentrators are:

- RW-4 pipeline from 90 to 120 m³/min,
- Lubin pipeline (RW-1) from 55 to 65 m³/min,
- Polkowice pipelines (R1, R2, R3 and R4) approx. 50 m³/min,
- Gilów pipelines (Gilów I and Gilów II) from 20 to 46 m³/min (periodically).

The key elements of the technological water transport network are presented in Figure 2 and they are:

- Tarnówek pumping station,
- Kalinówka pumping station,
- Gilów pumping station,
- technological water distribution station,
- Polanka retention reservoir,
- Świnino II chamber,
- Water discharge node.

2.2. Hydro transport network of flotation tailings

The hydro transport network of flotation tailings is also a part of the technological water transport network, because along with the flotation tailings from the concentrators, mine and process waters are also transported in the same pipeline to Żelazny Most TMF. Thanks to this - after clarification - it becomes possible to reuse them in the concentration processes and/or discharge them to the Odra River, according to current needs. For this reason, the hydro transport network of flotation tailings is also an important component of the WTMS, in which it performs the following tasks:

- transport of flotation tailings from individual ZWRs to Żelazny Most TMF,
- transport of mine water from individual ZWRs to Żelazny Most TMF (together with waste slurry).

Within the Żelazny Most TMF network itself provides also:

- selective discharge of coarse tailings to the beach near the embankment crown. This part of tailings is designated for dam construction,
- selective discharge of fine-grained tailings into the canopy of TMF to seal the bottom of the basin,
- discharge of all tailings into the Żelazny Most TMF canopy - only during the period of negative temperatures.

Flotation tailings from concentrators (Regions: Lubin, Polkowice, and Rudna) are supplied in the form of a hydrated mixture to Żelazny Most TMF with a network of large-diameter main pipelines. Then, through a network of distribution and discharge pipelines, the waste slurry is directed to the selected parts of beaches, so-called sections, where discharging is carried out.

IOP Conf. Series: Materials Science and Engineering **641** (2019) 012021 doi:10.1088/1757-899X/641/1/012021

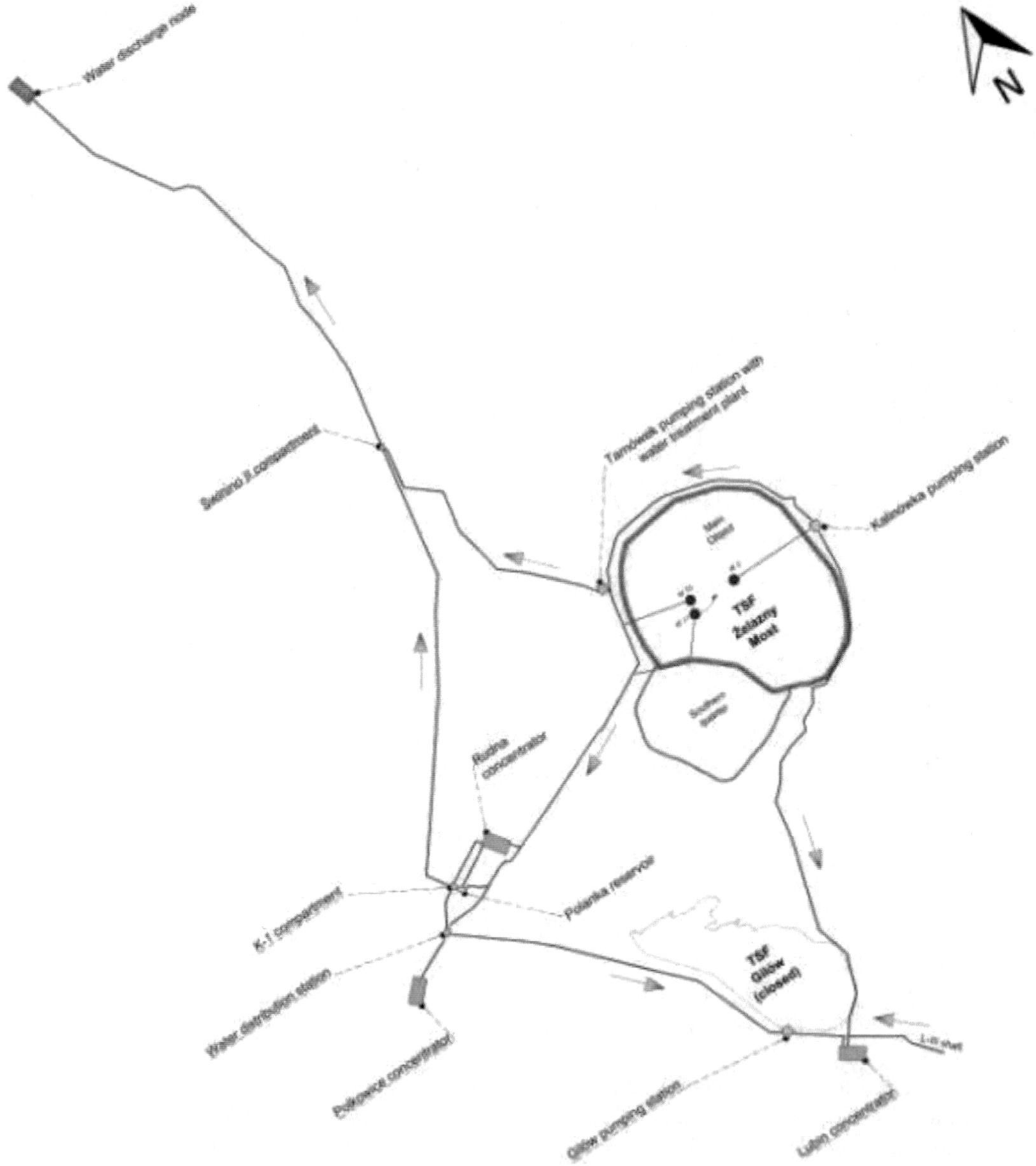

Figure 2. Horizontal projection of the Water Management System of KGHM Polska Miedź S.A.

The general principle of tailing depositing in TMF is ring discharging - around the whole TMF circuit, whereby sandstone type tailings (Lubin and Rudna concentrators) are directed to the drainage slope of the dams, whereas the clay-carbonate tailings (Polkowice concentrator) are directed into the canopy of the facility through pipelines located on so-called piers (dams). In addition to the pillars for the discharge of Polkowice tailings, there are also piers for other tailings, but they are intended only for winter operation, because during periods of negative temperatures discharging tailings into beaches cannot be performed. In the winter period tailings are directed to the deepest regions of the water reservoir. Supernatant water, after sedimentation of tailings, is captured by overflow tower and drained from the facility.

The hydro transport network of flotation tailings includes (Figure 3):

- first-stage flotation tailings pumping stations at:
  - Lubin concentrator,

- Polkowice concentrator
- Rudna concentrator, A side,
- Rudna concentrator, B side,

- discharge pipelines of tailings from the above pumping station,
- LG and RG tailings distribution stations with PG and RG chambers,
- tailing pipelines from the distribution station to the boundaries of TMF,
- pumping stations,
- pipelines distributing tailings around the TMF dams,
- discharging pipelines on the beaches.

The network of tailings transport pipelines consists of overhead pipelines laid in earthwork and excavations, made of steel, reinforced concrete and plastic pipes (HDPE), diameters from 500 to 1,200 _mm. The pipeline network is run in a strip of land up to 20_-m wide and with a total length of approx. 100 km. In the case of renovation and maintenance works, the pipelines are emptied into dedicated settling tanks, located at the foot of the Żelazny Most TMF barrage.

Due to the systematically progressing wear of pipelines, they are cyclically rotated, as well as systematically exchanged and modernized. With currently modernized slurry pipeline networks, steel and reinforced concrete pipes are exchanged for plastic pipes. Plastic pipelines are characterized by very high abrasion resistance and lack of corrosion, while their unfavorable feature is lower resistance to high pressures.

IOP Conf. Series: Materials Science and Engineering **641** (2019) 012021 doi:10.1088/1757-899X/641/1/012021

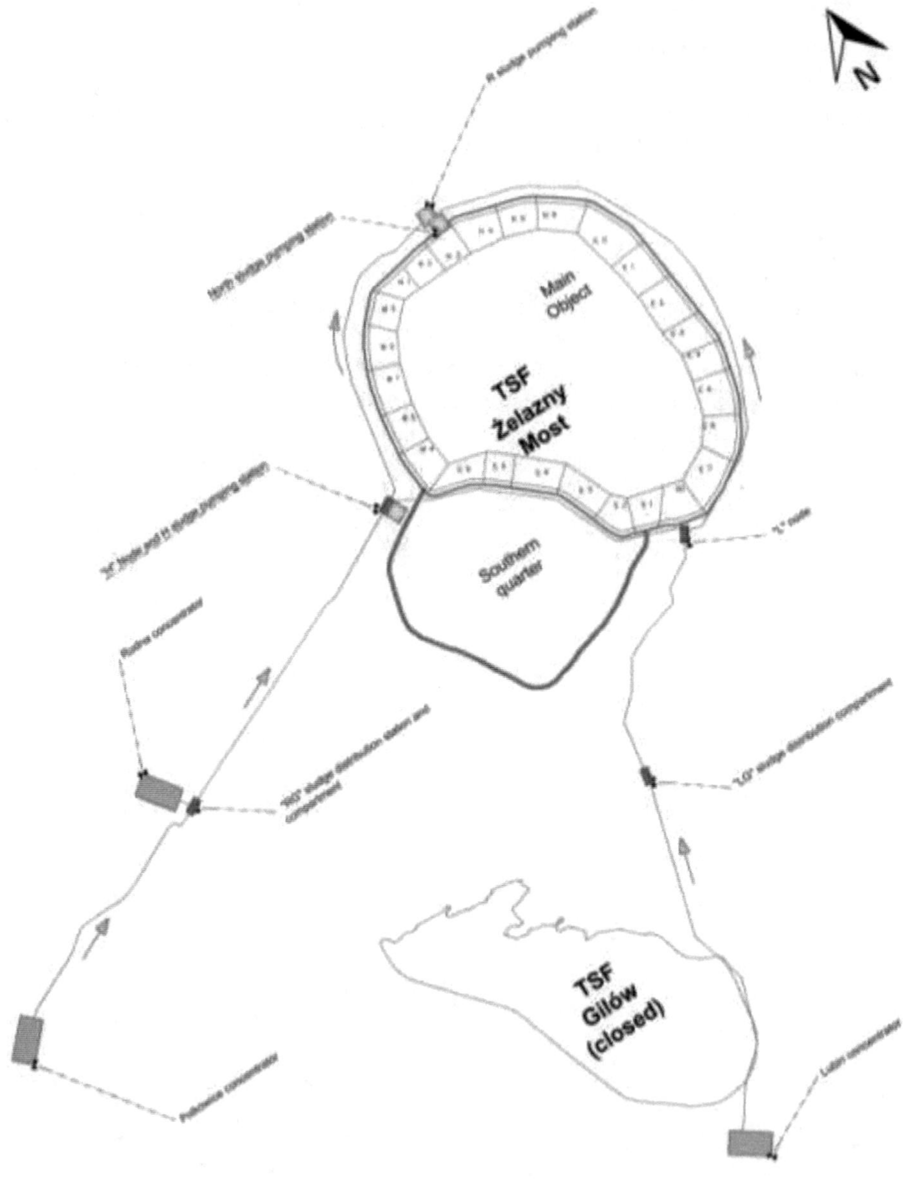

Figure 3. Horizontal projection of the Tailings Management System (TMS) of KGHM Polska Miedź S.A.

3. Environmental aspects of the WTMS

Many global studies, as well as water management protocols (Water Stewardship Protocols) define guidelines for sustainable water management in a given region [39]. The mentioned studies indicate the necessity of rational use of water by limiting the use of fresh water and more efficient recycling of process waters, while ensuring their appropriate parameters. This can be achieved by using such water management technologies that meet the following requirements:

- all potential water sources are taken into account already at the stage of planning the water needs of a plant,
- technology ensures the use of available waters according to their nature (quality), and the use of high quality water should take place only in the necessary cases or when another source of water is unavailable, while ensuring the least possible side effects,
- water introduced into the water system is used to the maximum extent, especially in areas with a significant water shortage, to minimize the uptake of water from the environment,
- surplus water, in or outside the plant, are used in an optimal way to maximize efficiency and reduce environmental impact.

Thanks to a significant increase in environmental awareness, the European Union has introduced the Integrated Pollution Prevention and Control (IPPC) Directive, which imposes the Best Available Technology (BAT) standard, which allows enforcement of compliance with the emission limits imposed by industrial plants. In the scope of the best available technologies for water and waste management in mining, the European Commission in its recommendations defines the desired directions of actions [40]. The most important of them, already implemented by KGHM Polska Miedź S.A., include the reuse of technological waters, the use of sedimentation tanks for the separation of fines and the removal of suspended solids and metals from waters discharged to the environment.

The major accidents of traditional TMFs in the recent years have clearly indicated the technologies for storing thickened and dry waste as increasing the safety of the facility, due to the limitation or complete elimination of the main factor of potential failure which is a water reservoir located inside of TMF [42]. In the case of using the technology of thickened tailings in e.g. the Southern Quarter [41], in addition to the increased safety of local residents, the degree of infiltration of saline water into the reservoir bed will be also reduced, which had a measurable impact on the environmental impact of the facility [43].

The "circular economy" principle introduced in the recent years requires the possibly highest usage (recovery) of waste products [44]. In the case of waters used in flotation process, virtually every concentrator in the world - although to varying degrees - fulfills this principle. Similarly, the KGHM Polska Miedź S.A., where the water management takes place through WTMS, guarantees repeated use of each type of water introduced into this system. On the other hand - as the overview of global solutions shows - meeting the requirements of a circular economy with respect to flotation tailings is very far from satisfactory because cases of a significant use of flotation tailings practically does not exist, and if they appear, are caused by very specific factors. In the case of flotation tailings generated by KGHM Polska Miedź S.A. the situation is slightly better because they are used to construct TMF embankments, to seal the water reservoir canopy and to neutralize the waste sulfuric acid [1]. Application of such methods for tailing utilization (recovery) became possible due to the effects of many years of research conducted by KGHM Polska Miedź S.A. focusing on reuse of flotation tailings [45-50]. Such studies are still being continued to increase the stream of tailings reused.

The recent analysis of the possibility of meeting the requirements of the closed-circuit economy indicated that in the case of flotation tailings, compliance with these requirements is excluded [51], due to the lack of the possibility of managing the entire tailing stream [1]. The authors pointed out that in the case of certain specific wastes, such as flotation tailings (including tailings from KGHM Polska Miedź S.A.), the implementation of this principle is impossible so far, despite the indisputable rightness of the closed-circuit economy philosophy.

4. Summary

Water and flotation tailing management at KGHM Polska Miedź S.A. has been taking place for over 60 years and is conducted through the Water and (flotation) Tailing Management System (WTMS). The system is the result of many years of experience and uses specific solutions, continuously adapted to the changing environmental, legal and technological conditions. In contrast to many global systems, the waters circulating in the WTMS come entirely from own company sources, mainly from the drainage of mines. The elimination of the need to intake additional quantities of water from the environment due to the use of own waters and recycling of technological waters allows for sustainable water management of KGHM Polska Miedź S.A. and fully complies with the principle of closed-circuit economy.

In the field of tailings disposal, both the technology currently used at Żelazny Most TMF and planned to be implemented at the South Quarter satisfactorily meet the requirements of both BAT and the "circular economy" principles. It became possible due to many years of experience and constant adaptation of applied technologies to the changing internal and external conditions.

5. References

[1] Grotowski A, Mizera A i Grotowska M 1995. Możliwości i warunki zagospodarowania odpadów wydobywczych powstających przy eksploatacji i przeróbce rud miedzi. *Konferencja: Problemy Zagospodarowania Odpadów Mineralnych*, Wisła.

[2] Grotowski A, Witecki K, Ziętkowski L i Rubaniuk A 2016. Dokumentacja Systemu Gospodarowania wodami kopalnianymi i przemysłowymi w ciągu górniczo-przeróbczym KGHM Polska Miedź S.A. *KGHM Cuprum Sp. z o.o.* – report not published.

[3] Liu W, Moran C J & Vink S 2011. Quantitative risk-based approach for improving water quality management in mining. *Environmental Science and Technology* **45**(17) pp 7459–7464.

[4] Moreno P A, Aral H, Cuevas J, Monardes A, Adaro M, Norgate T & Bruckard W 2011. The use of seawater as process water at Las Luces copper-molybdenum beneficiation plant in Taltal (Chile). *Minerals Engineering* **24**(8) pp 852–858.

[5] Freitas A, Magrini A 2013. Multi-criteria decision-making to support sustainable water management in a mining complex in Brasil. *Journal of Cleaner Production* **47** pp 118-128.

[6] Aitken D, Rivera D, Godoy-Faúndez A, Holzapfel E 2016. Water Scarcity and the Impact of the Mining and Agricultural Sectors in Chile. *Sustainability* **8**(128) pp 1-18.

[7] Valdés-Pineda R, Pizarro R, García-Chevesich P, Valdés J B, Fuentes R, Helwig B 2014. Water governance in Chile : Availability , management and climate change. *Journal of Hydrogeology* **519** pp 2538-2567.

[8] Kotarska I 2012. Odpady wydobywcze z górnictwa miedzi w Polsce – bilans, stan zagospodarowania i aspekty środowiskowe. *Czasopismo Naukowo-Techniczne Górnictwa Rud* **4**(65) pp 45-63.

[9] Jian-ming C, Run-qing L, Wei S & Guan-zhou Q, 2008. Effect of mineral processing wastewater on flotation of sulfide minerals. *Trans. Nonferrous Met. Soc. China*, **19**, 454-457.

[10] Chavez-Crooker P, Obreque-Contreras J, Perez-Flores D & Contreras-Vera A 2015. Desalination Plants: Technology to Supply Water to Mining Processes and Local Populations, Opportunities and Environmental Impact. *Current Biotechnology* **4**(3) pp 1-14.

[11] Quinn J J, Kracht W, Gomez C O, Gangon C & Finch J A 2007. Comparing the effect of salts and frother (MIBC) on gas dispersion and froth properties. *Mineral Engineering* **20** pp 1296-1302.

[12] Jeldres R I, Forbes L, Cisternas L A 2016. Effect of Seawater on Sulfide Ore Flotation: A Review. *Mineral Processing and Extractive Metallurgy Review* **37**(6) pp 369-384.

[13] Yousef A A, Arafa M A, Ibrahim S S i Khalek M A 2003. Sea Water Usage in Flotation for Minerals Beneficiation in Arid Regions – Simulation and Application. *Proceedings of XXII International Mineral Processing Congress* (Cape Town, RPA).

[14] Slatter K A, Plint N D, Cole M, Dilsook V, De Vaux D, Palm N & Oostendorp B 2009. Water Management In Anglo Platinum Process Operations Effects Of Water Quality On Process Operations. *Abstracts of the International Mine Water Conference* (Pretoria, South Africa).
[15] Jeldres R I, Forbes L, Cisternas L A 2016. Effect of Seawater on Sulfide Ore Flotation: A Review. *Mineral Processing and Extractive Metallurgy Review* **37**(6) pp 369-384.
[16] Laskowski J 1969. Chemia fizyczna w procesach mechanicznej przeróbki kopalin. *Wydawnictwo Śląskie* (Katowice).
[17] Castro S, Venegas I, Landero A, Laskowski J S 2010. Frothing in seawater flotation systems. *Proc. XXV Int. Mineral Processing Congress* (Brisbane) pp 4039-4047.
[18] Castro S, Ramos O, Cancino J P, Laskowski J S 2012a. Frothing in the Flotation of Copper Sulfide Ores in Sea Water. *Water in Mineral Processing – Proceeding of The First International Symposium* SME pp 211-223.
[19] Castro S, Toledo P and Laskowski J S, 2012b. Foaming Properties of Flotation Frothers at High Electrolyte Concentration. *Water in Mineral Processing – Proceeding of The First International Symposium* SME 51-60.
[20] Laskowski J S, Castro S, Ramos O 2014. Effect Of Seawater Main Components On Frothability In The Flotation Of Cu-Mo Sulfide Ore. *Physicochem. Probl. Miner. Process.* **50**(1) pp 17–29.
[21] Muzenda E 2010. An investigation into the Effect of Water Quality on Flotation Performance. *International Journal of Chemical and Molecular Engineering* **4**(9) pp 562-566.
[22] Lekki J, Laskowski J S 1975. Wpływ chlorku sodu w wodach kopalnianych LGOM na flotację rudy miedzi. *Physicochem. Probl. Miner. Process* **5**(1) pp115–123.
[23] Fourie A 2009. Preventing catastrophic failures and mitigating environmental impacts of tailings storage facilities. *Procedia Earth and Planetary Science PROEPS* **1**(1) pp 1067–1071.
[24] Yilmaz E 2011. Advances in reducing large volumes of environmentally harmful mine waste rocks and tailings. *Gospodarka Surowcami Mineralnymi* **27**(2) pp 89-111.
[25] Collective elaboration 2017. Mine Environment Neutral Drainage (MEND) Project - Study of tailings management technologies. *Klohn Crippen Berger* (Canada).
[26] Davis M 2011. Filtered Dry Stacked Tailings – The Fundamentals. *Proceedings Tailings and Mine Waste 2011* (Vancouver, Canada).
[27] Thompson N & Moreno P 2017. Thickened Tailings Deposition for Closure. *20th International Seminar on Paste and Thickened Tailings* (Beijing, China).
[28] Martin T E, Davies M P, Rice S, Higgs &, Lighthall P C 2002. Stewardship of Tailings Facilities. *Mining, Minerals and Sustainable Development* **20**.
[29] McPhail G 2015. The high density thickened discharge tailings storage facility at Osborne Mine – a case history from inception to closure. *Proceedings of the 18th International Seminar on Paste and Thickened Tailings* (Cairns, Australia).
[30] Davis M, Lupo J, Martin T, McRoberts E, Musse M & Ritchie D 2010. A Dewatered Tailings Practice –Trends and Observations. *Proceedings of Tailings and Mine Waste '10* (Vail, , USA).
[31] Park J H, Han Y S & Ji S W 2018. Investigation of mineral-processing waste water recycling processes: A pilot study. *Sustainability* **10**(9) 1–10.
[32] Raposo N, Bahia R, Afonso E & Topa Gomes A 2014. Optimization of thickened tailings deposition. *Proceedings of Paste 2014* (Vancouver, Canada).
[33] Lepoudre D C 2015. Examples, Statistics and Failure modes of tailings dams and consequence of failure. *SNC LAVALIN, REMTECH* - October 15.
[34] Larrauri P C & Lall U 2018. Tailings Dams Failures: Updated Statistical Model For Discharge Volume and Runout. *Environments* **5**(28) 1-10.
[35] Pomykała R & Tora B 2017. Circular economy in Mineral Processing. *Proceedings of Mineral Engineering Conference 2017* (Wisła, Poland).
[36] Matinde E, Simate G S & Ndlovu S 2018. Mining and Metallurgical wastes: a review of recycling and re-use practices. *The Journal of the Southern African Institute of Mining and Metallurgy* **118** pp 825-844.

[37] Tayebi-Khorami M, Edraki M, Corder G & Golev A 2019. Re-Thinking Mining Waste through an Integrative Approach Led by Circular Economy Aspirations. *Minerals* **9**(286) pp 1-13.

[38] Czaban S, Lewiński J, Rubaniuk A & Tarasek W 2008. Składowiska Odpadów. *Monografia KGHM Polska Miedź S.A.* pp 855-877.

[39] Collective elaboration 2013. Western Australian water in mining guideline. Department of Water (Australia) **12**.

[40] Cusano G, Gonzalo M R, Farrell F, Remus R, Roudier S & Sancho L D 2017. Best Available Techniques (BAT) Reference Document for the Non-Ferrous Metals Industries. *Industrial Emissions Directive 2010/75/EU (Integrated Pollution Prevention and Control)*

[41] Stefanek P, Serwicki A 2014. Ograniczenie oddziaływania OUOW Żelazny Most na środowisko poprzez zmianę technologii składowania odpadów. *Workshops: Górnictwo-człowiek-środowisko* pp 394-406.

[42] Chambers D M & Higman B 2011. Long Term Risks Of Tailings Dam Failure. *http://www.csp2.org/technical-reports/*

[43] Stefanek P & Wrzosek K 2015. Zmiana technologii składowania odpadów w procesie rozbudowy Obiektu Unieszkodliwiania Odpadów Wydobywczych Żelazny Most. *Inżynieria Morska i Geotechnika* **3** pp 382-386.

[44] Hansen K, Braungart M & Mulhall D 2012. Resource Repletion. *The Springer Encyclopedia of Sustainability Science and Technology.*

[45] Janiec R & Nowak J 1973, Odpady z przeróbki rud i ich mieszaniny z piaskiem jako materiał podsadzkowy. *Rudy i Metale Nieżelazne* **9**(18) pp 428-432

[46] Chmielewski T, Grotowski A, Kołodziej B & Adamski Z 1995. Możliwości zastosowania ługowania cyjankowego do odzysku miedzi z odpadów flotacyjnych. *Rudy i Metale Nieżelazne* **8**(40) pp 318-321.

[47] Kudełko J, Nitek D 2011. Wykorzystanie odpadów z działalności górniczej jako substytutów surowców mineralnych. *CUPRUM - Czasopismo Naukowo-Techniczne Górnictwa Rud* ***3***(60) pp 51–64.

[48] Raciborski R 1975. Badania przydatności odpadów flotacyjnych Lubińsko-Głogowskiego Okręgu Miedziowego do mas bitumicznych - część I. *KGHM Cuprum sp. z o.o.* – report not published

[49] Szczap J 1997. Gospodarcze wykorzystanie odpadów flotacyjnych do dosadzania starych zrobów zawałowych przy pomocy instalacji rurowych w O/ZG "Lubin". *KGHM Cuprum sp. z o.o. – CBR* – report not published.

[50] Dobrzański J, Garbaczewski J, Grotowski A, Mizera A & Piątkowski J 1999. Gospodarka odpadami w KGHM Polska Miedź S.A. bilans odpadów, technologie wykorzystania, efekty ekonomiczne i ekologiczne – stan i perspektywy. *V Conference - Problemy zagospodarowania odpadów mineralnych* (Wisła).

[51] Kotarska I, Mizera B & Stefanek P 2018. Mining Waste in the Circular Economy – Idea Versus Reality. *Proceedings of IIIrd International Innovative Mining Symposium* (Kemerovo, Russian Federation) **41** pp 1–7.

Investigation of the process of grinding of a char coal obtained from tires waste pyrolysis

J Sidor[1], S Budzyń[2], C Czosnek[2], G Kozub –Budzyń[3] and B Tora[4]

[1] Faculty of Mechanical Engineering and Robotics,
[2]Faculty of Energy and Fuels,
[3]Faculty of Geology, Geophysics and Environmental Protection,
[4]Faculty of Mining and Geoengineering
AGH University of Science and Technology, Mickiewicza 30 Av., 30-059 Krakow, Poland

E-mail: tora@agh.edu.pl

Abstract. The paper contains results of examinations of grinding of char obtained from waste car tires. The grinding of the char was conducted in a laboratory vibratory mill of low vibration frequency. The examinations concerned the possibility of using a char as raw material in industry, particularly as a substitute for carbon black applied for the production of rubber. One of the basic parameters characterizing carbon black is particle size distribution as well as specific surface area. In the examinations, the char was obtained with following characteristic sizes of particles: d_{50} = 2.5 ÷ 9.3 μm , d_{90} = 13.3 ÷ 35.0 μm and specific surface area 74 ÷ 163 m^2/g matching the particle size distribution and specific surface area characteristic of carbon black, which means that in order to grind a char, the vibratory mill can be used.

1. Introduction

In the EU countries, around 3.4 million Mg of car tiretires are withdrawn from operation every year; in Poland it is about 0.24 million Mg. About 23% of that amount is reused. The remaining amount needs putting into appropriate use in accordance with the current regulations. This involves the reuse of the tires after retreading, energy recycling - combustion, pyrolysis - conversion to liquid and solid fuels, material recycling - after mechanical processing and modification (devulcanization and regeneration), and putting into use in different sectors - after mechanical processing[1].

The processing of waste tires and other rubber waste through pyrolysis is one of the methods of their recycling, and its products are: gas with a composition similar to that of natural gas, pyrolytic oil, and a solid residue - a char. The char contains 70 ÷ 80% of carbon, is featured by low contents of volatile matter and the presence of inorganic matter, the composition of which depends on the kind of rubber blends produced [2, 3, 4]. The carbon contained in the char comes from carbon black, but its structure and properties are different because of the influence of technological processes to which carbon black was subjected (production of rubber blends, vulcanization and pyrolysis). In the technology of rubber blends production, different additives are applied, such as vulcanizing agents and accelerators, plasticizers, fillers, pigments, anti-ageing substances, and others. These are mainly inorganic substances, which remain in the char after the pyrolysis process. Also, a significant amount of sulphur (up to 3%), which is used for vulcanization of rubber blends, stays in the char [4, 5]. The properties of a char depend on the kind of rubber waste, time-temperature conditions of the pyrolysis process and type of plant in which pyrolysis is conducted [8, 9, 10].

In the technological process of rubber blends production, various kinds of organic and inorganic substances are used as additives - fillers, which aim at imparting the required physico-chemical properties to the rubber products. The basic substance used as a filler is carbon black, which, depending on the type, is characterized by the specific surface area (BET) of 20 ÷ 130 m^2/g. Carbon black is a relatively expensive component of rubber blends, therefore, in rubber products with lower quality requirements, substitute substances are applied.

Laboratory examinations showed that in certain cases carbon black can be fully or partly replaced with a char obtained from pyrolysis of waste tires, without significant changes in the properties of the resulting rubber [11]. The price of the char is much lower than that of carbon black, which makes it possible to reduce the production costs of rubber blends. This also creates the possibility to recycle waste rubber products, to the benefit of the environment, by developing a wasteless technology of utilizing rubber waste in the pyrolysis process. One of the conditions for obtaining a char, which can be used as a filler in the production of rubber blends, is its size reduction to an appropriate limit and obtaining an appropriate specific surface area [12]. A char can also be used in different sectors of industry, e.g. for producing pigments, activated carbons, plastics, as a mercury adsorbent, an additive to asphalt, as well as a component of suspensions and liquid coal, where its appropriate size reduction is also required [8-11].

The paper contains results of investigations of a very fine grinding of a char conducted in a laboratory vibratory mill with a low vibration frequency [13, 14]. The diameter of the milling chamber used in this research, corresponding to that of industrial milling chambers will, in the future, facilitate the selection of grinding parameters and the dimensions of the mill adequate for the required milling efficiency of chars on an industrial scale [15,16].

2. Characteristics of char

The basic properties of the char intended for the examinations are presented in Table 1. The char was obtained in an experimental plant for pyrolysis of organic waste operating periodically. The maximal pyrolysis temperature was 600 °C, and the residence time of waste in the reactor was 18 hours.

Table 1. Physico-chemical properties of the char.

Moisture content [%]	Ash content [%]	Volatile matter content [%]	Sulphur content [%]	Carbon content [%]	Hydrogen content [%]	BET specific surface area [m^2/g]
W	A	V	S	C	H	S_{BET}
1.1	20.2	2.2	2.66	76.3	0.95	50

Table 2. contains the determination results of particle size distribution for the char before grinding, and Fig.1 shows a typical SEM image of the char with the results of elemental analysis. The particle size distribution of the char was determined with the use of the dry method, according to the standards PN-71/C-04501 and PN-ISO 2395-2000, by means of a laboratory vibratory screen.

Table 2. Particle size distribution of the char before grinding.

Size fraction [mm]	>1.6	1.6-1.0	1.0-0.63	0.63-0.40	0.40-0.315	0.315-0.10	0.10-0.063	<0.063
Yield of size fraction [%]	0.0	6.7	14.2	12.9	8.8	6.4	32.2	18.8

Figure 1 shows the results of examinations of char conducted by means of a field emission scanning electron microscope (FESEM) FEI QUANTA 200. The results of the elemental analysis are given in Figures 1B ÷ 1F. The char contains 76.3% of the carbon element and 20.2% of ash (Table 1). The presence of inorganic matter in the char is a result of applying mineral components for rubber blends. It is composed mainly of SiO_2, ZnO, CaO, Al_2O_3, Na_2O, and Fe_2O_3 [6]. Car tires subjected to pyrolysis were not cleaned at all; therefore, the char can also contain components originating from the impurities.

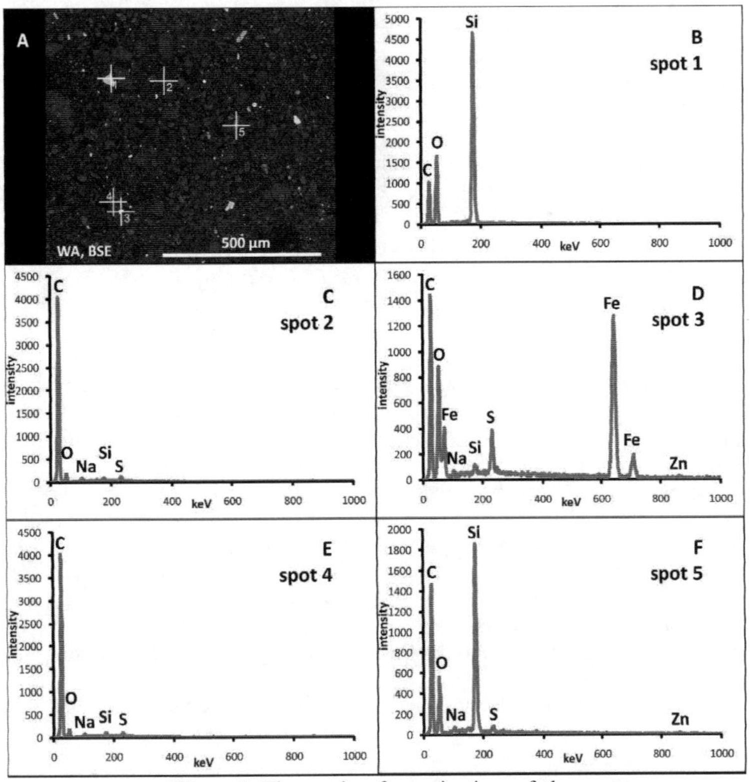

Figure 1. The results of examinations of char.

3. Objective and method of examination of char grinding

The main aim of the investigations was to obtain a ground char with a specific surface area close to that of activated carbon black and with the maximal particle size of 45 μm, at standard parameters of the mill, within the shortest possible grinding time. The material for grinding was a char from a periodically operating industrial plant for pyrolysis of organic waste, in which waste from worn out car tires was subjected to pyrolysis. The investigations of the process of char grinding were conducted in a laboratory vibratory mill, operating periodically, in a chamber with steel lining with the capacity of 2.2 dm^3. As the grinding media, steel balls were used. Their mass was 8 kg. The variable parameters were grinding time and mass of the char. Grinding time varied from 10 to 60 minutes, except one test where the grinding time was 120 minutes. The mass of the char was 0.32 kg in the sa1 to sa4 tests, and in the remaining ones it was 0.25 kg. The grinding was performed using the dry method, in a tightly-sealed chamber. The vibration frequency of the chamber was 14 Hz. The test stand with the original laboratory vibratory mill of low vibration frequency is presented in Figure 2.[13, 14].

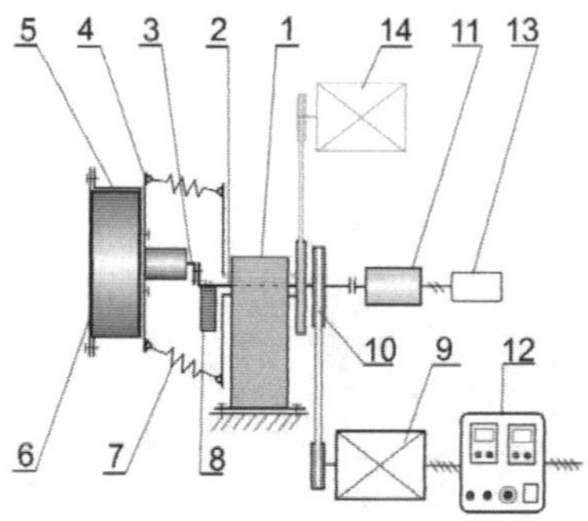

Figure 2. Constructional diagram of the vibratory mill: 1 - the unit of propulsion, 2 - the shaft of vibrator, 3 -the shaft of chamber, 4 - shield, 5 - chamber, 6 - cover of the chamber, 7 - clutch, 8 - filler, 9 - the engine of vibrator, 11 - sensor, 12 - the power system, 13 - measuring system, 14 - the engine of the chamber.

The test equipment enables investigations of the vibratory grinding process within a broad range of changes of technological parameters (in the conditions of air, inert gas, water and other liquids), stabilization of the temperature of the grinding process within the range of 20 ÷ 80 °C in chambers with capacities from 100 cm^3 to 5 dm^3 with a lining of steel and ceramics - corundum or polyamide). The parameters of vibratory motion can also be changed: the frequency of chamber vibrations within the range of 0 ÷ 25 Hz, the amplitude of chamber vibrations 2.5 ÷ 14 mm, and the chamber can also be set in additional rotary motion. The power output of the vibrator engine is 3.5 kW, and of the chamber engine (not used in these experiments), 0.75 kW - see item 14 in Figure 2.

4. Program, implementation and results of investigations

The program of preliminary investigations of char grinding involved the determination of char grinding process kinetics for the adopted mill parameters - these tests were labelled with symbols from sa1 to sa4, two tests with a lowered char mass (sa4 and sa8) and one test labelled sa9, with a grinding time two times longer when compared to the maximal time adopted in the grinding kinetics examinations. The kinetics of the grinding process concerned the impact of the char grinding time on the change of characteristic particle size fractions, particle size and the specific surface area.

The results of the investigations of particle size distribution of the char after grinding, determined with the use of an ANALYSETTE 22 apparatus (Fritsch), are shown in Table 3. Figures 4 and 5 represent the impact of the grinding time on the contents of particle size fractions 0-5 μm, 0-10 μm, as well as 0-20 μm, and the size of particles d_{97}, d_{90} and d_{50} of the char ground during particular tests. Figure 6 represents the particle size distribution for the char after 60 minutes of grinding in the test labelled as sa4.

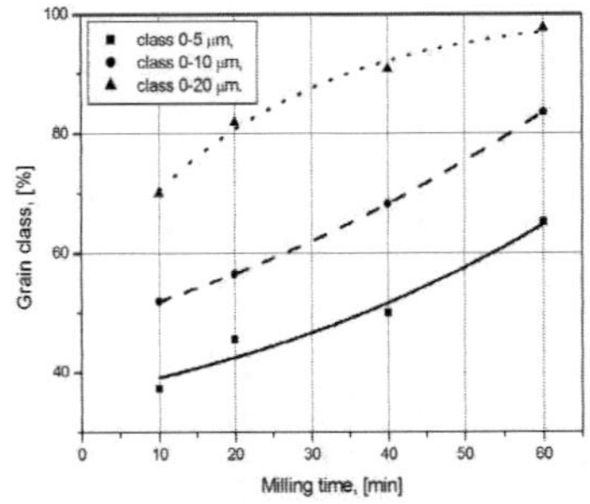

Figure 3. Impact of grinding time on size fractions content in tests sa1 – sa4.

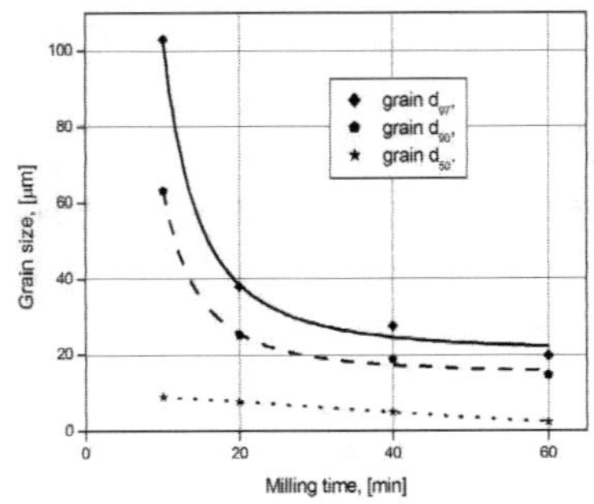

Figure 4. Impact of grinding time on particle sizes d_{97}, , d_{90}, and d_{50} in tests sa1 – sa4.

Table 3 provides also BET specific surface areas of the samples of ground char. The specific surface area results were obtained using the method of low temperature nitrogen sorption by means of a Micrometrics Gemini V 2380 apparatus. Nitrogen adsorption isotherms were determined at liquid nitrogen temperature, using nitrogen gas of 99.999% purity. Before the adsorption measurements, the samples were degassed at 200 °C for the removal of any incidentally adsorbed matter, and thus obtaining a clean surface for adsorption. The specific surface areas of the samples were calculated by means of the standard BET method using five data points on the adsorption isotherms in the P/P_0 range of 0.05 to 0.30 and taking the molecular cross-sectional area of 0.162 nm^2.

Table 3. Results of examinations of particle size distribution of the char after different grinding times.

Sample → Particle size	sa1	sa2	sa3	sa4	sa6	sa8	sa9
d_{10} [μm]	0.86	0.79	0.68	0.51	0.78	0.67	0.79
d_{37} [μm]	4.84	4.04	2.65	1.47	3.00	2.49	2.59
d_{50} [μm]	9.29	7.87	5.01	2.52	5.50	4.53	4.28
d_{80} [μm]	33.46	19.03	14.18	8.79	16.26	14.40	14.91
d_{90} [μm]	35.00	25.14	19.85	13.32	22.79	21.98	22.63
d_{99} [μm]	124.99	40.91	31.92	23.41	30.78	38.07	49.42
BET specific surface area [m^2/g]	74	88	103	141	140	141	163
Grinding time [min]	10	20	40	60	60	60	120

The impact of grinding time on the change of the specific surface area of the char is shown in figure 5. The specific surface area of the char before grinding was 50 m^2/g.

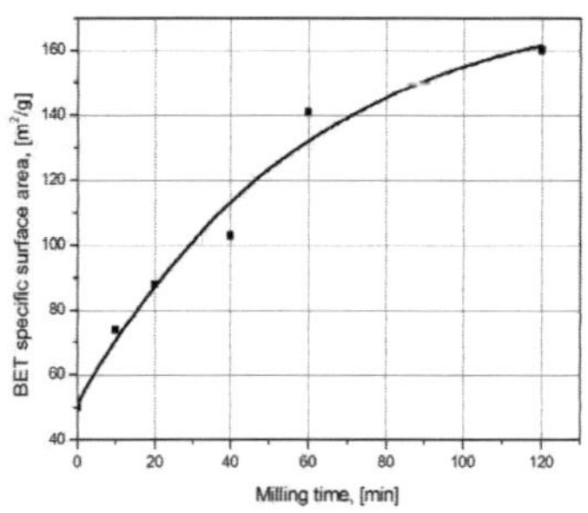

Figure 5. Impact of grinding time on the specific surface area of the char.

Observations and chemical analyses were performed using a FEI QUANTA 200 Field Emission Gun Scanning Electron Microscope (SEM) equipped with an energy dispersive spectrometer in the Phase, Structural, Textural and Geochemical Analyses Laboratory at the Faculty of Geology, Geophysics, and Environmental Protection, AGH University of Science and Technology (Krakow, Poland). Analytical conditions included low vacuum, accelerating voltage of 20 kV, 10 mm working distance, and secondary electrons (SE) imaging of particles sprinkled on the SEM mount with an adhesive carbon duct tape.
Figure 6 represents typical SEM images of the char from the tests sa2, sa8 and sa9.

IOP Conf. Series: Materials Science and Engineering **641** (2019) 012022 doi:10.1088/1757-899X/641/1/012022

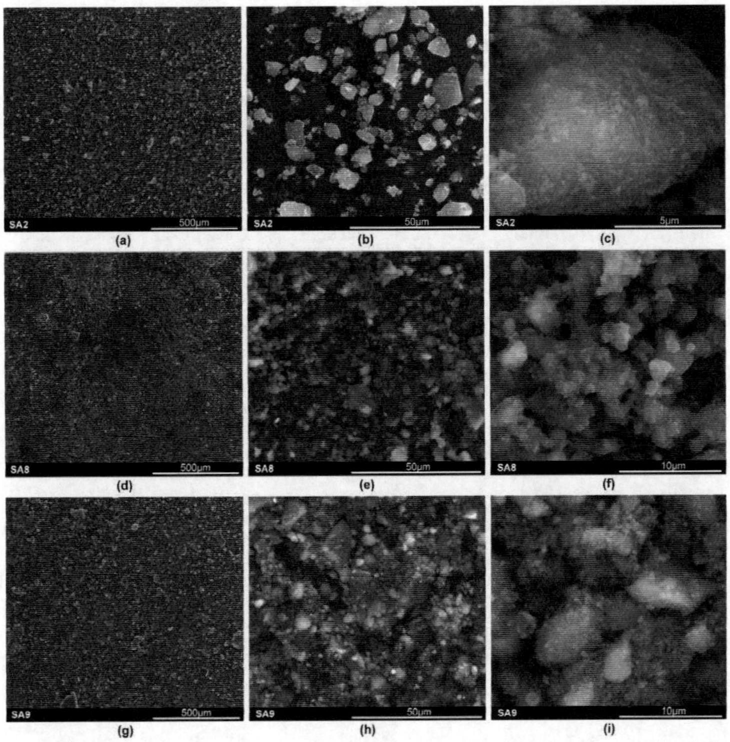

Figure 6. SEM images of the char after grinding tests: a, b, c - after 20 minutes of grinding; d, e, f - after 60 minutes of grinding; g, h, i, - after 120 minutes of grinding.

5. Conclusions

The results of preliminary investigations of char grinding conducted in a laboratory vibratory mill confirmed the possibility to use it for a very fine grinding of that material. The results of the examinations of particle size distribution of ground char contained in Table 3 as well as in Figures 3 and 4 indicate a clear impact of the grinding time on the selected size fractions and characteristic sizes of particles d_{50}, d_{80}, d_{90} and d_{99}. After 20 minutes of char grinding (test sa2), a 99% concentration of particles below 31.92 μm was obtained, while, for carbon black this requirement concerns particles of 45 μm. An increase in the grinding time up to 60 minutes (test sa6) reduced the upper limit of particle size to 23.41 μm. The results of microscopic observations (SEM) presented in Figure 7 indicate a very high dispersion ratio and the occurrence of large amounts of particles with sizes below 10 μm and 5 μm.

In accordance with the standard ASTM D1765, activated carbon black should have a specific surface area from 71 m^2/g to 130 m^2/g. The lower value of that range can be obtained in a vibratory mill already within 10 minutes of grinding. The char ground for 60 minutes had, in each of the tests, a specific surface area which was greater by nearly 8% (140 m^2/g) than the required maximal value of the specific surface area of carbon black. The specific surface area was greater by about 90 m^2/g than the specific surface area of the char before grinding (50 m^2/g). The increase of grinding time up to 120 minutes resulted in a growth of the surface area by only 23 m^2/g, without a significant change of the particle size distribution.

The particle size distribution and the specific surface area of a char are basic and indispensable, but, at the same time, not the only parameters determining its usefulness as a component for producing rubber. Therefore, in order to determine if a char is fully useful as a substitute of carbon black, it is necessary to examine the remaining properties, such as: iodine number, tinctorial strength, pH, and DBP number. The final result of determining the usefulness of the char for the production of rubber will be verified through examinations of its impact on physical and quality properties of rubber blends and rubber products.

In the paper it has been demonstrated that a char obtained from waste tires can be used to produce a material with the basic parameters (particle size distribution and specific surface area) similar to those of activated carbon black applied in the rubber industry. It has also been shown that a vibratory mill allows obtaining a char with a varying particle size distribution, including a significant amount of size fraction with dimensions of the order of a few dozen nanometers. It means that in a vibratory mill, a machine with a simple structure and a low power input, it is possible to produce powdered char, which can be used not only as a component for rubber production, but also as a valuable material for other purposes, e.g. as a component for manufacturing pigments , water-coal suspensions, a filler for polymer materials, as well as an adsorbent for removing mercury or other impurities. As a result, it is possible to reduce the costs of recycling of waste tires.

References

[1] Krajowy plan gospodarki odpadami 2022, Warszawa, 2016, Załącznik do uchwały nr 88 Rady Ministrów z dnia 1 lipca 2016 r. (poz. 784)

[1] S. Stelmach (2011) Potencjalne metody zagospodarowania karbonizatów z opon samochodowych, Archiwum Gospodarki Odpadami i Ochrony Środowiska, 13 (2011) 37-52.

[2] S. Budzyń, J. Jakóbiec, B. Tora, W. Żmuda, (2013) Laboratory analysis of rubber wastes in order to their utilization in energy sector, AGH Journal of Mining and Geoengineering, 37 (2013) 9-13.

[3] K. Jastrząb, S. Stelmach, J. Figa, (2013) Adsorbenty węglowe otrzymane ze zużytych opon przeznaczone do usuwania rtęci z gazów spalinowych, http://www.is.pcz.czest.pl/konferencje/weg2013/2008/19 (26.07.2019).

[4] Stanisław Budzyń, Barbara Tora (2015) Analysis of carbon black from tires pyrolysis, Inżynieria Mineralna = Journal of the Polish Mineral Engineering Society ; ISSN 1640-4920. — 2015 R. 16 nr 2, s. 149-154.

[5] Stanisław Budzyń, Victor Iwanicki, Andrzej Sumara, Wieslaw Żmuda, Christian d'Emal (2012) *Procédé de transformation de caoutchouc pour produire du carbonisat semi-actif et du plastifiant.* [Rubber granulate conversion process for producing a semi-active carbonized substance and a plasticizer] Patent, FR 2946054 B1

[6] Stanisław Budzyń, Victor Iwanicki, Andrzej Sumara, Wiesław Żmuda, d'Emal Christian, (2012) Rubber granulate conversion process for producing a semi–active carbonized substance and a plasticizer, Patent US 2012136112 A1 http://patenty.bg.agh.edu.pl/pelneteksty/US20120136112A1.pdf

[7] Jan J. Hycnar, Karel Honysch, Barbara Tora, Stanisław Budzyń (2017) – Physico-chemical Characteristics of Selected Alternative Fuels and their Mixtures with Carbon Fuels, Inżynieria Mineralna – Journal of the Polish Mineral Engineering Society, No 2(40), pp. 201-206

[8] Juan Daniel Martínez, Neus Puy, Ramón Murillo et all (2013) Waste tire pyrolysis – A review, Renewable and Sustainable Energy Reviews 23:179–213, DOI 10.1016/j.rser.2013.02.038

[9] Jaswinder Singh (2017) A review paper on pyrolysis process of waste tire, International Journal of Applied Research 2017; 1(13): 258-262

[10] N Cardona, F Campuzano, M Betancur, L Jaramillo and J D Martínez (2018) Possibilities of carbon black recovery from waste tire pyrolysis to be used as additive in rubber goods -a

review, IOP Conf. Series: Materials Science and Engineering 437 (2018) 012012 doi:10.1088/1757-899X/437/1/012012

[11] Barbara Tora, Stanisław Budzyń, Wiesław Żmuda, Peter Fecko, Vlastimil Kriz., (2013), The methode of organic waste pyrolysis oils utilisation] Patent PL 214925 B1 http://patenty.bg.agh.edu.pl/pelneteksty/PL214925B1.pdf

[12] Xue Zhang, Hengxiang Li, Qing Cao, (2018) Upgrading pyrolytic residue from waste tires to commercial carbon black, Waste Management & Research, 2018, Vol. 36(5) 436–444 DOI: 10.1177/0734242X18764292

[13] Jan Sidor, (2005) Badania, modele i metody projektowania młynów wibracyjnych, Rozprawy Monografie nr 150, UWND AGH, Kraków 2005

[14] Jan Sidor, (2014) Preliminary studies of production of glass micropowder in a vibratory mill, Materiały Ceramiczne - Ceramic Materials 66 (2014) 292-297.

[15] J. Sidor, (2011) The development of powder producing technology with using the vibratory mills, Powder & Bulk - Materiały Sypkie i Masowe; ISSN 1899-2021. - 2011 wyd. spec. [SyMas 2011], s. 19-23.

[16] Jan Sidor (2011) Projecting of vibrating mills. Advanced grinding: 25 th anniversary of the comminution in Bydgoszcz, eds. A. Mroziński, M. Macko, Wyd. Fundacji Rozwoju Mechatroniki, Bydgoszcz p. 225-24.

Acknowledgements
The research was supported by AGH University of Science and Technology under a subsidy No. 16.16.100. 215 and 16.16.210.476

Physical separation methods, Part 1: A Review

N Poloko

Department of Chemicals, Materials & Metallurgical Engineering, Botswana International University of Science and Technology, Private Bag 6, Palapye 10071, Botswana

Email: nengubap@biust.ac.bw

Abstract. Herein, the importance of physical separation methods of ores in mineral processing is widely acknowledged. Of interest is the magnetic separation, gravity concentration and sensor-based separation methods. The process of separating elements of value from gangue in ores depends on its chemical nature and mineralogical attributes hence the need for a profound characterization prior to physical separation. Some ores especially copper sulphides are readily available in nature in low grades usually less < 1% while some may appear relatively in small isolated deposits (Baba et al, 2012). Therefore, it is costly to extract a small portion of a purified metal from such ores. To circumvent high energy and costs when conducting relevant extraction operations, ores directly from mines can be processed physically before smelting, leaching, purifying or other recovery processes. Most physical separation plants and processes are adjunct to the mines to avoid transportation of a heavy ore with only a small portion of valuables. The aim of this review is to present an understanding on physical separation methods with emphasis on how they take advantage of ore physical properties to achieve separation. In addition, developments of these methods with growing technology is also presented.

1. Introduction

Extractive processes done on ores after mining activities are smelting, hydrometallurgy, floatation and electro-technologies. Due to diminution of high grade metal ores, extracting valuables directly from ores without physical separation practices first, consumes high energies and are costly processes. Therefore, physical separation techniques are important as they increase the metal grade and makes it easier to render valuables from gangue materials. The physical separation can be achieved by a few processes which includes; gravity concentration, dense medium separation, magnetic separation, sensor-based separation etc. These processes take advantages of the ore physical properties such as shape, size, density, color or light adsorption, magnetic susceptibility, and electrical conducting properties etc. For instance, particles of magnetite although they are minute, they are highly magnetic and if passed through poles of a magnet they will attach to that magnetic material, this magnetic property they exhibit allows them to be removed from gangue material with ease [2].

Physical separation follows crushing, a particle size reduction activity which liberates particles and increase surface areas. This is of benefit to separation processes and for drastic increase in chemical reaction rates during concentration. In physical separation of ores, a metal concentrate is attained without chemical decomposition since it does not occur at molecular level but rather it involves separation of aggregates [3]. The run of mine ores are readily available with non-uniform constituents and mostly available as low grades <1% to utilize for economic purposes or worst case scenario may even be too course to process. Considering the structure of chalcopyrite, which is $CuFeS_2$ and according to atomic weight, 1 part of copper entails 3.46 parts of chalcopyrite. Taking account that the chemistry of chalcopyrite is not changed during physical processing, a Cu-concentrate with 29% ([1/3.46] *100) copper grade will be achieved. If copper was to be extracted from the very same chalcopyrite through smelting or dissolving chemically enormous heat will be required hence high cost. Physical separation can be considered dry or wet depending on the requirement of water (wet) as the processing medium. Most of physical separation process requires large volume except a few such as electrostatic methods (dry). In wet processing it is important to have water treatment plants connected in series with the physical separation plants so that water can be purified and recycled for the next batch of the physical separation process.

2. Physical separation methods

Valuable minerals can be separated from gangue materials by means of physical separation. Some physical separation techniques such as gravity concentration have been in practice as early as sixteenth century. Egyptians monuments from 3000 BC also depicts the use of film concentration used in the washing of gold. Evidence of further theoretical and experimentations on physical separation methods is believed to have been performed in nineteenth century (Aplan F, F, 2003)

Physical separation methods such as medium separation, magnetic separation, gravity concentration and sensor-based separation method can be applied to fresh ores from mines or tailings or even recycling plants for scavenging useful elements. Fig 1. Shows a typical scavenging flow sheet for a combination of processes from stockpiles of metallurgical wastes to physical separation techniques.

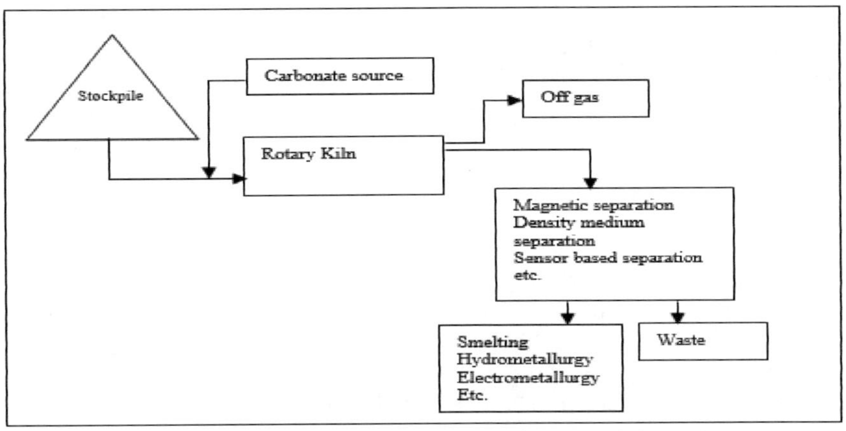

Figure 1. Process flow for waste materials.

2.1. Gravity Concentration

This is a natural geological separation process that takes advantage of gravity or centrifugal force to separate mixed particles either in suspension or in dry condition. These particles are usually of different shapes, sizes and specific gravity being the latter. The property of density is paramount during separation, but size and shape of the components also plays a significant role in separation efficiency. If there is a wide variation on these properties, then separation is affected [5]. The most prominent advantage about this method is its low operational cost and reduction efficiencies. Literature has shown that more on gravity concentration is yet to be studied. Nonetheless, some countries like USA use roughly about 25% for degritting coal and most ores by this method more than its counterpart, which is flotation [3]. Other applications of gravity separation techniques are in industries for separating food grains, in paper pulp, toxic waste pipes, recycling solid waste etc. The principle of gravity concentration center around utilizing specific gravities of particles for success separation but to some extent can also take account of some physical properties such as size and shape

[3, 5]. The best working range for gravity concentration is course particle size of 130 mm- 74μm. Fine particles (< 74 μm) are difficult to treat by gravity separation method. The settling kinetics of finer particles is quite slow [6]. Mineral processors use the concept of concentration criterion to determine the suitability of gravity concentration on particles below it can be applied. This criterion is defined as the CC equation 1. Given below.

$$CC = \frac{\text{SG(heavy mineral)}-\text{SG(fluid)}}{SG(light\ mineral)-SG(fluid)} \quad \text{.........(1)[8]}$$

And if CC is greater than 2.5, then the separator is suitable for working with particle size above 74 μm, for CC in the range 1.75 -2.5 the separator can work with particle size above 150 μm while any CC value between 150-1.75 the separator is suitable for degritting particles above 1.7 mm by size. For CC from 1.25-1.50 by value the working size for a separator is above 6.35 mm. If the value of CC is 1.25 then the separator is considered not suitable for any size [8].

Recent research and developments to focuses more on invention of devices that accommodates for finer particles [6]. Physical properties of ore particles dictates their behavior when subjected various degritting devices. Some concentrating devices and corresponding size particles they work well with are given in table 1.

Table 1. Concentrating devices and corresponding size ranges [3].

Course +6.4 mm	Intermediate 6.4-100mm	Fine concentration -0.150 mm
Jigs, Heavy media, handheld device, Heavy media hydrocyclone, hindered-settling classifier, pneumatic jigs etc.	Jigs, heavy media hydrocyclone, water-only cyclone, Sluices, shaking tables, Humphreys-type spirals, cannon concentrator etc.	Kelsey Jigs, Round table, vanners. Cannon concentrator, Reichert cone, falcon concentrator, Mozley multigravity concentrator etc.

2.1.1. Mechanics of gravity concentration. This method separates particles with different specific gravities. Specific gravity is simply the ratio of a particle's density to some standard fluid usually with s a unit equal to 1 [7]. According to Thomas, J (1978), the law of specific gravity was discovered by Archimedes in about 250 BC. The findings on this discovery were that if a floating particle is submerged in a liquid, the force that buoy the particle is equal to the to the weight of the liquid they displace. In mineral processing this principle is applied to separate components of differing gravities when lifted by a vacuum over a screen with vibrational effects. This leads to a lighter material being suspended in air while heavier impurities remain on the screen and are discarded out. Separation can be achieved in 2 main ways i) subjecting finely liberated particles in dry conditions under a gravitational or centrifugal force that enhances the settling kinetics of these particles, this is known as hydraulic separation and ii) subjecting particles to a wet media with a counter current flow which affect the fluid-particle interaction leading to a hindered settling phenomenon. The wet media is usually water, and this is known as pneumatic separation. Water has a high density which make separation in wet sharper than in dry conditions though it requires dehydration of the concentrate and tailings after separation [5, 8]. This problem is common during coal cleaning which results in the product with 10 % moisture. On the other hand, when using hydraulic separation, concentration can be achieved in a short period of time mainly because the centrifugal forces enhances gravity making particles to arrange and settle in the radial direction (Sarkar et al, 2018) . Particles can experience a free settling or hindered settling phenomenon. In hindered settling there is resistance due to a pull force from external sources while in free settling the particles to be separated falls freely without any opposing forces from other particles. Assuming spherical particles under separation, a Newtonian relationship has been developed to calculate the terminal or free settling velocity of these free falling particles.

2.2. Magnetic separation (M-S)

Magnetic separation is applied in ore processing for separating magnetic materials, particularly Iron [4]. The advent of magnetic separation found favour in mineral processing for over 200 years ago. The knowledge and use of magnetic concepts can be traced back to Thales of Miletus, A Greek philosopher, mathematician and an astronomer who lived from c. 624 – 546 B.C [9]. In this approach, separation of particles is archived by passing finely liberated ore particles through a spectrum of a magnetic field preferably of sufficient magnitude. The resulting effect is the retention of magnetic particles (paramagnetic) to the vicinity of the separator's magnetic component. On the other hand non-magnetic (diamagnetic) components deflects and falls off. At least one component of the particles should have magnetic susceptibility properties thereby responding to a magnetic field. Iron and magnetite are strongly magnetic materials therefore classified in a special group called ferromagnets. A reddish bronze ore pyrrhotite, hematite, Ilmenite, Ferberite, Franklinite and siderite etc. are paramagnetic materials. Diamagnetic materials includes Silica, bismuth, cobaltite, and skutterudite etc. The most common application of this method is in separation of Iron and iron bearing substances, ferrous and non-ferrous containing materials [10]. The recovery process of magnetite ore from blast furnaces is not 100% efficient since massive tailings are produced with substantial amount of iron losses. According to estimations, about 1 tonne of iron ore recovered from beneficiation produces 400 kg of tailings containing Iron grade equal or marginally more than iron grade found in other iron ores exploited. Also discard from gravity concentration of iron-bearing ores contains >39 wt. % of iron (Dauce, P.D, 2018). Recovery rates of iron can be increased by processing of tailings using magnetic separators. Such a practice is fast, efficient and can be of economic benefits and helps reduce the volume of tailings in landfills which is of interest to environment sustainability [12].

2.2.1. Separation mechanism

A real practical example which demonstrate the concept of magnetic separation is very common in scrap yards for sorting metals. A heavy magnetic metal is used to lift only magnetic materials and what remains behind is the non-magnetic components. The magnet is so strong such that it can withstand the gravitational forces of components. In mineral separation, besides force of gravity there are some external competing forces such as centrifugal, inertia, hydrodynamic forces etc. These forces can hinder separation therefore for successful separation of strong magnetic particles, the magnitude of magnetic force of the separator must be greater than that of competing forces summed together. Whereas, for weak magnetic particles the force of the separator must be smaller than the sum of external competing forces (Svoboda, J, 2005). However the two divergent forces should be of comparable magnitude such that the difference is too small. Otherwise if there is a large difference between the magnetic force of the separators and sum of competing forces i.e. $F_{separator} \gg \Sigma F_{opposing}$, then separator cannot distinguish different magnetic components which respond differently to applied magnetic field. The attraction and deflection occurs along the line of a magnetic field until a point where the magnetic field intensity is large for paramagnets or small for diamagnetic components (Will, 2016). Another important factor in separation is the magnetic field gradient. Magnetic susceptible materials will mostly respond to a non-uniform field therefore the magnetic component of the separator should be capable of producing a significant field gradient (Wells, 1991).

2.2.2. Magnets for separators

The growing technology and research has led to development of more advanced tools for separation. Magnetic separators can be equipped with conventional magnets, permanent magnet and superconducting magnets depending on the physical attributes of components to be separated. The efficiency of the separator depends on the type of magnet used (its strength, to be specific), as well as the volume and magnetic susceptibility of the component.

Permanent magnets were developed to address problems associated with conventional magnets during processing. These types are also called rare earth magnets, have a much higher intensity and are capable of producing high magnetic field gradient as compared to conventional magnets. This enable them to separate weakly paramagnetic components. Permanent magnets manufactured around the 1970's were made of samarium and cobalt. With advancing manufacturing technology, engineers were able to design even high intensity rare earth magnets composed of neodymium, iron and boron. The two examples of the rare earth magnets are the rare-earth drum (RED) and the rare-earth roll (RER) magnets. RED is an NdFeB magnet with about 0.9 T strength that align uniquely to perpendicular to the drum surface. RED separates two or more weakly magnetic particles. RER has low operational capacity and effective in treatment of finer particles less than 1mm compared to its counterpart. This magnets on separators usually acts as pulley heads and as fines are fed on the pulley at higher velocities they experience a magnetic field which separates them according to their susceptibility (Dobbins et al, 2007). A typical separator installed with such magnets is the boxmag rapid mgnaroll magnetic separator. This separator was mostly commonly used for the removal of ash and sulphur containing components from coal (Wells, 1991). Another application is separation of iron bearing impurities from non-magnetic minerals. Permanent magnets can be applied separators for application in mining industries and solid state chemistry [15]. The latest permanent magnetic roll separator (permroll) is capable of producing field strength of up to 1.6 T.

Conventional magnets are divided into 2 main groups, the ones used in High intensity magnetic separators and the other group used in low intensity separators. These are designed to remove deleterious tramp iron components in mineral processing equipment's e.g. during production of silica, feldspar and zircon etc. it's necessary to remove iron that occurs alongside these compounds to avoid damage to the equipment. These magnets are capable of separating components of different susceptibility. High intensity magnetic separators are used for either wet or dry applications for separation of weakly magnetic particles with low susceptibilities (Norrgran, 1988). Magnets with such high intensities are used in Induced-roll separators (IRM), jones separators and Frantz Isodynamic separator. IRMs are for dry applications most commonly in sand circuits. But for better capacity the RERs are good replacement [14]. IRMS are used for cleaning of quarts, calcite and other non-magnetic particles by removing paramagnetic compounds with an attractive force of about 2.2 Tesla and high field gradient [17]. The Jones separator was designed for wet applications. In wet applications the main competing forces are the magnetic field force and the hydrodynamic drag forces (Shao et al, 1996). So for successful separation the field of the separator must be greater than the drag force. Jones separators have a plate-box like design with steel structure on the box edges mainly for support. The Jones separator is also grooved such that the magnetic field is concentrated on the tip of ridges and it can reach values above 2 Tesla. Addition to the list of conventional magnets for high intensity separators is the Frantz Isodynamic separator (FIS) which also separate mineral particles according to their magnetic susceptibility and how the individual particles in question behave towards applied field vs gravity. This process is effective but takes time and can only with particle size range of ~74 -700 μm. Otherwise very coarse will clog the separator. Conventional magnets can be applied in low intensity magnetic separators to produce flux densities around 0.2 T for mostly winning ferromagnetic particles such as magnetite, taconite and pyrrhotite etc. and other paramagnetic particles with high susceptibilities from non-magnetic materials. This low intensity separators can also be done in wet and dry applications. Examples of the low intensity are the protective (dry) (figure 3) and wet magnetic separators. The protective magnets are installed on conveyer heads mainly for removal of tramp magnetic materials from diamagnetic materials. To date most coal industries apply these technique to separate coal from magnetite in wet conditions. Traditionally low intensity wet separators have been used as the workhorse for winning iron from its ore magnetite.

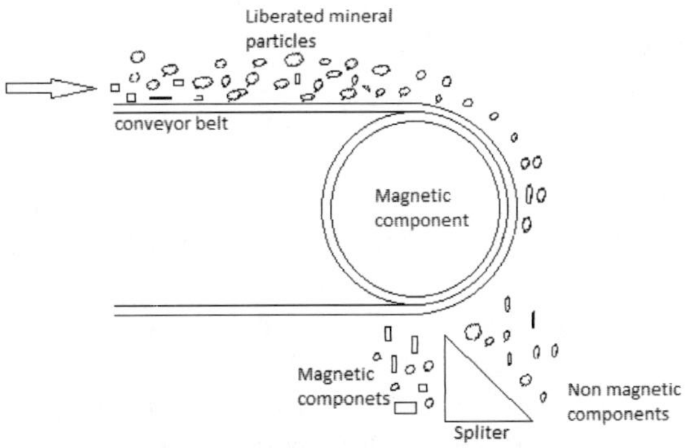

Figure 2. Removal of tramp magnetic materials by protective magnets [4].

Though traditional permanent magnets are still widely applied in separators for mineral processing, they are limited to other applications e.g. separation of relatively weak magnetic components against hydrodynamic and opposing forces especially under liquid and gaseous streams has its own problems and complexity. This has made significant demands on the manufacturing industry to design more stronger and efficient magnets**.** Fortunately the magnet technology has expanded well enough to produce strong **superconducting magnets** that can produce more than twice the magnetic field of permanent magnets (up to 5 tesla). This permits for separation of small particles in liquid or gaseous streams [20]. Though some text dates the use of first conductor with strength of up to 20 T in 1950 in physics and research astronomy community [19], the first reported superconductor used in the USA was 1986 mainly for minerals and in 1986 they successfully installed a superconductor separator with twice the magnetic field as the previous. In the following years these separators started to get attention in Germany and Brazil [21]. The magnetic field of superconductors is produced by inducing an electrical current through resistive coil. They can also be generated by permanent magnets. The field strength is maxed my altering the geometry of magnets. However but both the solenoid coil and the permanent magnet have limits, for instance the magnetic field of the resistive coil is limited by windings which produce some form of intrinsic resistance (Vankatraman, 2004). In operation of superconductor separators, low power is required for cooling rather than to offset the ohmic losses from the magnet's coil. So the use of these separators offers great economic efficiency which is proportional to the field strength. (Svoboda, 2005) One distinct feature of the superconducting separators it the solenoid coil. Examples of the superconducting magnets includes the high gradient wet magnetic separator (HGMS) and the Open gradient dry separator (OGMS). OG separators offers deep strong magnetic field which renders for large volume for separation. The magnet can be inclined such that feed material falls over and as they reach the neighbourhood of the magnetic zones deflection of the magnetisable species in an inhomogeneous manner according to their size and magnetic susceptibilities. So with this separators the geometry of the magnet makes it easy to generate the required field gradient for rather than incorporating a matrix (Svoboda). The HGMS offers a higher magnetic intensity mainly form the superconductor coil instead of a solenoid coil used for open gradient separators. Contrary to a read by Vankatraman, (2004) the coil has no resistance so much lower power is required to charge the magnet. This coil is also capable of storing energy which enables a once off charge. The trapped particles are removed using a ram, so step determines the separation efficiency of the magnet. The magnet also allows for charge and discharge incase for demagnetization purposes at the end of the separation cycle (Svoboda, 2005).

2.2.3. Magnetic separation equipment.

Magnetic separation equipment has been classified accordingly as 3 main groups namely; equipment for tramp iron removal, magnetic separation equipment for purification or concentration and lastly equipment designed for product cleaning. Tramp iron separators act as protection to handling and processing devices such as screens, crushers, pulverizing machines etc. in mineral processing mainly to avoid abrasion wear, discolouration or contamination by tramp iron. These should be applied on materials which are dry or with surface moisture. The separators for tramp iron removal includes rare earth magnets applied in pulleys of conveyor belts, plates magnets found in chutes, grate magnets incorporated and various magnetic drums that are installed as separate units in separators [23]. Concentration equipment such as magnetic pulley separator, magnetic drums, induced roll magnets, wet intensity magnetic separators and high gradient magnetic separator (HGMS). HGMS can be used for purifying limestone and other minerals such as kaolinite. Concentration separators can also be used as cleaning separators and have been used for recovering elements that are lost along gangue materials. Some research conducted in mid-90s shows that Boliden Mineral AB had a high gradient magnetic separation installed adjunct to the flotation tank to recover zinc lost along lead concentrate after flotation of their main target product copper.

2.3. Sensor based separation method

Sensor based separation commonly known as sensor based sorting is a dry separation technology for separation of coal, diamonds and various minerals according to physical properties calibrated on the sensor. These properties include reflectance, color, magnetism, atomic density, visual fluorescence brightness etc. (Wills, 2016). The principle of the particle detection technology is simply the actuation of impulses of the detector by identification of sample particles which report back ''yes/no'' ejection decisions [25]. First, individual particles are eminently identified by a sensor followed by rejection mechanisms of an amplified mechanical or pneumatic processes [26 Hand sorting in some extent can be considered as a conventional technique for sensor based separation. Hand sorting involves the sorting on mineral particles based on visual examination while sensor based it the automation counterpart. Hand sorting has been years ago in mining separation but due to the demand of processing of extremely low grade ores and fine particles its application has declined with time and growing technology. However hand sorting can still be applied as a preliminary separation technique e.g the removal of timber components from tramp iron. It is also still applied in countries with low pay rates (Wills mineral processing, 2016) . According to research there is evidence of patents from late 1920s that proves the application of optical based sorting (a technology along the lines of sensor based sorting) to have a long history in mineral processing. Application of sensor based separation techniques in mineral processing without any doubts offer a wide range of advantages. The use of such a technique addresses certain challenges by other separation methods. The use of this method results in improvement of critical areas i.e. consumes less energy, solves ore dilution problems, reduced water usage and environmental impacts (Mahlangu et al, 2016). From processing of fines point of view traditional sensor based methods have lost popularity since the development of more advanced sensor based separators. Modern separators solves limitations associated with previous techniques such as inability to separate a media with both coarse and fine particles, Impreciseness resulting from fluctuating particle movements and conventional sensors are limited to separation by color variations [26]. The diamond industry profit from using this technique to separate diamond from its ore kimberlite. This method on separation of diamonds enables the removal of waste rocks embedded in its ore which deems difficult with other separation techniques [27].

Sensor based sorters are divided in accordance to the work they form. Use of conventional techniques poses significant challenges hence the ideology of development of efficient and sustainable techniques to address challenges in question while maximizing profit e.g. Development of high temperature sensors to increase durability in high temperature applications, introduction of sensors for processing fines and many more to reduce energy usage and improves life of mine in a challenging landscape. The two main sorter are the chute-type and belt type figure 3a and 3b respectively. Other types include the channel-type, bucket-wheel type and the cone-typer sortes. In the chute-type sensor the ore particles are introduced to the sensor system through an inclined chute of some angle sufficient enough to allow for free fall. Before the particles reach the reject or accept chambers they encounter an optical beam of the sensor mounted on both sides to allow detection of properties on both sides. The belt system consists of a moving belt in a fixed point like a pulley system. Particles are introduced into the belt on one end and allowed to settle prior to detection on the other end by a sensor fixed on a location above belt. Because there is enough settling time this gives a better resolution as compared to the chute -type system [28].

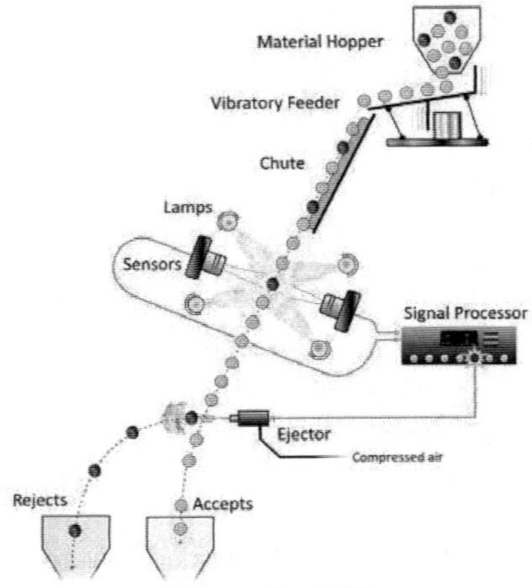

Figure 3a [29]

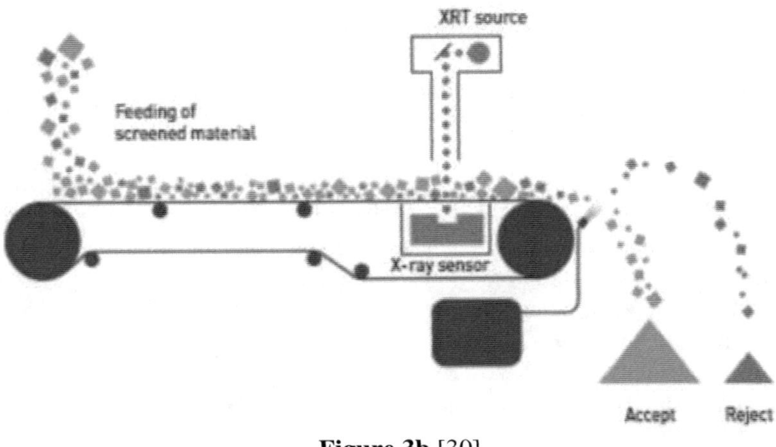

Figure 3b [30]

These types can be further classified according to two groups which are transmitting and reflecting technologies. The reflection system is composed of the optical camera which captures particles according to surface features while the X-ray of the transmission system identifies particles in accordance to the difference in density. ''Yes or no'' decision causes the individual particles to be removed from the mainstream through the mechanism of air jels [25]. The transmitting technology analyses the inner constituent's features of individual particles while the reflecting scans and interprets surface information. So with reflecting technology the sample particles need to be free from contaminants as much as possible for accurate interpretation of information. The main disadvantages of reflecting types the inability to achieve 100% probability of detecting all components of the particle. Examples of transmitting technologies include but are not limited to X-ray transmission (XRT), electromagnetic sensor (EM). X-ray luminescence is a reflecting sorter.

2.3.1. XRT

It is a dry separation process that identifies materials based on particle properties such as specific atomic density, regardless of its size, moisture content or pollution level. XRT is capable of sorting high atomic mass particles and also provides high quality data of both the internal structure and information on contaminants (Kolacz, 2012). It is used in sorting or separation of diamonds, gold, coal and sulphide ores. It upgrades the grade of gold especially in gold bearing sulphide. Crushed ore particles are fed into screens prior to introduction onto a conveyor belt (belt-type sorter). The XRT for identification is equipped with an x-ray source such as an electrical tube which creates a broad-band radiation that penetrates the material and provides absorption data. This data which records on the x-ray camera as a digital dense image. The material is scanned at a rate of about 3m/s. The sensor system consists of 2 distinct channels which records the image depending on energy levels i.e. one captures images of low density while the other captures high density images so thickness and atomic weight of particles plays a major role in quantification in this process. Density is usually measured as shades of grey. The commands instructions of the system then allows the valves to open and close for the identified particles to exit the system. The individual identified material is pulled from the rest of the material by jets or compressed air. Materials separates in two different chambers the ''reject'' and "accepted''. An example of the XRT such as the dual energy x-ray transmission (DE-XRT) is very useful in separation of coal from torbanite which often results in contamination of coal. This separation also removes pyrite sulphur (Ketelhodt et al, 2010, tombra ref). Another application of this automatic sorting technique is in classification of base metals according to respective atomic densities of the constituents (Mesina et al 2006).

2.3.2. Near-infrared (NIR)

It is a recent technology in the world of mineral processing and mining industry (mahlangu). It analyses materials based on particle behavior under reflected light in the near infrared spectrum of the sensor. NIR spectroscopy of the sorter analyzes information such as chemical compositions as well as the context of associations and occurrence. The belt moving at 3m/s usually accommodates a throughput of up to 300tonn/hr with particles sizes not greater than 300mm due to mechanical constraints. The working principle of the NIR is simply the emittance of radiation from the NIR source above the belt. The radiation then penetrates the material and a polygon mirrors mounted perpendicular to the belt axes reflects point signals to the spectrometer of the detector unit. The mirror is mounted such that it allows for rotation so that the point scanner covers the whole belt width. the data is interpreted by the spectrometer as a hypercube with 3 point coordinate x, y and λ (spectral response) (Robben 2012).There are well known advantages associated with the use of NIR such as lo operational cost, non-destructive, offers reduced processing time in mineral processing and provides higher resolution and extended frequency ranges [36]. It can be applied to discriminate between kimberlite and waste materials.

3. Summary

Physical processing of ores is important in mineral processing. Physical processes offers a wide range of advantages when rendering elements of values from low grades ores such as energy efficiency, reduced processing time, ability to separate finer particles etc. This enables mines to up its economic reserves. Some ores naturally occurs as low grades and extraction of minerals of interest from these ores with smelting, hydrometallurgy and electrorifing processes is very costly. Separation of the ore physically prior to these activities helps reduce the operational cost and ease up extraction processes. Physical sorting is important as a start-up activity. From the listed physical separation methods, a choice of sorting technique to use is selected based on the nature of ore, its size particles after crushing and surface properties and other physical properties.

References

[1] Baba, A. A., Ayinla, I. K., Adekola, F. A., Ghosh, M. K., Ayanda, O. S., Bale, B. R., Sheik, A. R., and Pradhan, S. R., A Review on Novel Techniques for Chalcopyrite, International Journal of Mining Engineering and Mineral Processing, vol. 1, pp. 1-16, 2012.A

[2] [Mastermagnets.com. (2019). Magnetic Separators For Mineral Process | Master Magnets. [online] Available at: https://www.mastermagnets.com/magnetic-separators-for-mineral-processing/ [Accessed 04 Jun. 2019].

[3] Ahindra Ghosh, Hem Shanker Ray, Principles of extractive metallurgy,

[4] Aplan, F.F, chapter 6, principles of mineral processing, society for mining, metallurgy, and exploration, Inc. (SME), Littleton, Colarado, USA, 2003.

[5] Triple/S Dynamics. (2019). How Gravity Separators Work | Density Separation Equipment. [online] Available at: https://www.sssdynamics.com/resources/news-and-articles/genius-action-gravity-separators-work-part-ii/ [Accessed 30 Jun. 2019].

[6] Das, A and Sarkar, B, Advanced Gravity Concentration of Fine Particles: A Review, An International Journal, Vol. 39, no. 6, pp 359–394, 2018.

[7] Thomas, J, Principles of gravity separation, Oliver Manufacturing Company, Rocky Ford, Colarado.

[8] Balasubramanian, A, Gravity separation in ore dressing, Centre for Advanced Studies in Earth Science, University of Mysore, Mysore, 2017.

[9] Svoboda, J, Magnetic Techniques for the treatment of materials: Science and Technology (2nd Edition), Kluwer Publishers, pp 1-7, 2005

[10] Rao, S.R.R, Resource Recovery and Recycling from Metallurgical Wastes, Technology and Engineering, 2011.

[11] Dauce, P.D, de Castro, G.B, Lima, M.M.F and Lima, R.M.F, Characterisation and magnetic concentration of an iron ore tailings, Journal of Materials Research and Technology, Volume 8, Issue 1,pp 1052-1059 ,2018

[12] Wills, B.A, Chapter 13: Magnetic and Electrical Separation, Wills' Mineral Processing Technology: An Introduction to the Practical Aspects of Ore Treatment and Mineral Recovery, Seventh Edition, 2016.

[13] Wells, I.S, Application of rare earth magnets in mineral processing, Gordon and Breach Science Publishers S.A, Magnetic and Electrical Separation, Vol. 3, pp. 105-111, 1991

[14] Dobbins, M., Domenico, J., and Dunn, P. A discussion of magnetic separation techniques for concentrating ilmenite and chromite ores. The 6th International Heavy Minerals Conference 'Back to Basics', The Southern African Institute of Mining and Metallurgy, 2007.

[15] Iranmanesh, M and Hulliger, J, Magnetic separation: its application in mining, waste purification, medicine, biochemistry and chemistry, Chem. Soc. Rev, Vol 46, pp 5925-5934, 2017.

[16] Norrgran, J.A and Wernham, Production and Processing of Fine Particles, proceedings of Metallurgical Society of Canadian Institute of Mining and Metallurgy, Montreal, August 28–31, 1988.

[17] Mastermagnets.com. (2019). Magnetic Separators For Mineral Process | Master Magnets. [online] Available at: https://www.mastermagnets.com/magnetic-separators-for-mineral-processing/ [Accessed 07 Jun. 2019].

[18] Shao, Y, Veasey, T.J and Rowson, N.A, Wet high intensity magnetic separation of iron minerals, Magnetic and Electrical Separation, Vol.8, pp.41-51, 1996

[19] Anon, (2019). [Online] Available at: https://www.researchgate.net/profile/Arvind_Singh56/post/Heavy.../1.pdf [Accessed 7 Jun. 2019].

[20] Beharrell, P.A, Applications of Superconducting Magnetic Separation, Cooperate headquarters, Quantum Design Inc, San diego, USA

[21] Watson, J.H.P, Status of superconducting magnetic separation in the minerals industry, Journal

of Minerals Engineering, Vol 7, pp 737-746, 1994.
[22] Svoboda, J, Chapter 2 , A review on magnetic separators, Magnetic Techniques for the treatment of materials: Science and Technology (2nd Edition), Kluwer Publishers, pp 130-133, 2005
[23] Morgan, D.G and Bronkala, W.J, The selection and application of magnetic separation euipment. Part I, Applied Magnetic Systems, Inc., Greenfield, Magnetic and Electrical Separation, Vol. 3, pp. 5-16, 1991.
[24] Ciesla, A, Application of superconducting magnets to magnetic separation. some selected aspects, Electrical Power Institute, The Academy of Mining and Metallurgy, Cracow, Poland, Vol. 3, pp. 219-240, 1991
[25] Outotec.com. (2019). [online] Available at: https://www.outotec.com/globalassets/products/dry-comminution-and-sorting/ote_outotec_tomra_sensor-based_ore_sorting.pdf [Accessed 17 Jun. 2019].
[26] Kolacz, J, Wieniewski, A, Advanced separation methods in the X-ray-optical sorting systems, Cuprum Ore Mining Scientific and Technical Magazine, Vol 2 (75), pp 137-146, 2015.
[27] Mahlangu, T, Moemise, N, Ramokokovhu, M.M, Olubambi, Shongwe, M.B, Separation of kimberlite from waste rocks using sensor-based sorting at Cullinan Diamond Mine, Journal of the Southern African Institute of Mining and Metallurgy, Vol 116, 2016
[28] AusIMM Bulletin. (2019). Sensor-based ore sorting to maximise profit in a gold operation | AusImm Bulletin. [online] Available at: https://www.ausimmbulletin.com/feature/sensor-based-ore-sorting-maximise-profit-gold-operation/ [Accessed 22 Jun. 2019].
[29] Quora.com. (2019). What are the sensors which detect plastics bottles? - Quora. [online] Available at: https://www.quora.com/What-are-the-sensors-which-detect-plastics-bottles [Accessed 30 Jun. 2019].
[30] Outotec.com. (2019). Ore sorting: The Road to Optimizing Your Operation. [Online] Available at: https://www.outotec.com/company/newsletters/minerva/minerva-issue-2--2017/ore-sorting-the-road-to-optimizing-your-operation/ [Accessed 21 Jun. 2019].
[31] Kolacz, j, Advanced sorting technologies and its potential in mineral processing, AGH Journal of Mining and Geoengineering, vol 36 (4), 2012
[32] Von Ketelhodt, L, Bergmann, C, Dual energy x-ray transmission sorting coal, Commodas Ultrasort (Pty) Ltd, South Africa; Mintek, South Africa, The Southern African Institute of Mining and Metallurgy, 2010.
[33] SA, T. (2019). X-ray sorting of minerals - COM XRT - How it works. [online] Tomra. Available at: https://www.tomra.com/en/sorting/mining/sorting-equipment/com-series/com-xrt/how-it-works-xrt [Accessed 30 Jun. 2019].
[34] Mesina, M.B, De Jong, T.P.R, Dalmijn, W.L, Automatic sorting of scrap metals with a combined electromagnetic and dual energy X-ray transmission sensor
[35] Robben, M.R, Knapp, H, and Wotruba, H, Applications of near infrared sorting in the minerals industry. Unit of Mineral Processing, German, Vol. 23 (6), 2012
[36] Mintek.co.za. (2019). [online] Available at: http://www.mintek.co.za/Mintek75/Proceedings/K02-vonKetelhodt.pdf [Accessed 30 Jun. 2019].

IOP Conf. Series: Materials Science and Engineering **641** (2019) 012024 doi:10.1088/1757-899X/641/1/012024

Investigation of mineral deportment in a copper ore from Botswana

N Poloko[1], L K Moatlhodi[2], G Danha[3]

[1].Department of Chemicals, Materials & Metallurgical Engineering, Botswana International University of science and Technology, Private Bag 6, Palapye 10071, Botswana.

Email: nengubap@biust.ac.bw

Abstract. Understanding the characteristics of minerals is key in developing effective techniques for copper ore processing to maximise recovery hence income. Most studies have focused on understanding the fundamentals and principles of dissolution kinetics, oxidation and leaching of copper minerals. New developments and technologies have made it possible to reveal that copper ores are fascinating and complex minerals. Other research concentrates on chemical and mineralogical analysis, hence revealing information such as properties, compositional change and analysis. In this paper X-Ray Diffraction (XRD) and Quantitative Evaluation of Minerals Scanning Electron Microscopy (QEMSCAN) are used as tools in quantifying chemical and mineralogical attributes of a copper ore (chalcocite bearing mineral) from Botswana as the objective. Obtained information was not limited to grain size and distribution, mineral associations and liberations characteristics of economic minerals in the ore and quantitative information being the latter. XRF indicates that the copper ore contains phases such as Al203, CaO, MgO, TiO2, V2O5 and SiO2, which is the dominant mineral with 60.6 wt% as well as traces of elements Fe, S, Pb, and Co with wt% of <0.02. Scanning Electron Microscope (SEM) peaks also confirmed these elements to exist in the mineral. Quantitative X-Ray Diffraction (QXRD) analysis entailed phases present with silicates being the dominant phases and their existence on the mineral by wt%. SEM peaks showed evidence of Fe, Si, Cu, S etc. which is consistent with XRF data. In addition QESCAN also revealed grain size of cuprite particles to be greater than 45 μm with < 0.24 % liberated. The copper ore is characterized with a possibility of extracting metals or elements of economic value.

1. Introduction

China has been the largest market for most of the world's copper consuming nearly 40% annually. The reduced demand of copper from china that started in the year 2011 has caused a decline in the price of copper worldwide [1]. This circumstance has led to most mines to operate under strict financial and environmental regulations, using careful processing techniques that are less costly. This measures are incorporated to generate better income hence compensating for the declining market. Like most minerals, understanding copper ores through characterization is detrimental in development of efficient processing routes. A throng of copper sulphides such as chalcopyrite, chalcocite and covalite are slowly replacing bornite as a copper ore due to gradually decreasing grade [8]. This has created a problem for plant operators as they are facing a task to comprehend which minerals contribute to the grade since individual minerals are likely to behave uniquely during mineral processes such as comminution and beneficiation. Minerals which are likely or goes misidentified during processing may inhibit recovery of minerals of interest or increase processing costs. Many mining operations today face recovery problems due to insufficient data on ore properties from characterization [2, 3]. Mineralogical data generation in the physical metallurgy (characterization) stage is an operation that has recently been adopted by most processing plants for copper ores and most minerals [4]. Copper ores as complex minerals usually contains pyrite, sulphides, zinc nickel non-metallic gangue such as quartz, feldspar and trace elements such as Te and Re etc. [16]. The copper ore (Chalcocite-bearing mineral) in question was obtained from Khoemacau mine near Maun, Botswana. Khoemacau is one of the copper mines affected by the world's declining of copper prices which adds to a list in Botswana. According to Haest et al, 2011 chalcocite usually appears on 3 stage veins which are high angle veins, underdeveloped and associated haloes as a dark grey to black mineral, it has the formula Cu_2S. It is a secondary sulphide formed by alteration of other minerals such as copper leached away from near-surface sulphides. Its formation through atom by atom replacement makes it a pseudomorph mineral [10, 12]. Its formation from chalcopyrite ($CuFeS_2$) is explained as a reduction mechanisms of water table conditions due to oxygen attack. Lessening of such conditions favours the dissolution of Cu hence Cu displaces Iron in the iron sulphide to form Cu_2S [6]. Previous microscopy analysis on chalcocite indicated that the crystal system of chalcocite is orthorhombic in its natural state and at temperatures below $105^{o}C$, however it exhibits a hexagonal configuration at temperatures above $105^{o}C$ [11]. Chalcocite is processed through hydrometallurgy and pyrometallurgy beneficiation techniques.

Effective parameters for processing can be established to optimize recovery of valuable minerals from chalcocite at reduced processing costs after a comprehensive mineralogical and chemical deportment is closely studied [2]. The objective of this research is to study the deportment of a copper ore hence revealing useful information such as chemical and mineralogical attributes and how they affect processing routes and steps. Techniques used to obtain such information include QEMSCAN and XRD. XRD coupled with quantitative analysis by QEMSCAN (based on SEM and equipped with XRF) facilitates much improved ore control hence recoveries are optimized. QEMSCAN is a recent technology based on scanning electron microscopy (SEM). XRF of QEMSCAN determines the compositional analysis of minerals while XRD provides crystalline phases existing in in the ore [14]. A recent research by Gitari et al, 2017 studies focused on XRD and XRF physicochemical and mineralogical characterization of a copper ore to reveal major and trace species present. In this context, knowledge on chemistry and mineralogical nature of the copper ore such as liberations and associations, grain size distribution, constituents and phase composition etc. it is possible to suggest a processing route since this factors affect recovery rates.

2. Materials and methods

2.1. Sample preparation

A sample of CuS (as shown in Figure 1.) was collected from Khoemacau mine and sent to SGS South Africa for QEMSCAN and XRD analysis. It was crushed to a powder with granules of 1 mm particle sizes and the powder split into 2 for further experimental analysis. 10-15 g was split out to make 900 blocks to be examined by QEMSCAN and about 50g of the other split was pulverized for XRD analysis.

Figure 1. Sample of chalcocite from khoemacau mine.

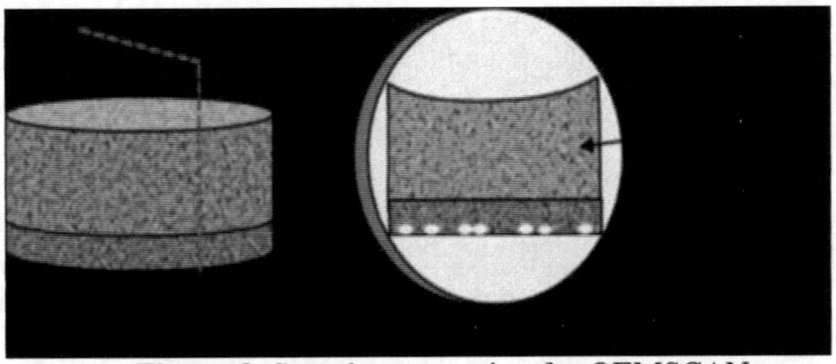

Figure 2. Sample preparation for QEMSCAN.

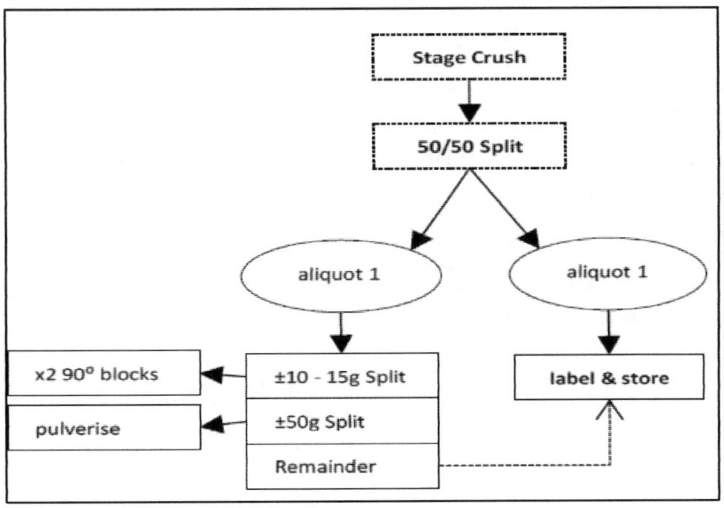

Figure 3. Sample preparation schematic diagram (SGS, S.A).

These steps are summarized in figure 3. The blocks prepared for surface analysis by QEMSCAN were cut at transverse angle in the manner shown in figure 2.

2.2. Mineralogical analysis (QEMSCAN)
QEMSCAN 650 (Quantitative Evaluation of Minerals SEM) is a technology is based on secondary electron microscopy (SEM). It an auto modified SEM, It has four light –element Dispersive X-ray Spectrometers (EDS) and provides quantitative and reliable data as compared to the traditional optical microscopes. QEMSCAN specific mineral search (SMS) was used to provide details of Cu speciation and elemental deportation, grain size distribution as well as liberations and associations, quantitative analysis of major elements and grain size distribution [18]. X-ray diffraction (XRD) analysis an inexpensive technique that quantifies ores to obtain phases present in the ore. Co-radiation has recently replaced the use of Cu-radiation in XRD characterization of copper ores. Copper ores are likely to contain elements such as Fe, Cr, Co and Mn that can cause X-ray fluorescence hence background scattering often associated with the use of cu-radiation [17]. XRF data of QEMSCAN was then validated with results from XRD.

2.3. Chemical analysis (X-Ray Fluorescence Spectroscopy XRF)
XRF borate fusion and ICP sodium peroxide fusion (Including. Ag) was used to conduct the chemical analysis of the copper ore, most base metals are analysed by XRF. It can detect trace elements

Occurring at sub ppm levels, Enzweiler et al (1996). It was used to detect major and trace oxides together with their respective proportions.

3. Results and discussions

3.1. Chemical analysis

XRF Analysis XRF elemental analysis results are shown in table 1.0. The results shows minerals of economic value, routine oxides as well as gangue materials. The ore sample consisted of mostly quartz as a gangue material which recorded a high wt. % (60.6). Even on visual examination of the sample evidence of quartz could be seen on the surface of the mineral samples collected. Most of land in Botswana is covered with $Si0_2$ hence the high amount of quartz occurring alongside mineral of interest. $Si0_2$ is have very low solubility in solutions hence remains as a impurity solid .The abundance of quartz in the ore contributes to the overall hardness of chalcocite hence milling time for this ore will be increased during processing [16]. The presence of CaO is known to occur the ore due to calcium leaching by solution and consequent reprecipitation [13]. The sample also contained high Al_2O_3 which is likely to be present in mica and significant amounts of Cu, Fe, K_2O and minor quantities of TiO_2, V_2O_5 as well as affinity of Cr etc.

According to Kotoky et a Mn present in mineral samples may indicates a warm and humid environment in which the ore exist. This correlates with climate in botswana which is warm/hot and humid. Quantities of Cu and S present in the sample are not related to chalcopyrite and exists in the form of Cu_2S (chalcocite). All the lower limit of detection (LLD) for all the phases fall in the range 0.01-0.05 %.

Table 1.0 XRF chemical analysis of chalcocite

Element	Cu Ore %	Ldetection %	Udetection %
Al_2O_3	13.7	0.05	100
CaO	4.4	0.01	100
Co	<0.02	0.02	100
Cr	<0.05	0.05	100
Cu	1.09	0.05	100
Fe	2.74	0.05	100
K_20	3.82	0.01	100
MgO	2.83	0.05	100
Mn	0.17	0.05	100
Na_2O	1.62	0.05	100
Ni	0.06	0.05	100
P_2O_5	0.164	0.01	100
Pb	<0.05	0.05	100
S	0.18	0.01	100
SiO_2	60.6	0.05	100
TiO_2	0.64	0.01	100
V_2P_5	0.02	0.01	100
Zn	<0.05	0.05	100

3.2. Mineralogical analysis

SEM analysis In this subsection phase distributions in the ore are analysed. SEM imaging shown in the following figure shows that a large spot A the sample scanned is composed of Cu and S likely occurring in the form of Cu_2S. This is proved by SEM Cu peaks at ~0.9 KeV and ~8.08 KeV which shows copper dominating the spot with ~41% above S with ~19%. Spot B which is a little darker than A represent Fe (~40%) as shown by the second Peak mapping. Other analysis on different spots are shown in appendix section.

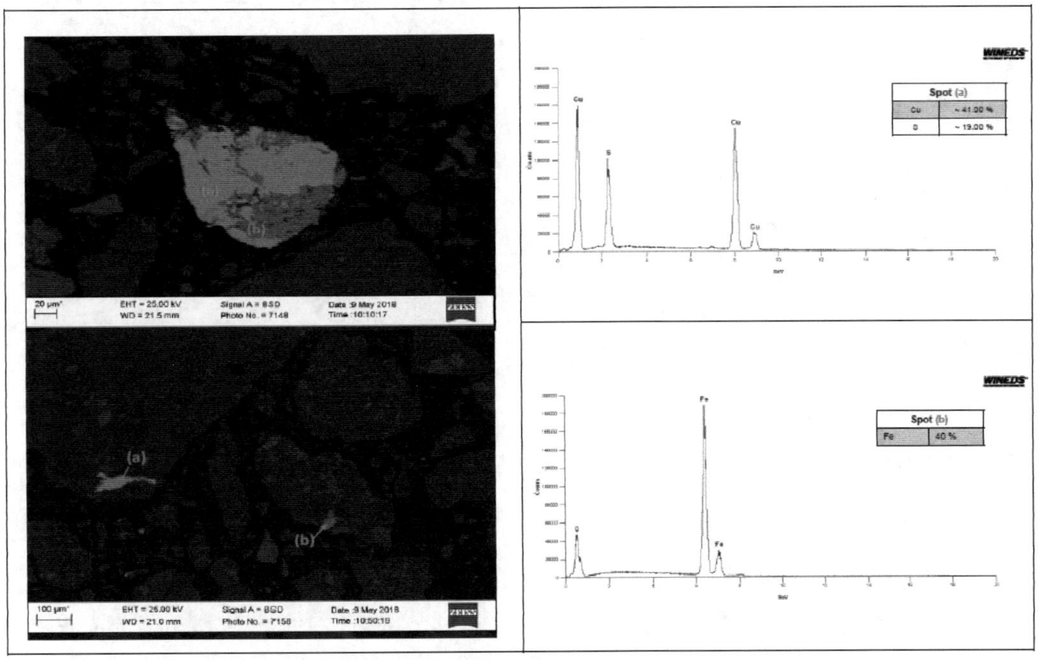

Figure 4. SEM images showing minerals detected in the copper ore.

3.2.1 XRD

Table 2.0 XRD crystalline phases of minerals and their abundance in %.

Mineral	Approx Formula	Approximate Abundance %
Quartz	SiO_2	28.40
Mica	$KAl_2(Si_3Al)O_{10}(OH,F)_2$	18.35
Plagioclase	$NaAlSi_3O_8$ - $CaAl_2Si_2O_8$	25.62
Chlorite	$(Mg,Fe)_6(Si,Al)4O10(OH)_8$	19.30
K-feldspar	$KAlSi_3O_8$	*trace*
	Total Silicates	~ 92.48
Calcite	$CaCO_3$	7.52
	Total Carbonates	~ 7.52
Cuprite	Cu_2O	*trace*
Chalcopyrite	$CuFeS_2$	*trace*
Covellite	CuS	*trace*
	Total Cu oxide/sulphide	*trace*

Table 2.0 shows crystalline phases that occurs within the sample as detected by quantitative X-ray diffractometer (QXRD). XRD peaks of these respective phases are shown in figure 5.

The results obtained from QXRD indicated that the copper ore investigated consisted of mostly silicates followed by carbonates at % of 91 and 8 respectively. The rest was negligible amount of copper oxides/ sulphides traces in the form of cuprite, chalcopyrite and covellite. Quartz was the most abundant silicate as a gangue material with 28.40 abundance %. This results are consistent with XRF results analysed. The peaks in the next figure shows quartz recorded the highest peaks and the sharp peaks represents the material being brittle.

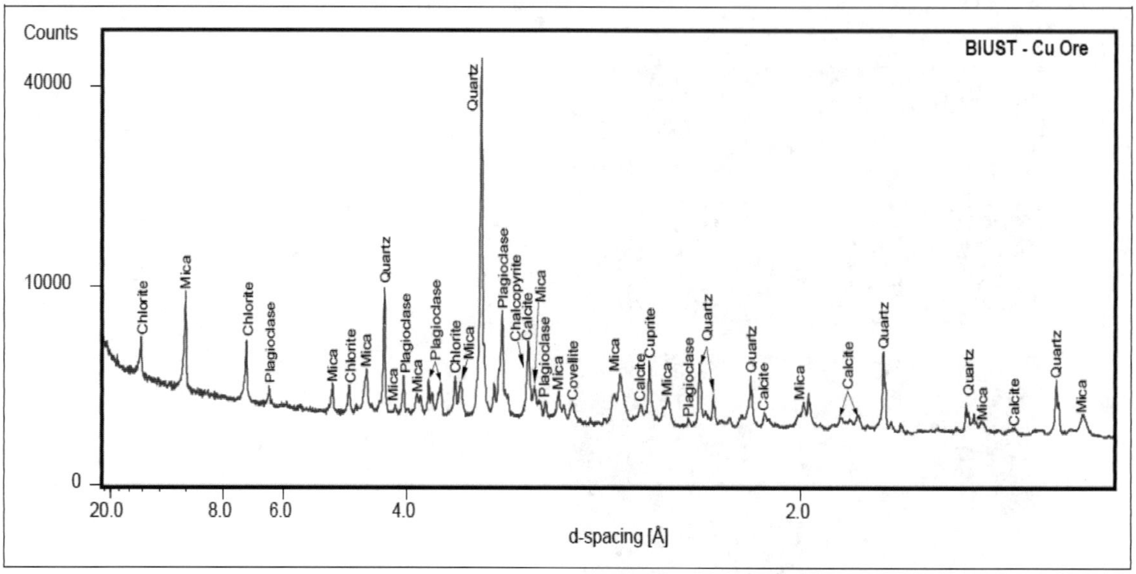

Figure 5.0 xrd peaks recorded for the copper ore.

*3.2.2 QEMSCAN t*his results of mineral phases detected by QEMSCAN are also consistent with data detected by XRD where silicates occurrences dominates in the sample. In addition to these minerals. Other included minerals, listed in Table 3. 0 below, were found occurring in trace amounts. The grain size distribution (GSD) analysis in Figure 6 shows the sample has fine to coarse size fractions

Table 3.0 shows bulk modal mineralogical date as analysed by QEMSCAN

Mineral	Approx Formula	Approximate Abundance %
Silicates	$-[SiO_{4-x}{}^{(4-2x)-}]n$	91.78
Calcite	$CaCO_3$	4.96
Other	-	0.71
Cc/Cov	Cu_xS_y	1.68
Cuprite	Cu_2O	0.57
Other Oxides	$-[O_2-]$	0.3
	Total	100

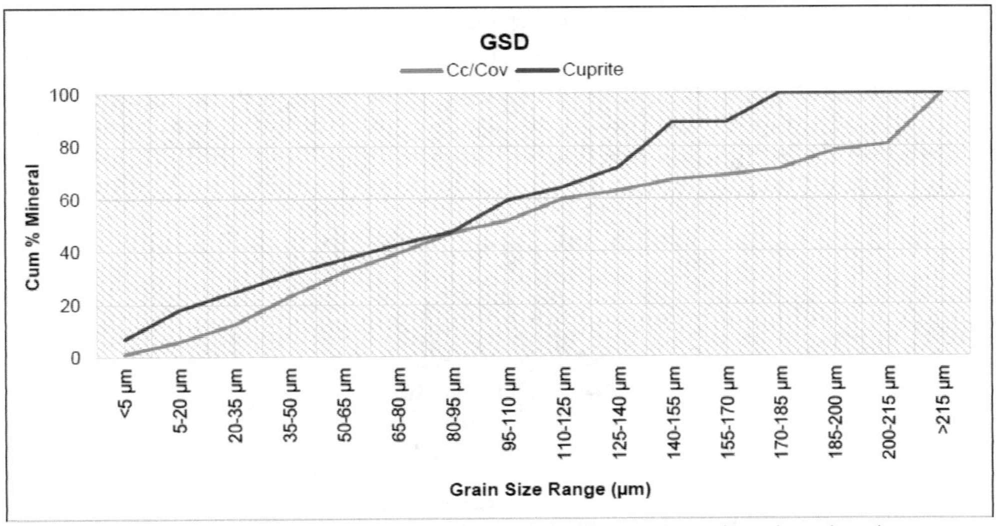

Figure 6. Grain size distribution (GDS) of Cc/Cov and cuprite mineral grains .

80% of Cc/Cov is greater than 45 µm grain size range, while 70% of the cuprite is greater than 45 µm grain size. QEMSCAN takes advantage of point counting technique in order to determine the degree of liberation of the copper ore. The grains of copper minerals were counted as well as gangue materials locked into the ore and the relative percentages are given in table 4.0. Figure 7 (below) indicates that ~28% of Cc/Cov and ~49% of cuprite is fully liberated. If particles are liberated it means more than 80 % of the particle is the mineral of interest. Liberation can dictate recovery rate of minerals. Poor liberation rates leads to lower recovery of coarse particles [9] therefore for efficient recovery of minerals of interest from gangue the ore must be adequately liberated. However in real practices a 100 % liberation is not possible hence particles with locked gangue and minerals of interest are produced (Sutherland et al). Locked particles are those that contains more than one interface between phases (Fuso, 2015). Locked particles also have less than 30% of particles being the mineral of interest. In High (Hi) Middlings 50-80% of particle is the mineral of interest as compared to Lo Middling with 30-50 being the mineral of interest.

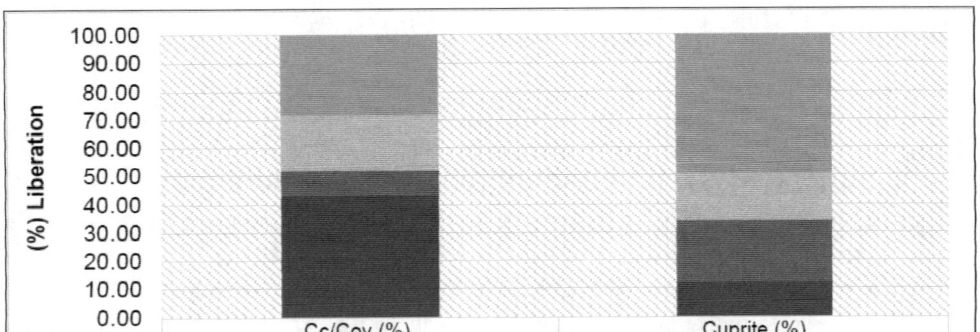

	Cc/Cov (%)	Cuprite (%)
Liberated	28.47	49.39
Hi Midd	19.59	16.46
Lo Midd	8.64	21.95
Locked	43.31	12.20

Figure 7. Cc/Cov & Cuprites liberations.

The rest of the Cc/Cov and cuprite minerals, which are classified as *Hi Midd*, *Lo Midd* and *Locked*, are associated with other minerals present in the sample. The associations, are shown in Table 4.0. The associations are summarized by pie chart shown in Fig 8 which reveals that 70% of the total Cu in the total sample occurs as Cc/Cov, and 26% in the cuprite. Chalcocite liberation with cuprites is fairly good hence the reason for low association values.

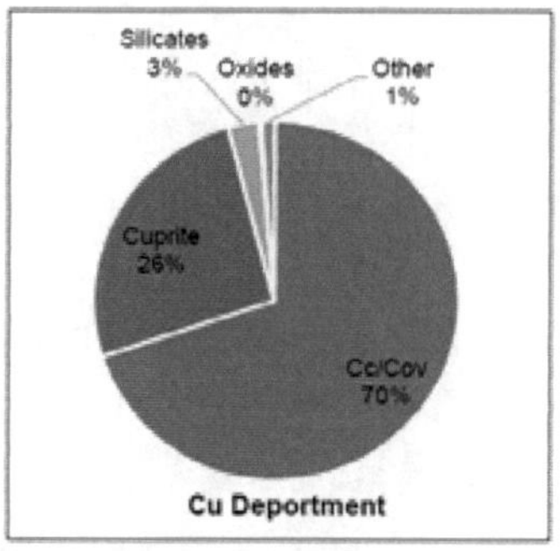

Figure 8. Distribution of total Cu in different phases.

Table 4.0 liberations and associations of Cc/Cov

Liberation and Association of Cc/Cov	
Liberated Cc/Cov	27.41 %
Cc/Cov, Associated with Cuprite	6.09 %
Cc/Cov, Associated with Silicates	38.61 %
Cc/Cov, Associated with Calcite	3.05 %
Cc/Cov, Associated with Oxides	0.12 %
Complex (Cc/Cov and more than two other minerals)	27.73 %
Other (Associations without Cc/Cov)	0.00 %

Conclusions

1. QXRD data showed that the Cu ore sample is mostly comprised ~91% silicates, ~8% carbonates and trace amounts (<1%) of Cu oxide/sulphide were recorded. Quartz being the most dominant as a gangue material.
2. SEM images shows a fine dissemination of element Cu throughout the sample.
3. The XRF and XRD characterization showed no substantial variations in chemical analysis of major occurring elements. However a slight deviation in other trace elements is observed.
4. Cc/Cov and cuprite are the only two Cu-bearing minerals detected by QEMSCAN analysis. ~28% of the Cc/Cov and ~49% of the cuprite was found to be liberated. 70% of the Cu in the total sample occurs in the Cc/Cov group, and 26% in the cuprite. The ore consists predominantly quartz which increases hardness, it is suggested that this ore be milled to 80% <106m and subjected to

flotation by initially adding a sulphidizing reagent (to sulphidise the cuprite) and then perform sulphide flotation.

References

[1] Chalcocite, MineralsUk Centre for sustainable mineral development, [Online] Available: www.mineraluk.com, Sep 09, 2018.
[2] Curtiss B, Developing Automated Copper Ore Processing Using NIR Analysis and XRD, ASD inch. Boulder, Colo, 2012.
[3] Bonnici, N. K, The mineralogical and textural characteristics of copper-gold deposits related to mineral processing attributes, School of Earth Sciences, ARC Centre of Excellence in Ore Deposits, 2012
[4] Baum, W, Ore characterisation, process mineralogy and lab automation a roadmap or future mining. Minerals Engineering. Vol 60, pp 69-73.
[5] Haest, M and Muchez, P, Stratiform and vein-type deposits in the Pan-African Orogen in Central and Southern Africa: evidence for multiphase mineralisation. Geologica Belgica, vol 14, pp 23-44, 2011.
[6] Muthur, R, Ruiz, J, Titley, S., Liermann, L, Buss, H, Brantley, S, Copper Isotopic fractionation in the supergene environment with and without bacteria. Geochimica et Cosmochimica Acta. Vol 69, pp 5233-5246, 2005.
[7] Gitari, M,W, Akinyemi, S,A, Thobakgale, R, Ngoejana, P,C, Ramugondo, L, Matidza, M, Mhlongo, S,E, Dacosta, F,A, Nemapate, N, Physicochemical and mineralogical characterization of Musina mine copper and New Union gold mine tailings: Implications for fabrication of beneficial geopolymeric construction materials, Journal of African Earth Sciences, vol 137, pp 218-228, 2017.
[8] Ridge, D,J, Annotated bibliographies of Mineral Deposits in Africa, Earth sciences, Elsevier Publisher, pp 496-497, 2003.
[9] Rao, D,S, Rath, S,S, Dash, N, Mohanty, S and Biswal, S,K, Mineralogy, liberation and leaching characteristics of iron oxide phases in an Indian diaspore sample, Trans. Nonferrous Met. Soc. China Vol 28, pp 1640−1651, 2018
[10] Howe, S,S, Mineralogy, Textures, and Relative Age Relationships of Massive Sulfide Ore in the West Shasta District, California, Economic Geology, Vol. 80, pp. 2114-2127, 1985.
[11] Wuensch, B,J and Buerger, M, J, The Crystal structure of chalcocite, International mineralogical associations, vol 1, pp 164-170, 1963.
[12] Smith Jr, A,E, The mineralogy of Texas, 1st Ed, Brett Smith Publisher, pp 56, 2016.
[13] Darwis, A,J, and Massina, M, A, X-Ray Fluorescence (XRF) to identify chemical analysis of minerals in Buton island, SE Sulawesi, Indonesia, IOP Conf. Ser.: Earth Environ. Sci., Vol 118, 2018.
[14] Amponsah-Dacosta, M and Reid, D,L, Mineralogical Characterization of Selected South African Mine Tailings for the Purpose of Mineral Carbonation, An Interdisciplinary Response to Mine Water Challenges - Sui, Sun & Wang (eds), vol pp 686-689, 2014.
[15] Li, G, Cheng, H, Xu, C, Lu, C, Lu, X, Zou, X, and Xu, Q, Mineralogical analysis of nickel/copper polymetallic sulfide ore by x-ray diffraction using rietveld method, Characterization of Minerals, Metals, and Materials, 2016

IOP Conf. Series: Materials Science and Engineering **641** (2019) 012024 doi:10.1088/1757-899X/641/1/012024

[16] Jacobs, T,T, Process Mineralogical characterization of the kansanshi copper ore, Nw Zambia Thesis, Department of chemical Engineering, University of Cape Town, 2016.
[17] Coetzee, L,L, Theron, S,J, Martin, G,J, Van Der Merwe, J,D. and Stanek, T, Modern gold departments and its application to industry. Minerals Engineering. vol 24, pp 565 - 575.
[18] Gottlieb, P, The revolutionary impact of automated mineralogy on mining and mineral processing. In: 24th International Mineral Processing Congress, pp 165-174, 2008.

Appendix

SEM images showing minerals detected in the copper ore A,B,C

A

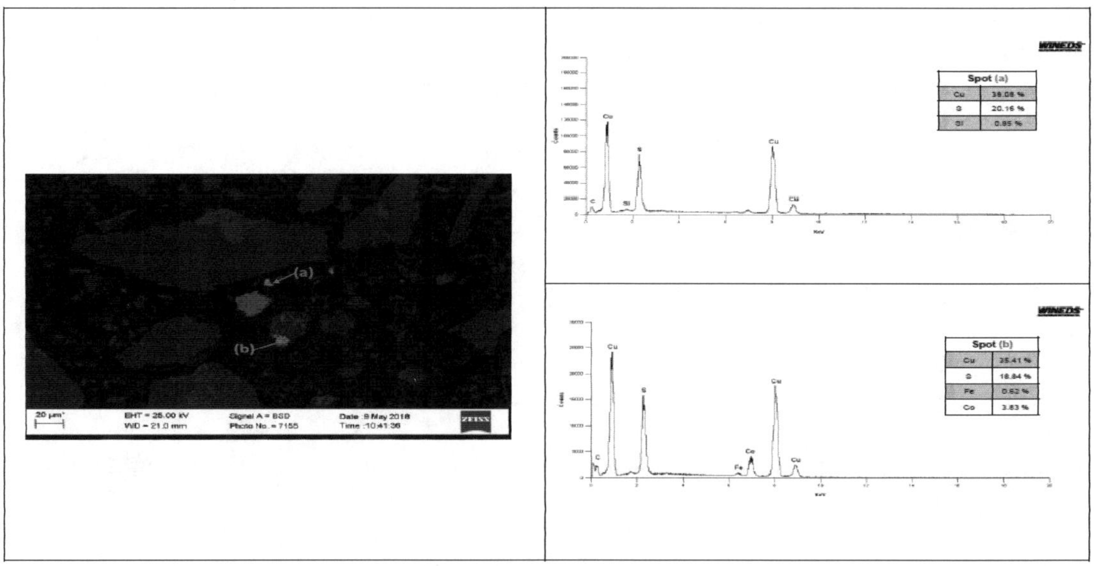

B

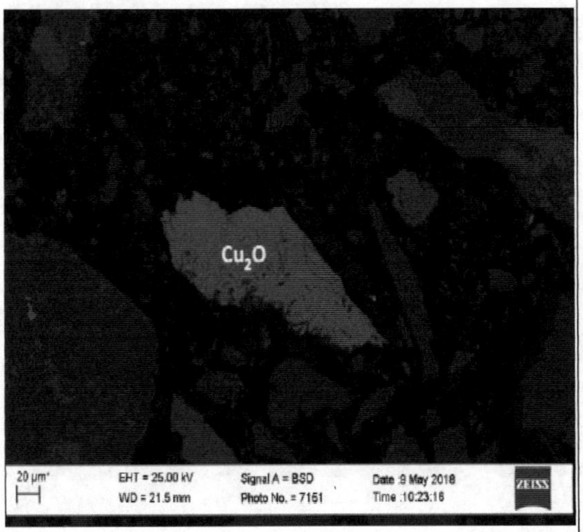
Cu2O
20 µm
EHT = 25.00 kV
WD = 21.5 mm
Signal A = BSD
Photo No. = 7161
Date :9 May 2018
Time :10:23:16
ZEISS

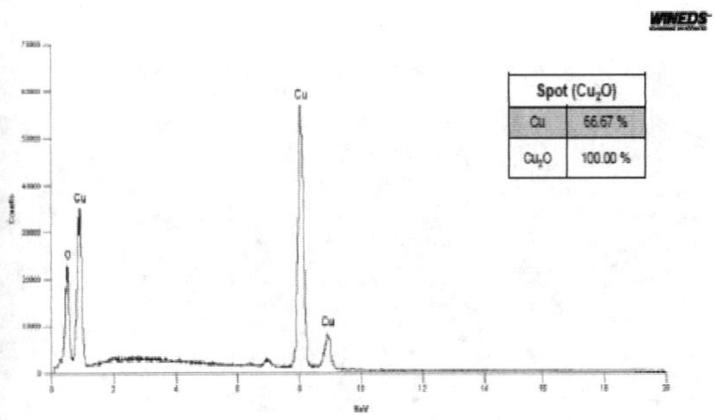
Spot (Cu2O)
Cu 66.67 %
Cu2O 100.00 %
O
Cu
Cu
Cu

C

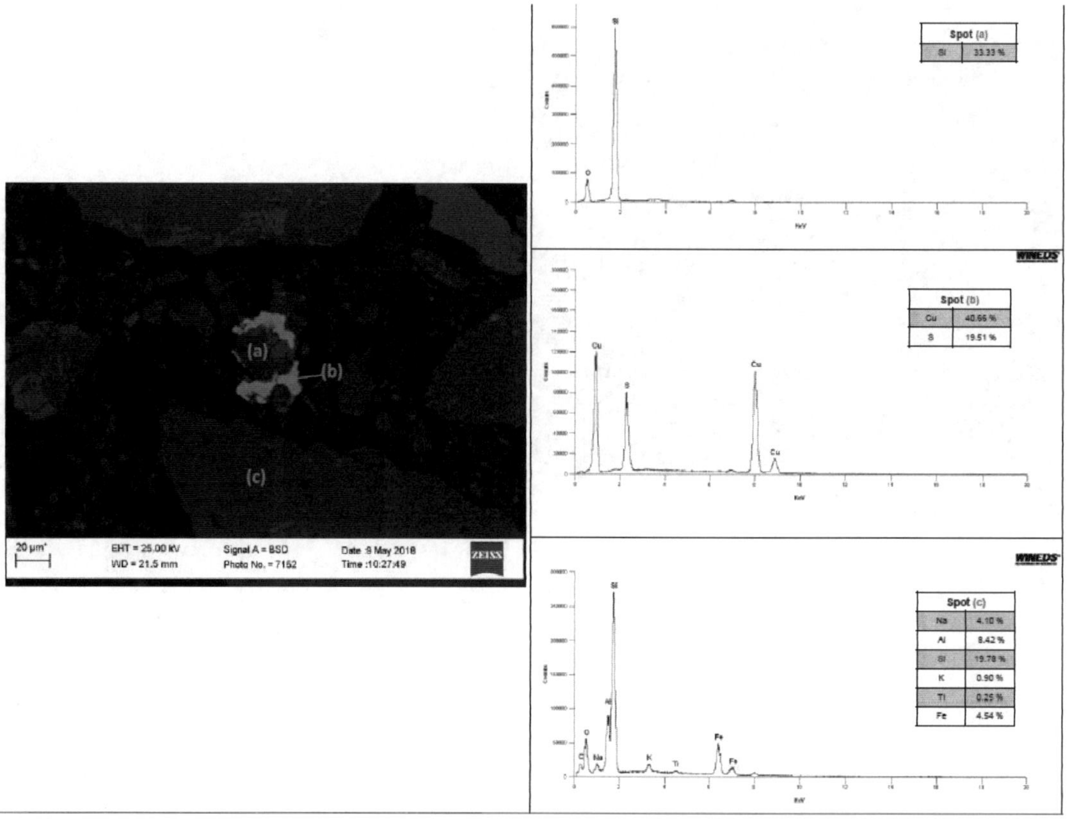

Acknowledgements
The authors will like to thank BIUST t for making resources available to our disposal in order to complete this research. Also special gratitude to Phuti Letswalo from SGS South Africa who played a major role in obtaining QEMSCAN, XRF and XRD results.

Mathematical model of dry coal deshaling by using FGX vibrating air table

W Mijał , T Niedoba and D Polek

Department of Environmental Engineering, Faculty of Mining and Geoengineering, AGH University of Science and Technology, Al. Mickiewicza 30, PL-30059 Cracow, Poland

E-mail: walmij@agh.edu.pl

Abstract. Dry coal separation process is a relatively new method for coal separation in Poland. First air separators which were used on bigger scale was in United States before Second World War in 1930s. Nowadays is widely used in China, United States, Russia and all those places where access to water is limited. Last year's very popular become separation by using vibrating air tables FGX where beneficiation process use air suspension which separate heavier particles from light coal grains. This separation process depends on different parameters like preparation of feed and it parameters, grain size fraction, air supply etc.. This paper will describe what is it a dry coal separation, modern separation techniques and in the main part focus on creating mathematical model which will present the quality of using this kind of process for coal deshaling. Mathematical model will base on dependence between calorific value and ash content in the tested samples.

1. Introduction

Coal preparation is based on many different methods like the most common gravity separation (by using jigs, dense medium separators, dense medium cyclones, shaking tables or typical physio-chemical method like flotation (commonly used for coking coals). One of old gravity separation methods is dry coal separation by using air jigs or air tables. In the beginning of 20th century this method was used in United States (air dense medium suspension created by air and sand in Frazer-Yancey dry separator). In 1930s in United States build few dry coal preparation plants. The biggest dry separation plant was in Lundale West Wirginia, the biggest separator in this plant had total capacity 200t/h. In the same time in Europe dry separation where used by countries such as England (1925), Belgium, Germany or Poland (1928). Dry enrichment is usually applied in places where there are water shortages to wet processes and in a harsh climate due to the possibility of freezing separation products after separation in a water medium. The raw materials that can be enriched with this method are mainly hard coals with a large proportion of coal-fired or waste fractions and for brown coals (hard types). In Poland common dry separation equipment is FGX air vibrating table and OSX optical sorter constructed by Comex group company (for separation are used difference in colours and content of usefull material inside tested feed). Those machines till this moment was not applied into existed coal preparation plants (wide tests were conducted on steam and coking coal by the team headed by Prof. I. Baic and W. Blaschke and Institute of Mechanized Construction and Rock Mining, optical separators was tested for example for pre-concentration of zinc and lead ore).

Last 20 years become a very fast developing time of new equipment for dry coal enrichment especially in China (CFX, TGX or FGX). Very popular become air vibrating table type FGX which is used in United States, Turkey, India, South Africa, Vietnam, Russia, Mongolia and a dozen other countries [1, 2, 3, 4, 5, 7, 8, 9, 11].

2. Dry deshaling principles

Dry beneficiation on air table work by using ever-rising stream of air. Work plate can also get vibration movement to increase the accuracy of separation. Receipt of products depends on construction of table. As an example of this type of separators is air vibrating table FGX. Second type of air separators are air jigs. The air is fed by pulsation under the material layer. The material is separated in the same way as during wet enrichment in a water jig. The raised material is loosening, and grains differing in density from each other begin to form layers of grains of the same density.
Vibrating air separator FGX consists of a funnel feed, dosing feeder, perforated work plate, vibrator, air chambers, dust removal module and a mechanism that allows to change the angle of inclination of the working plate and the frequency of vibrations. On the installation using a vibratory feeder a feed is fed which goes to a working plate inclined at various lateral and longitudinal angles set in a vibrating motion by means of a vibratory drive [13].

In order to ensure air supply under the working plate there are air chambers, which are fed by a centrifugal fan. The fine carbon material forms a fluidized bed (air-solid slurry) as a result of contact with air. As a result individual grains can fall relative to each other depending on their size or density. Under the influence of combined forces: air current and vibrations the coal bed is raised and then depending on the density it becomes stratified. The lighter material is suspended on the surface of the fluidized bed and the grains with a higher density sink deeper. An additional phenomenon is the liquefaction effect resulting from the interaction of small grains between them, which is a suspension and coarse grains. This phenomenon improves the efficiency of the separation of coarse fractions. Fine material located on the surface of the layer tends to slide over its surface and fall continuously under the influence of gravity through the partition at the edge of the plate (dumping of enriched coal). The heavy material falls to the bottom of the layer and is moved towards the waste collection point (gangue). Figure 1 shows the distribution on FGX working plate [4, 5, 6, 7, 8, 11, 13].

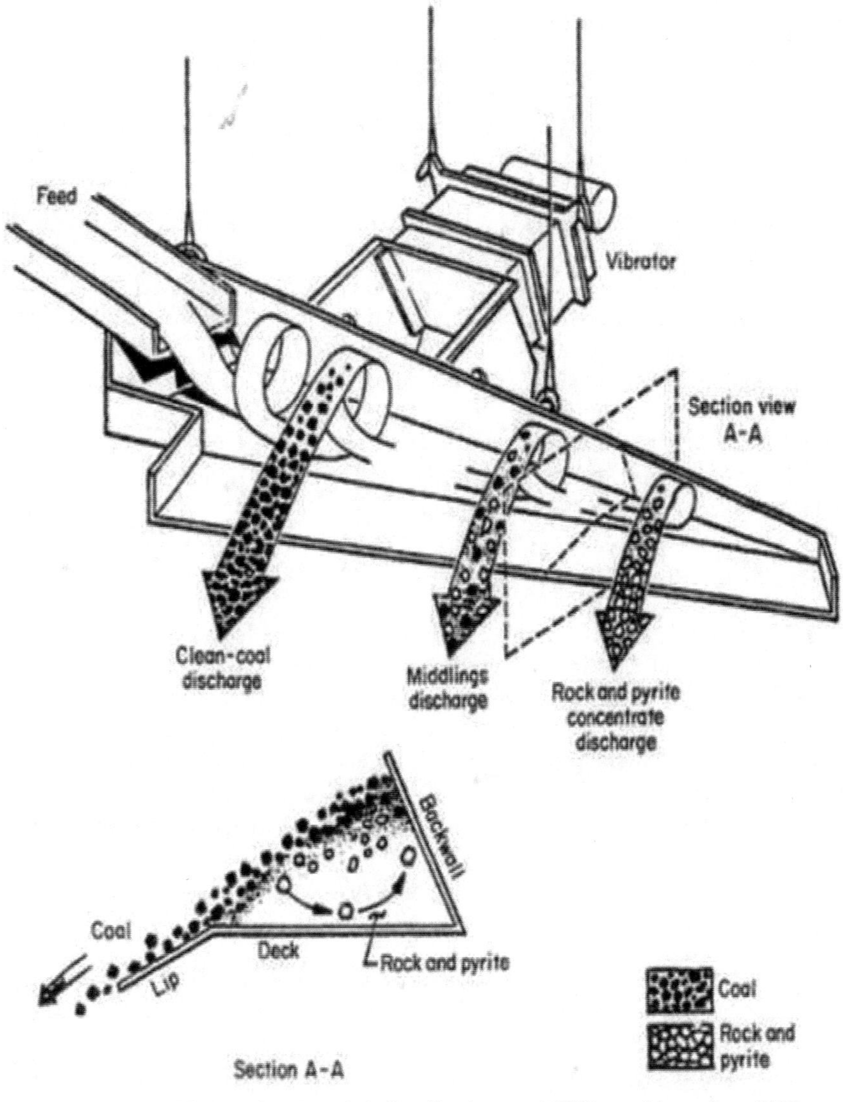

Figure 1. Material distribution on FGX working plate [12].

Previously mentioned scientific team lead other research to show possibilities of the applicability of FGX vibrating air table as a good solution to remove sulfur [16, 17], mercury [18, 19, 20, 21, 22, 23] or they are working on the application of this method as a supplement to the enrichment technology in jigs (initial averaging of feed using dry deshaling) [24, 25].

3. Parameters influencing the separation on the air table separator

Air separators have low separation accuracy. This process need to be conducted with strictly followed rules of enrichment. The separation process depends on many parameters [14, 15]:

- ***Initial preparation of the feed*** – with the low coefficient of equal fallen grains to separation process should be send narrow grain classes for example 50-25 mm or 25-6 mm etc.. Industry experience show that it is also possible to send for beneficiation process grains with size 80(75)-0 mm or 50-0 mm. Very necessary during separation process is to keep in the main fee the amount of small grains between 15 and 30%. Those grains are necessary to not lost the important static pressure (before it change into dynamic pressure),

- ***Grain size & weight feed composition*** – sometimes during separation processes in processing plants are separated even grains with maximum size 100 mm. Grain size smaller than 0,8(0,5)mm is not separated. Feed with high amount of middlings is also not good for separation process. In situations where is a lot of middlings it should be changed classification scale,
- ***Amount of air for separation process*** – this parameter is define by tests. If the feed have high amount of grains with big size and high humidity, thicker feed layer which is send to separation process the amount of air for separation process should be bigger,
- ***Height of the bar*** – this parameter it is chosen during separation process and depend on grain size of the feed and difficulty of enrichment process. Bars can be divided into two types: bar of working plate and edge bars. Edge bars control the layer of material which is on working plate and time for remove concentrate from separator. Working plate bars control the evenly distribution of the material at working plate surface,
- ***Angle of working plate*** – longitudinal angle affect the time of separation the wastes, middlings and wastes from feed. With increasing the longitudinal angle the time of separation wastes will be too short and wastes affect the quality of separated concentrates. Too low longitudinal angle will create the chance of losing useful minerals in waste fraction. In practical way the longitudinal angle can be changed between $0 - 2^{o}$. The transverse angle affect the separation time of concentrate. Low transverse angle cause longer time of separation of the feed at surface of working plate which affect separation efficiency. In practical way the transverse angle can be changed between $0 - 10^{o}$.
- ***Number of working plate swings*** – amount of swings depend on amount of waste fraction and humidity of the feed. With high amount of swings the separation process of wastes will increase. It is recommended to choose the about of swings which depends on longitudinal angle of working plate. The total amount of swings per minute should be between 200 to 450.
- ***Separator efficiency*** – the optimal efficiency of separator is determine experimentally. Most important factors are grain size of material, weight composition of feed and total amount of humidity in the feed.

Experience described by foreign users shows that separation process also depends on factors mentioned below [14, 15]:

- Total moisture,
- Dimension of the separated research material (maximum grains),
- Grain size fraction,
- Amount of grain size fraction 0 – 6 mm in the feed,
- Relation between amount of rock and coal grains in the feed,
- Total amount of ash in research material,
- Total amount of middlings in raw feed.

Other specific parameters and dependence of grain behavior on the surface of the working board and during the separation are described in this paper [26].

4. Characteristic of the research material

Research material was a steam coal from three different coal mines located in Poland (in total 12 samples). Total minimum weight of one sample used for test was 25 Mg, each sample was different to another by calorific value Q_u, ash content A_r or difficulties with coal separation process were different between samples.

In practical way comparing of those samples should not be applicable but for this paper and discussion we compare them by making correlation between calorific value Q_u & ash content A_r. After this comparison of results it will be created a theoretical mathematical equation which is define dependence calorific value Q_u and ash content A_r during dry separation process. This paper will be introduction to the further research over the issue of dry coal separation efficiency.

5. Results

From many published papers about dry coal separation in Poland and new vibrating air table separator was chosen some of important data which show the effects of deshaling etc.. Based on data published by team of Prof. Blaschke & Prof. Baic in Polish and foreign journals and descriptions about working principles of FGX vibrating air table and parameters which can affect the efficiency of beneficiation process we choose one characteristic which was very good base to create theoretical mathematical model of dry separation [1, 3, 4, 7, 10, 11, 14, 15, 16, 17, 18, 19, 20, 21, 22, 23, 24, 25, 26]. The main parameters taken for consideration were calorific value and ash content in raw feed and beneficiation products. Parameters mentioned and described in this chapter are widely described below:

- A_F – ash content in the feed,
- Q_{uF} – calorific value in the feed,
- A_C – ash content in concentrate,
- Q_{uC} – calorific value in concentrate,
- A_M – ash content in middlings,
- Q_{uM} – calorific value in middlings,
- A_T – ash content in tailings,
- Q_{uT} – calorific value in tailings.

Mathematical models were created for calorific value. To create these models two experiments were taken into consideration. One consisted of 12 samples for which 4 models were created, separately for the feed, concentrate, middlings and tailings. Second experiment consisted of 48 samples and the model was created generally for the whole sample, without partition of the products. Correlation matrices for both experiments are presented in Tables 1 and 2 and the occurring regressive models are positioned in Tables 3-7.

Table 1. Correlations between calorific value and ash content chosen for this research.

Variable	Mean value	Standard deviation	A_F	Q_{uF}	A_C	Q_{uC}	A_M	Q_{uM}	A_T	Q_{uT}
			Marked correlation indexes are significant with p < ,05000 N=12							
A_F	37,77	3,970	1,000000	-0,929142	0,566224	-0,302790	0,084312	-0,007712	0,566836	-0,566194
Q_{uF}	16403,67	1455,044	-0,929142	1,000000	-0,549374	0,392021	0,063238	-0,104686	-0,478539	0,508491
A_C	26,37	3,710	0,566224	-0,549374	1,000000	-0,833275	-0,072375	0,026067	0,597012	-0,545218
Q_{uC}	20129,08	1139,093	-0,302790	0,392021	-0,833275	1,000000	-0,059140	0,089404	-0,169609	0,126256
A_M	47,40	11,409	0,084312	0,063238	-0,072375	-0,059140	1,000000	-0,945973	-0,102543	0,118924
Q_{uM}	13022,42	4132,623	-0,007712	-0,104686	0,026067	0,089404	-0,945973	1,000000	0,146318	-0,155608
A_T	79,68	5,046	0,566836	-0,478539	0,597012	-0,169609	-0,102543	0,146318	1,000000	-0,988431
Q_{uT}	2422,58	1628,446	-0,566194	0,508491	-0,545218	0,126256	0,118924	-0,155608	-0,988431	1,000000

Table 2. General correlations between calorific value and ash content.

Variable	Marked correlation indexes are significant with p < ,05000 N=48			
	Mean value	Standard deviation	A	W_u
A	47,80	21,112	1,000000	-0,917829
Q_u	12585,78	7238,078	-0,917829	1,000000

Looking at the results of correlation indexes between calorific values and ash contents for experiment 1 it can be noticed that there are high values of these indexes for all products. The worst case occurred for the concentrate, but still the value is statistically significant. The same observations were found for the experiment 2. That was the basis to create regressive models, presented in Tables 3-7 and on Figures 2-6.

Table 3. Analysis of linear regression between calorific value and ash content in the feed – Experiment 1.

N=12	Summary of regression of dependent variable: Q_{uF} R= ,92914195 R^2= ,86330475 Adjusted R^2= ,84963523 F(1,10)=63,155 p<,00001 Standard error of estimation: 564,22					
	b*	Standard error from b*	b	Standard error from b	t(10)	p
Constant term			29265,17	1626,577	17,99187	0,000000
A_F	-0,929142	0,116917	-340,52	42,849	-7,94704	0,000012

where: b – value of parameter; b* - value of parameter of normalized distribution; t – value of t-Student test; p – significance level; R^2 – coefficient of determination; F – value of F-Snedecor test.

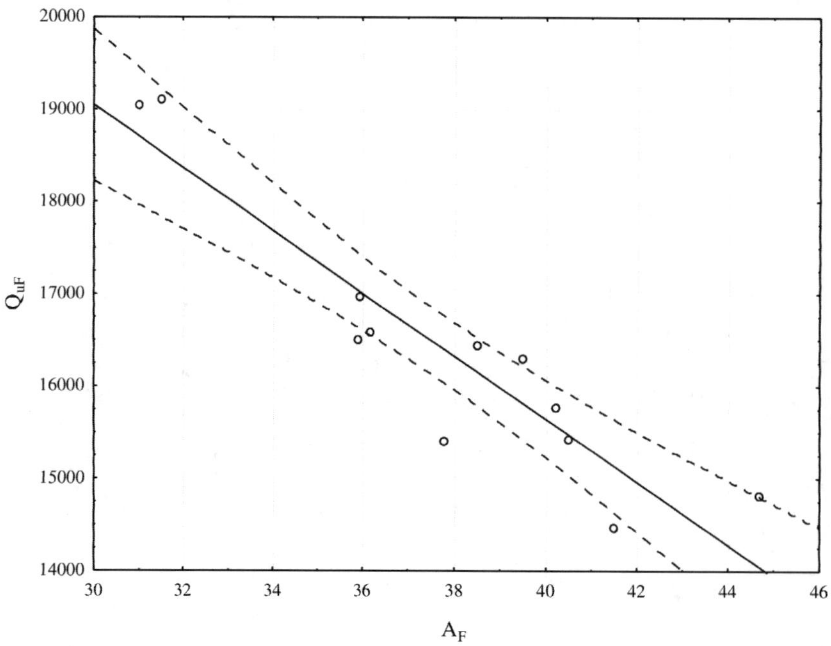

Figure 2. Regressive function for calorific value of the feed and ash content (Experiment 1, N=12)

$$\boldsymbol{Q_{uF} = -340,52A_F + 29265,17};\ R^2=86,33\% \quad (1)$$

Table 4. Analysis of linear regression between calorific value and ash content in concentrate – Experiment 1

Summary of regression of dependent variable: Q_{uC} R= ,83327499 R^2= ,69434720 Adjusted R^2= ,66378192 F(1,10)=22,717 p<,00076 Standard error of estimation: 660,50						
N=12	b*	Standard error from b*	b	Standard error from b	t(10)	p
Constant term			26876,63	1428,484	18,81480	0,000000
A_C	-0,833275	0,174829	-255,87	53,684	-4,76622	0,000761

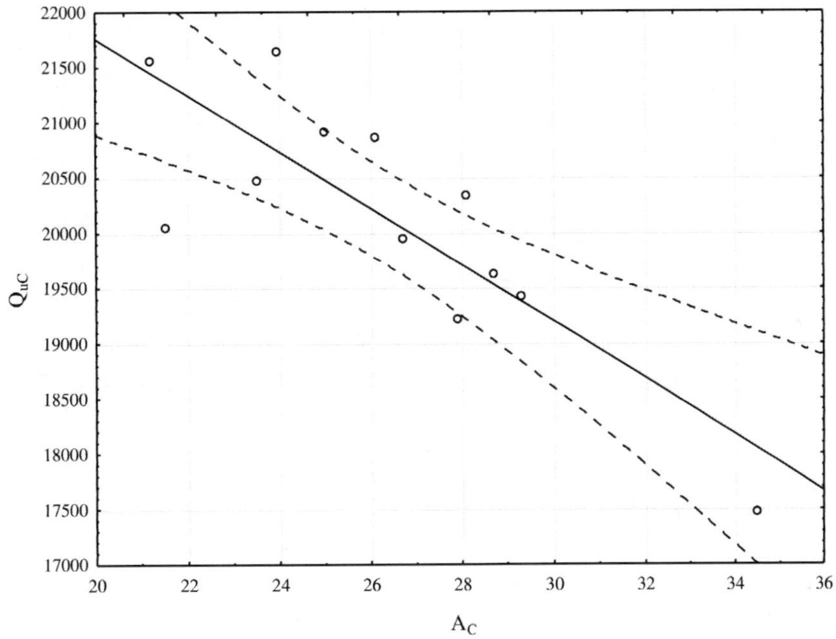

Figure 3. Regressive function for calorific value of the concentrate and ash content (Experiment 1, N=12)

$$Q_{uC} = -255,87A_C + 26876,63;\ R^2=69,43\% \tag{2}$$

Table 5. Analysis of linear regression between calorific value and ash content in middlings – Experiment 1

Summary of regression of dependent variable: Q_{uM} R= ,94597279 R^2= ,89486451 Adjusted R^2= ,88435096 F(1,10)=85,115 p<,00000 Standard error of estimation: 1405,4						
N=12	b*	Standard error from b*	b	Standard error from b	t(10)	p
Constant term			29263,37	1806,529	16,19867	0,000000
A_M	-0,945973	0,102536	-342,66	37,142	-9,22580	0,000003

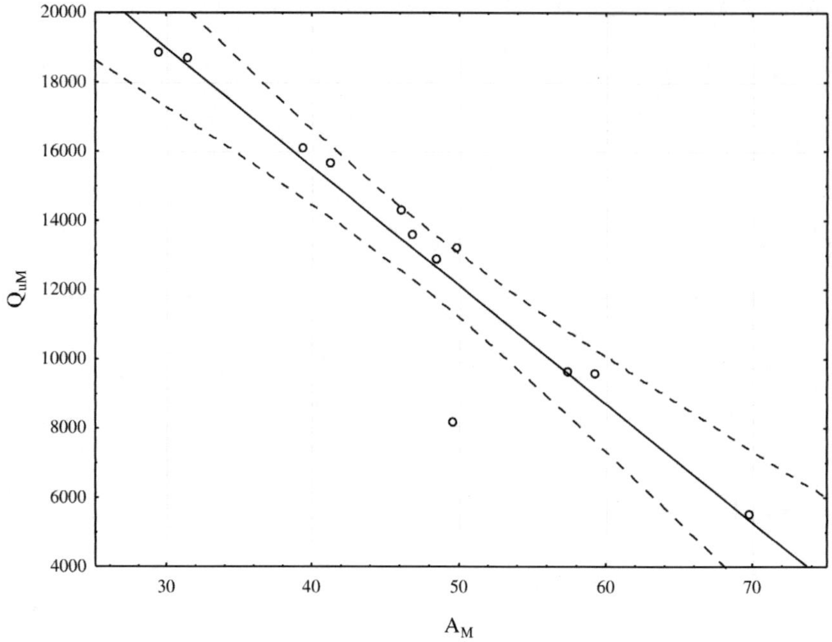

Figure 4. Regressive function for calorific value of the middlings and ash content (Experiment 1, N=12)

$$Q_{uM} = -342,66A_M + 29263,37;\ R^2=89,49\% \qquad (3)$$

Table 6. Analysis of linear regression between calorific value and ash content in tailings – Experiment 1

N=12	Summary of regression of dependent variable: Q_{uT} R= ,98843110 R^2= ,97699604 Adjusted R^2= ,97469564 F(1,10)=424,71 p<,00000 Standard error of estimation: 259,04					
	b*	Standard error from b*	b	Standard error from b	t(10)	p
Constant term			27839,13	1235,573	22,5314	0,000000
A_T	-0,988431	0,047962	-319,00	15,479	-20,6084	0,000000

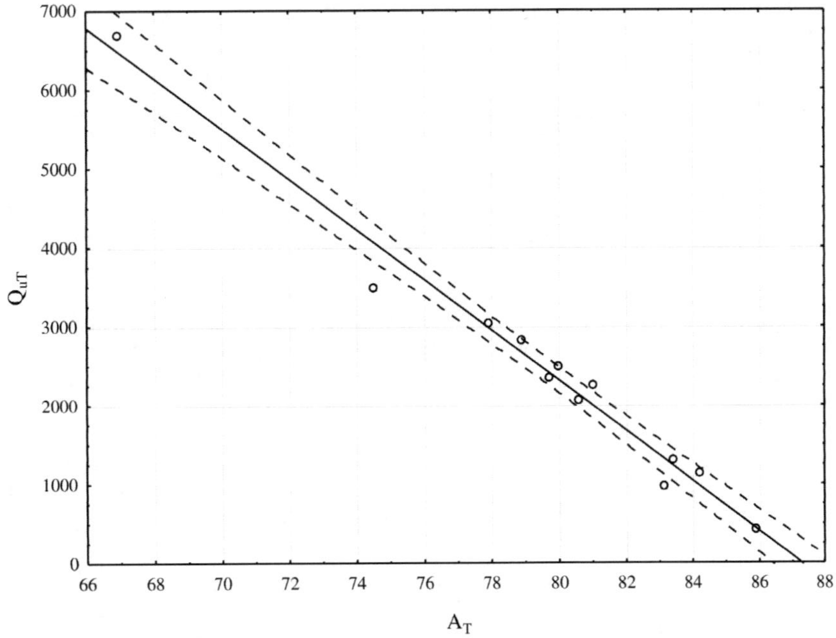

Figure 5. Regressive function for calorific value of the tailings and ash content (Experiment 1, N=12)

$$\boldsymbol{Q_{uT} = -319,00A_T + 27839,13};\ R^2=97,70\% \tag{4}$$

Table 7. Analysis of linear regression between calorific value and ash content – Experiment 2

Summary of regression of dependent variable: Q_u= ,91782903 R^2= ,84241012 Adjusted R^2= ,83898426 F(1,46)=245,90 p<0,0000 Standard error of estimation: 2904,4

N=48	b*	Standard error from b*	b	Standard error from b	t(46)	p
Constant term			27627,92	1046,856	26,3913	0,000000
A	-0,917829	0,058531	-314,67	20,067	-15,6811	0,000000

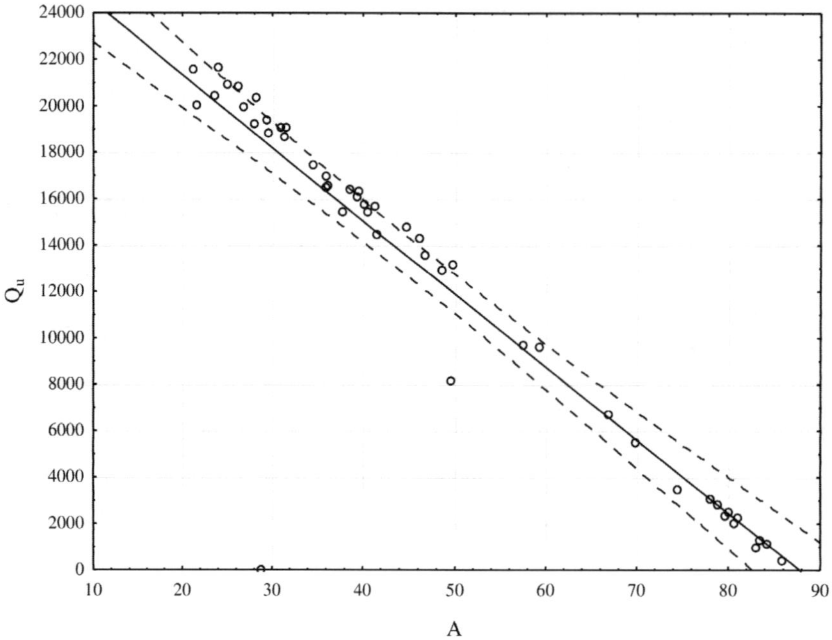

Figure 6. Regressive function for calorific value of the feed and ash content (Experiment 2, N=48)

$$Q_u = -314,67A + 27627,92; \ R^2=84,24\% \qquad (5)$$

6. Conclusions

Basing on the conducted calculations for both experiments considered in the paper it occurred that there are high correlations between calorific values and ash contents. That means that it is possible to forecast the calorific value of the coal sample knowing its ash contents. Dry coal separation method used in these experiments indicated that it can be efficient tool to divide the feed into subproducts (concentrate, middlings and tailings) and thanks to the models the appropriate tool or technique can be selected easier and more accurately. The amount of samples considered in this paper was not sufficient to claim that the results are representative for all circumstances. These samples were prepared especially for the purpose of evaluating the FGX dry separation method. In case of having more samples with more changeable conditions of the process conductance and more parameters being measured (like sulfur contents, phosphorus contents, mercury contents, different enrichment characteristic of coal) the results would be more adequate to describe the process itself. However, this method is not popular in Poland and requires more studies.

References

[1] Blaschke S 1951 *Przeróbka Mechaniczna Węgla i Rud* Państwowe Zakłady Wydawnictw Szkolnych Warszawa p 309-323
[2] Krukowiecki W 1965 *Przeróbka Mechaniczna Kopalin* PWN Warszawa p 154-159
[3] Blaschke S 1972 *Przeróbka Mechaniczna Kopalin* Wydawnictwo "Śląsk" Katowice p 314-321
[4] Baic I, Blaschke W and Szafarczyk J 2014 Dry Coal Cleaning Technology *Inż. Min. – J.of the Pol. Min. Eng. Soc.* **34** p 257-262
[5] Sobko W, Blaschke W and Baic I 2016 Constructional Improvements of FGX-1 Air Concentrating Table Aiming at Optimization of Operation *Inż. Min. – J.of the Pol. Min. Eng. Soc.* **37** 37-46
[6] Tangshan Kaiyuan Coal Preparation Technology Co. Ltd *Materiały promocyjne i katalogi*

http://www.kyxuanmei.com/
[7] Mijał W, Blaschke W and Baic I 2018 *25th World Mining Congress Proceedings* Astana Kazakhstan p 224-235
[8] Wieniewski A, Szczerba E, Nad A, Łuczak R, Kołacz J and Szewczuk A 2015 Ocena możliwości zastosowania nowoczesnych technik separacji do wstępnego wzbogacania rudy Zn-Pb *CUPRUM – Czas. Nauk.-Tech. Gór. Rud* **2** 109-122
[9] Comex Polska Sp. z o.o. *Materiały promocyjne i katalogi* http://www.comex-group.com/pl/
[10] Baic I, Blaschke W and Sobko W 2015 Badania nad odkamienianiem energetycznego węgla kamiennego na powietrznych stołach koncentracyjnych *Rocz. Och. Śro. - An. S. The Envir. Prot.* **17**. 958-972
[11] Mijał W, Blaschke W and Baic I 2018 Sucha metoda wzbogacania węgla w Polsce *Przeg. Gór.* **11** 9-18.
[12] Biuletyn informacyjny o suchej separacji w RPA *Dry Mineral Processing* http://www.genet.za.com/CMS/?page_id=188
[13] Mijał W and Tora B 2018 *IOP Conf. Ser.: Mat. Sci. and Eng.* Development of dry coal gravity separation techniques **427** 1–8 MEC 2018 : Mineral Engineering Conference : 26-29 September 2018, Zawiercie, Poland.
[14] Blaschke W 2013 Nowa generacja powietrznych stołów koncentracyjnych *Z. Nauk. IGSMiE PAN* **84** 67-74
[15] Blaschke W 2014 Zasady wzbogacania na powietrznym stole koncentracyjnym *Czas. Tech. KTT* **154-161** 10-14
[16] Blaschke W, Baic I, Sobko W and Biel K 2016 Usuwanie siarki z węgla kamiennego z wykorzystaniem stołu koncentracyjnego FGX *Z. Nauk. IGSMiE PAN* **95** 137-144
[17] Blaschke W, Baic I, Sobko W and Biel K 2018 Usuwanie siarki z węgla kamiennego z wykorzystaniem wibracyjno-powietrznego separatora typu FGX *Czas. Tech. KTT* **176-177** 10-14
[18] Baic I, Blaschke W, Dziok T, Strugała A and Sobko W 2017 Badania podatności węgli energetycznych na zmniejszenie zawartości rtęci na etapie pre-combustion *Z. Nauk. IGSMiE PAN* **98** 103-114
[19] Baic I and Blaschke W 2017 Badania wstępne nad ograniczeniem zawartości rtęci w energetycznym węglu kamiennym poprzez zastosowanie wibracyjnego powietrznego stołu koncentracyjnego *Rocz. Och. Śro. - An. S. The Envir. Prot.* **19** 480-496
[20] Dziok T, Strugała A, Chmielniak T, Baic I and Blaschke W 2017 *Z. Nauk. IGSMiE PAN* Koncepcja hybrydowego procesu usuwania rtęci z węgla kamiennego **98** 125-135
[21] Baic I, Blaschke W, Dziok T, Strugała A and Sobko W 2018 Badania podatności węgli na zmniejszenie zawartości rtęci w koncentratach metodą wzbogacania na sucho *Czas. Tech. KTT* **176-177** 15-23
[22] Baic I and Blaschke W 2018 Badania wstępne nad ograniczeniem zawartości rtęci w energetycznym węglu kamiennym poprzez zastosowanie wibracyjnego-powietrznego stołu koncentracyjnego *Czas. Tech. KTT* **176-177** 24-31
[23] Dziok T, Strugała A, Chmielniak T, Baic I and Blaschke W 2018 Koncepcja hybrydowego procesu usuwania rtęci z węgla kamiennego *Czas. Tech. KTT* **176-177** 32-37
[24] Blaschke W and Baic I 2018 Poprawa parametrów rozdziału węgla w osadzarkach poprzez wstępne uśrednianie nadawy metodą odkamieniania na sucho *Z. Nauk. IGSMiE PAN* **104** 163-172
[25] Blaschke W and Baic I 2018 Poprawa parametrów rozdziału węgla w osadzarkach poprzez wstępne uśrednianie nadawy metodą odkamieniania na sucho *Czas. Tech. KTT* **176-177** 45-50
[26] Baic I, Szafarczyk J and Blaschke W 2015 Matematyczny model pracy powietrznego stołu koncentracyjnego typu FGX *Z. Nauk. IGSMiE PAN* **90** 57-66

Influence of grinding on flotation of industrial semi-product from sedimentary copper ore upgrading process

K Ostrowski, A Bakalarz and M Duchnowska

[1]Wrocław University of Science and Technology, Faculty of Geoengineering, Mining and Geology, Wybrzeże Wyspiańskiego Street 27, 50-370 Wrocław

E-mail: alicja.bakalarz@pwr.edu.pl

Abstract. The effect of the grinding and liberation changes of sulphide minerals on their floatability in the flotation process of concentrate from rougher flotation from the Rudna Concentration Plant (KGHM Polska Miedz SA) was analyzed. It has been found that the upgrading selectivity decreases with the decreasing size of sulphide particles regardless of liberation degree. The best selectivity of flotation was observed for the fully liberated sulphides. Totally locked sulphides and minerals marginally liberated are characterized by very poor upgrading selectivity or even no upgrading. Moreover, for the smallest particles of sulphides (below 20 μm), despite of good liberation, very low selectivity of enrichment is observed. It was found that the application of one-stage grinding of concentrate from rougher flotation in separation circuit can result in higher upgrading selectivity of cleaning stages and higher content of useful minerals in final concentrate.

1. Introduction

Flotation is the most versatile technique used in mineral processing [1]. The selectivity and efficiency of flotation relies on various factors e.g. particle size, mineralogy, reagent type and dosage, air flow rate or solid content [1-4].

According to Pease et al [5], the finer particles tend to be more liberated, different than coarse particles. To achieve the liberation of valuable minerals, reducing of grain size should be conducted [6,7]. The possibility of achieving liberation by comminution is strongly related to textural relationship between minerals [7,8]. Three textural features appear as the most significant for mineral liberation characterization: grain size, grain boundary irregularity and the pattern of intergrowth type [8-10]. Quality and quantity of composites determine location of the mineralogical limit to flotation or theoretical grade recovery [7].

Inadequate liberation is often the main reason of the poor upgrading performance. This is the reason that process mineralogy study is highly required to control the plant performance [11]. It helps understand and predict flotation concentrate grade and recovery, and understand and predict causes of dilution to concentrate or losses to tailings [12].

Based on flowsheet of technological circuit at Rudna Concentration Plant (KGHM Polska Miedz SA), the concentrate from I and II cascade of rougher flotation is directed into first cleaning flotation operation. It is assumed that the grains in concentrate are too coarse and valuable minerals not liberated enough. The aim of this paper is the analysis of influence of one-stage grinding on the flotation selectivity and changes of sulphide liberation. The effect of comminution on upgrading of sulphide minerals liberated in various degree and upgrading of sulphide of different size was studied.

2. Experimental

2.1. Materials and methods

A representative sample of concentrate from I and II cascade of rougher flotation stage was collected from Rudna Concentration Plant (KGHM Polska Miedz SA). It was collected for 3 days, at each three work shifts. The content of copper in examined sample was 7.5%. The mass of flotation feed was 300 g. Two flotation experiments were performed. The first test was performed for the raw sample of concentrate, while in the second test the feed, before the upgrading process, was grounded in a laboratory ball mill in 30 minutes. All flotation tests were conducted in a Denver D12 laboratory flotation machine equipped with 1.5 dm^3 flotation cell, in the presence of process water salinity. The air flow rate was regulated during each flotation test using a rotameter. Industrial mixture of sodium ethyl and isobutyl xanthate and sodium O,O-diethyl dithiophosphate in proportion of 7:3 and the dose of 20 g/Mg was used as a collector. An aqueous solution of mixture of alkyl polyglycol ethers was utilized as a frother at a dosage of 5 g/Mg in each flotation tests. Both reagents were prepared directly before flotation test. Four concentrates and one tailing were collected in each flotation test. After the experimental part, all the products were dried and weighted. Mineral analyses were performed using the QEMSCAN® automated mineral analysis system. The content of copper was determined by using an iodic titration.

The analysis of the influence of sulphide minerals liberation on their flotation was carried out for five particle size fractions: 0–20 μm, 20–40 μm, 40–71 μm, 71–100 μm and above 100 μm. Liberation analysis was performed for liberation ranges as follows: 0–10% (totally locked particles), 11–20%, 21–30%, 31–40%, 41–50%, 51–60%, 61–70%, 71–80%, 81–90%, 91–99% (impregnations) and 100% (free particles). These data were calculated for main sulphides of copper (chalcocite/digenite/djurleite, chalcopyrite, bornite, covellite and tennantite), zinc (sphalerite), lead (galena) and iron (pyrite with marcasite).

2.2. Results and discussion

The results of particle size analysis are presented in Table 1. The results of flotation were evaluated by the mass balance of components and products of separation as well as by plotting recovery-recovery (the Fuerstenau upgrading curve) and grade-recovery separation curves (the Halbich upgrading curve).

As it can be shown in Table 1, the particle size decreased markedly after wet milling, especially it is noticeable for fines content.

The upgrading results for copper are presented in Figures 1 and 2. As it has been shown, significantly better upgrading results were observed in test with using grinding operation before the flotation. In this test the higher selectivity of process as well as the quality of flotation concentrate was observed. It is desired result because the concentrate from I and II cascade of rougher flotation is directed into cleaning stages. Improving the quality of concentrate and selectivity of cleaning flotation results in higher content of useful minerals in final concentrate.

Table 1. Particle size distribution of flotation feeds.

Particle size (mm)	Yield, γ (%)	
	Raw sample	Sample after milling
<0.020	38.1	50.6
0.020–0.040	29.0	32.2
0.040–0.071	21.7	14.7
0.071–0.100	7.2	2.2
>0.100	4.0	0.3

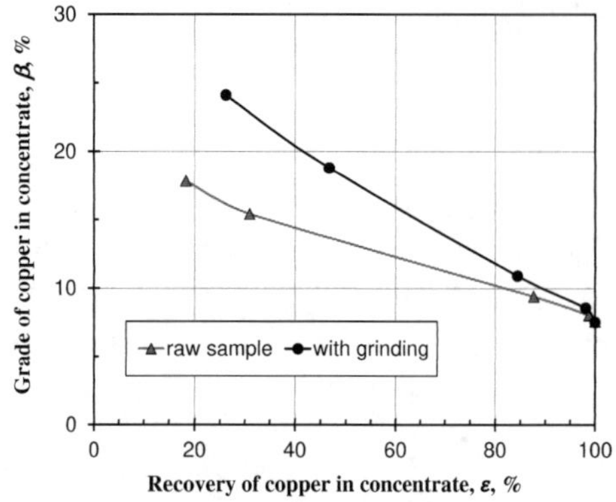

Figure 1. Copper grade in concentrate vs. recovery of copper in concentrate

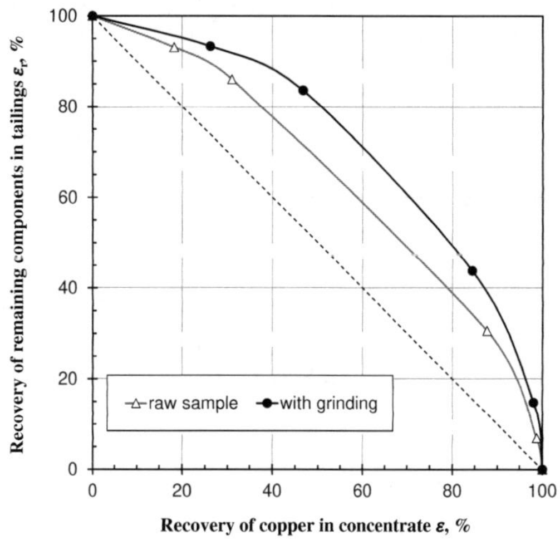

Figure 2. Recovery of copper in concentrate vs. cumulative recovery of remaining components in tailing

As it is presented in Figures 3-7, the applying the grinding has an impact on the enrichment of sulphide minerals in each size fraction and liberation degree. The greater degree of sulphides liberation the higher selectivity of flotation process is observed in each size fraction. Moreover, the differences in the position of each upgrading curves of the analysed liberation ranges are larger in test with applying of one-step grinding. It is the most visible for the particles size of 0–40 and 71–100 μm.

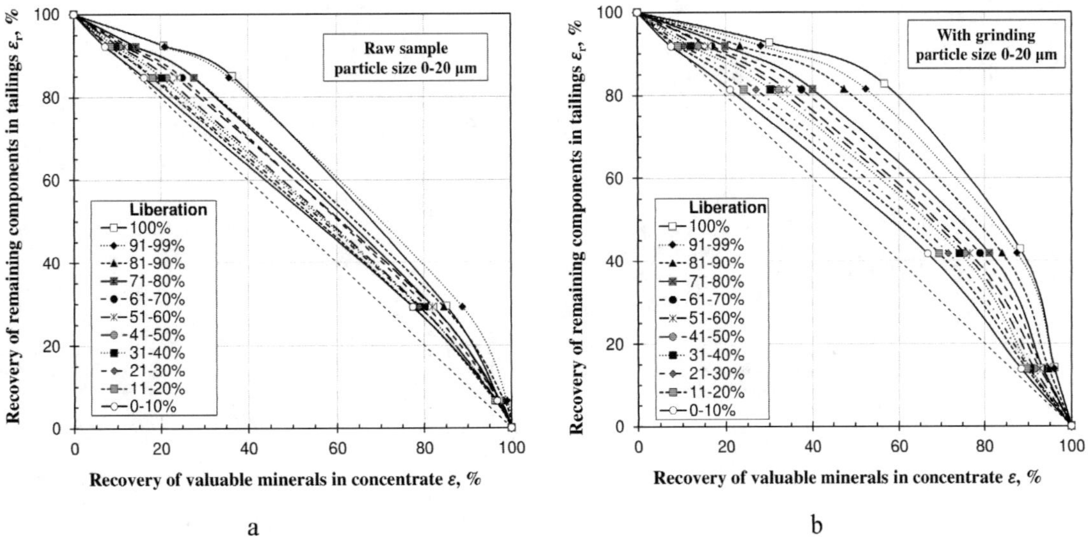

Figure 3. Recovery of sulphides in concentrate vs. recovery of remaining components in tailing in size fraction 0–20 µm for flotation test of raw sample (a) and with grinding stage (b).

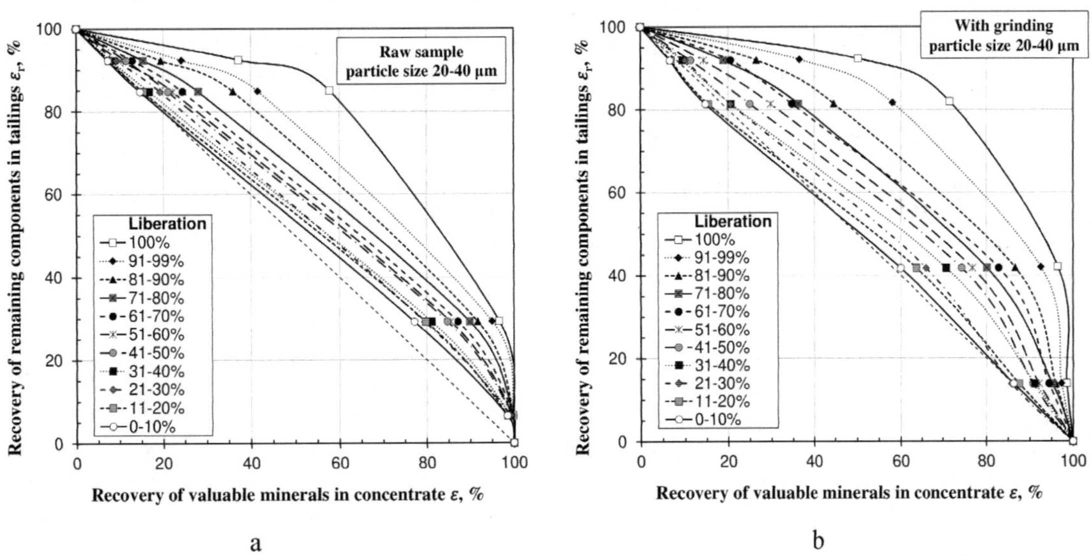

Figure 4. Recovery of sulphides in concentrate vs. recovery of remaining components in tailing in size fraction 20–40 µm for flotation test of raw sample (a) and with grinding stage (b).

IOP Conf. Series: Materials Science and Engineering **641** (2019) 012026 doi:10.1088/1757-899X/641/1/012026

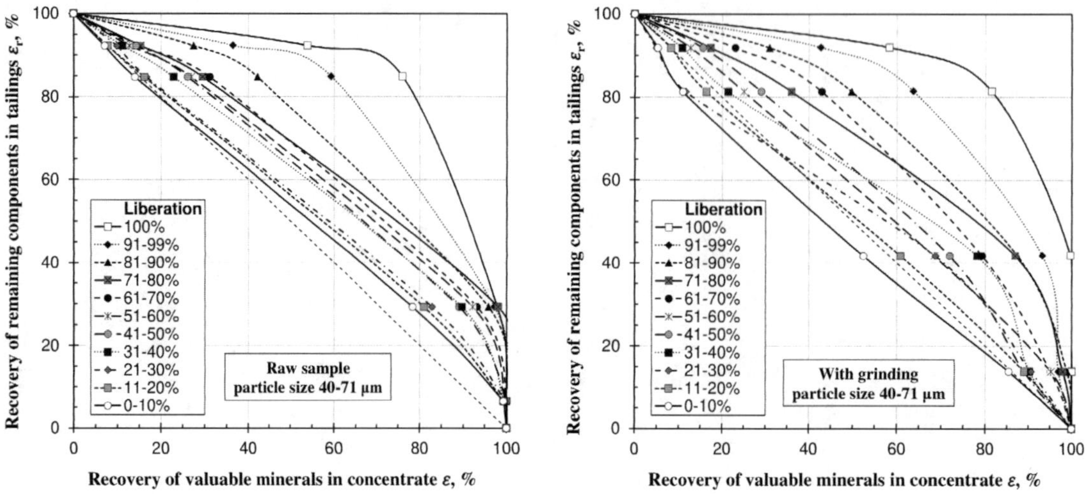

a b

Figure 5. Recovery of sulphides in concentrate vs. recovery of remaining components in tailing in size fraction 40–71 μm for flotation test of raw sample (a) and with grinding stage (b).

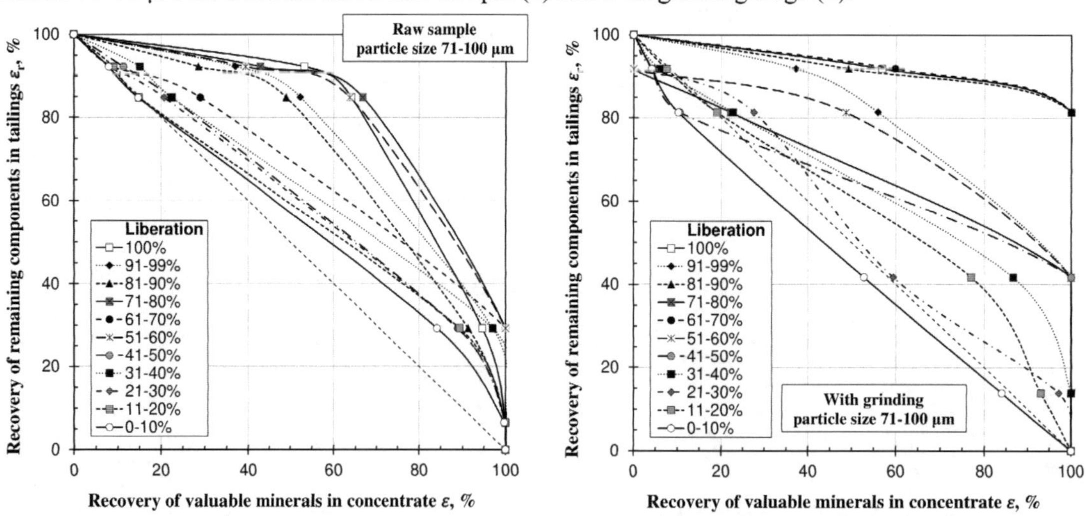

a b

Figure 6. Recovery of sulphides in concentrate vs. recovery of remaining components in tailing in size fraction 71–100 μm for flotation test of raw sample (a) and with grinding stage (b).

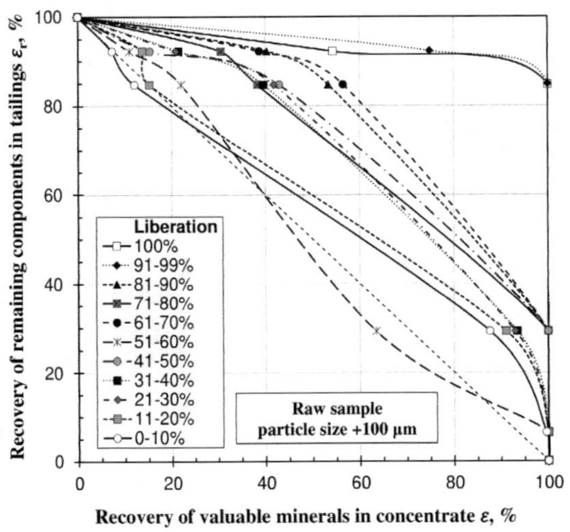

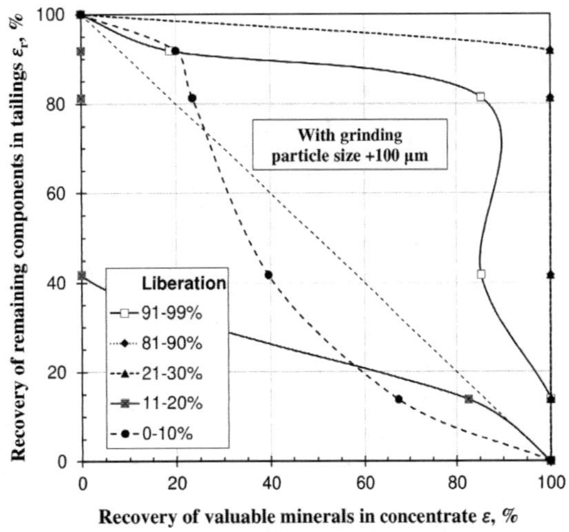

a b

Figure 7. Recovery of sulphides in concentrate vs. recovery of remaining components in tailing in size fraction +100 µm for flotation test of raw sample (a) and with grinding stage (b).

A very poor upgrading selectivity or no upgrading is observed for totally locked sulphides and minerals marginally liberated. It is noticeable mainly for smaller sulphides particles.

The highest selectivity of upgrading of fully liberated grains (100%) can be seen for the coarsest sulphides while poorer selectivity is observed with the decreasing of particle size. For the smallest particles (below 20 µm), despite of good liberation of sulphides, quite low selectivity of enrichment is observed (Figures 3a,b). These results confirm data from literature on the problems of flotation of fines. It is quite interesting, that e.g. for the sulphides liberated in 100% the applying of grinding improves their selectivity in all size fractions. Unfortunately, for the size fractions +100 µm, problems with the interpretation of the obtained results are observed (Figures 7a,b).

Additionally, the data points forming the Fuerstenau upgrading curve were approximated using the following equation [13]:

$$\varepsilon_r = a\frac{100-\varepsilon}{a-\varepsilon},$$

where ε stands for the recovery of useful minerals in concentrate while ε_r stands for the recovery of the remaining components in the tailing. This equation is a result of second-order flotation kinetics of useful and nonuseful components in the ore [14]. The upgrading results, fitted with this equation and plotted as the Fuerstenau separation upgrading curve, form a symmetrical plot with reference to diagonal. Ideal upgrading is observed for *a* equal to 100, and *a* values greater than 100 indicate lower selectivity. Therefore, the higher values of *a* the lower selectivity. Relationships between all possible to calculate selectivity indicators and particle size for all analyzed liberation ranges for flotation tests are presented in Figures 8a,b.

It can be seen in Figure 8a that the values of selectivity indicators increase with the decreasing size of sulphide particles regardless of liberation degree. Moreover, Figures 8a,b clearly show that applying one-stage grinding of concentrate from rougher flotation results in higher upgrading selectivity of sulphide minerals without regard to particle size. The lower values of selectivity indicator (greater efficiency of flotation) are observed in particular strongly for fine sulphides (below 40 µm) in test with additional grinding operation.

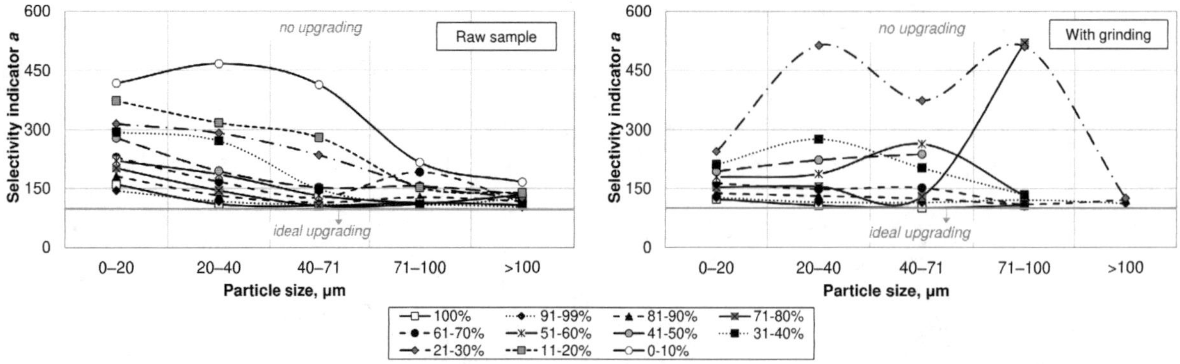

a b

Figure 8. Relationship between the selectivity indicator and particle size for all analyzed liberation ranges for flotation test of raw sample (a) and with grinding stage (b).

2.3. Summary and conclusions

In the paper two laboratory flotation tests of raw sample of concentrate from I and II cascade of rougher flotation (Rudna Concentration Plant, KGHM Polska Miedz SA) and with applying one-stage grinding operation were conducted. The effect of the grinding on the flotation selectivity and the changes of sulphide liberation was analysed in details. The analysis was performed for the main sulphides which occur in the sedimentary copper ore. It was found that the applying of one-stage grinding results in higher liberation of useful minerals from the gangue and improve the selectivity of the upgrading process. The upgrading selectivity decrease with the decreasing size of sulphide particles regardless of liberation degree. In both flotation tests, the best selectivity of flotation was observed for the fully liberated sulphides. Totally locked sulphides and minerals marginally liberated are characterized by very poor upgrading selectivity or even no upgrading. Moreover, among all analysed size fractions, for the smallest particles of sulphides (below 20 μm), despite of good liberation, very low selectivity of enrichment is observed.

In conclusion, an application of one-stage grinding of concentrate from rougher flotation in the technological circuit increases upgrading selectivity of sulphide minerals through the improvement of liberation degree in each particle size fraction. It can result in higher upgrading selectivity of cleaning stages and higher content of useful minerals in final concentrate.

3. References

[1] Wills B A and Finch J A 2016 *Wills' Mineral Processing Technology, An Introduction to the Practical Aspects of Ore Treatment and Mineral Recovery* (Eight Edition, Elsevier Ltd.)
[2] Asghari M, Nakhaei F and VandGhorbany O 2019 *Energ Source Part A* **41/6** pp 761–778
[3] Girgin E H, Do S, Gomez C O and Finch J A 2006 *Miner Eng.* **19** pp 201–03
[4] Shahbazi B, Rezai B and Koleini S M J 2010 *Chem Eng Process* **49** pp 622–27
[5] Pease J D, Curry D C and Young M F 2006 *Miner Eng.* **19** pp 831–840
[6] Ge B, Liu S, Nie Q, Li Q and Zhu Ch 2013 *Sep Sci Technol* **48** pp 1900–1905
[7] Bradshaw D 2014 *Proceedings of IMPC, Santiago, Chile, October 2014*
[8] Pérez-Barnuevoa L, Pirardb E and Castroviejo R 2013 *Miner Eng.* **52** pp 136–142
[9] Petruk W 2000 *Applied Mineralogy in the Mining Industry* (first ed.) Elsevier Amsterdam The Northerlands
[10] Gaudin A M 1939 *Principles of Mineral Dressing* McGraw-Hill New York
[11] Celik I B, Can N M and Sherazadishvili J 2011 *Min Proc Ext Met Rev* **32** pp 30–46
[12] Cropp A F, Goodall W R and Bradshaw D J 2013 *The Second AusImm International Geometallurgy Conference* (Brisbane, QLD, 30 September-2 October, 2013) pp 279–291
[13] Bakalarz A, Duchnowska M and Pawlos W 2018 *Miner Metall Proc* **35(1)** pp 19–23
[14] Bakalarz A, and Drzymala J 2013 *Physicochem Probl Mi* **49(2)** pp 443–451

Acknowledgments
The research presented in the paper is the part of project titled "Development of highly effective technology of Polish copper ore beneficiation". This project is carried out by the consortium with the Wroclaw University of Science and Technology as leader, agreements No.: NCBR: CuBR/I/7/NCBR/2015 and KGHM Polska Miedz SA: KGHM-BZ-U-1023-2015. Financial support by the Polish Statutory Research Grant (0402/0044/18) is also greatly acknowledged.

PSG method for the simulation of carbon particles accumulation in the flotation process

D. Kalisz[1], K. Kuglin[1], A. Młynarczykowska[2]

[1] AGH University of Science and Technology, Faculty of Foundry Engineering, 23 Reymonta Street, 30-059 Kraków, Poland

[2] AGH University of Science and Technology, Faculty of Mining and Geoengineering, 30 Mickiewicza Street, 30-059 Kraków, Poland

E-mail: dak@agh.edu.pl

Abstract. Carbon agglomeration on the surface of gaseous bubbles in the flotation process has been modeled in this paper. The calculations were based on the PSG method and performed for five strictly defined size groups of carbon particles (M=5) for initial sizes 100-400 μm, and mixing energy $\varepsilon = 0.01$ [m^2 s^{-3}]. The analysis of the obtained results revealed that the process was much faster for particles with bigger initial size 300 and 400 μm. In this case the time needed for the removal of particles in particular size groups was shortest. It was observed for all analyzed cases that the process was most dynamic in the initial phase, whereas at the end of it the agglomerations considerably lowered because of the decreased number of particles in specific groups.

1. Introduction

One of the methods of separating gangue from coal is flotation. The optimal conditions of flotation depend on the concentration of solids in feed, temperature, ph of the solution, size of flotated grains, amount of introduced air as well as time and intensity of mixing. In the course of flotation the carbon particles are separated from the mineral part in the course of Surface phenomena taking place at the air bubble/particle division interface. The hydrophobic force makes the grain adhere to the gaseous bubbles. Heuristic models of flotation kinetics based on the stochastic approach to the process description taking into account the birth and death of flotation aggregates, are described by Brożek and Młynarczykowska [1-3]. The possible agglomeration of carbon particles on the bubble surface is usually analyzed theoretically or experimentally on aqueous models. One of the mathematical methods of agglomeration modeling is the Particle Size Grouping Method. Authors used this method in earlier works to describe agglomeration of nonmetallic inclusions in the process of liquid steel refining from nonmetallic inclusions during flotation [4-5].

2. PSG Method

The process of carbon particle agglomeration during flotation was simulated with the Particle Size Grouping (PSG) method. The algorithm is based on dividing particles into M groups. Each group has a strictly defined size range, which is given and which is changed with the predefined coefficient [6]:

$$R_V = v_k v_{k-1} = \text{constas} \quad (1)$$

where:
v – volume of particle (coal),
k – index of a group.

If $R_v = 2$, the critical particle v_k was formed by two level-lower particles v_{k-1}. Index k describes the number of smallest elements making up the particle. Hence the conclusion that with the agglomeration of particles representing two size-groups, e.g. *k-l* and *k-l*, we can obtain a new particle with a size beyond this group. This new agglomerate is classified as *k* if its size exceeds the initial threshold of group *k*, otherwise it belongs to group *k-l*. This classification of particles affects the change of density of the groups, because:
- two particles form one particle, thus reducing the total number of particles,
- remaining in the group, a particle decreases the number of constituent elements.

If a collision of particles belonging to the interval $i_{c,k-1}$ to *k-l* generates a particle k, then the balance of the population can be calculated with the equation (2) [4-8]:

$$\frac{dn_k}{dt} = \sum \xi_{i,k-1}(r_1 + r_{k-1})^3 n_i \, n_{k-1} + \sum \varsigma_{i,k}(r_i + r_k)^3 n_i \, n_k - \sum(1 + \delta_{ik})(r_i + r_k)^3 n_i \, n_k \quad (2)$$

where :

dimensionless number denisity of size i particles are definied as:

$$n_k = n_k / N_0 \quad (3)$$

$$t = 1{,}3\alpha r_1^3 (\varepsilon/v)^{1/2} N_0 t \quad (4)$$

N_0 – initial total number density of particles (m^{-3}),
N_M – number of fundamental particles making up the biggest agglomeration,
r_I - radius of elementary monomers,
t* - dimensionless time of turbulence collision,
n_i, n_{i-k}, n_k -number density of size *i* ,*i-k* and *k* particles ($/m^3$)
$\xi_{i,k-1}$, $\zeta_{i,k}$ – correction coefficient of particle density in a group,
v – kinematic viscosity (m^2/s^3),
ε – turbulent energy dissipation rate (m^2/s^3),
α – agglomeration coefficient

$$\xi_{i,k-1} = (v_i + v_{k-1})/v_k \quad (5)$$

$$\zeta_{i,k} = v_i/v_k \quad (6)$$

$$r_k = r_k/r_1 \quad (7)$$

$i_{c,k-1}$- size of a particle,
v_i – volume of i-particle (m^3),
δ_{ij} –Kronecker's delta ($\delta_{ij} = 1$ for i=j, $\delta_{ij} = 0$ for i≠j).

If k=3, then i_k=1, at R=2, the sum will consist of two elements, i.e. collision of particles k-2=1 and k-1=2, and the other one k-1 and k-1. Parameter $\xi_{i,k-1}$ represents the fraction of total volume of two colliding particles, which tend to the volume of class „k" :

$$\xi_{i,k-1} = \frac{V_i + V_{k-1}}{V_k} \tag{8}$$

i.e. $\xi_{1,2} = \frac{V_1+V_2}{V_3} = \frac{3}{4}$ for R=2 (9)

and $\xi_{2,2} = \frac{2V_2}{V_3} = 1$ (10)

3. Results of calculations

The collisions of carbon particles during flotation were simulated based on data presented in table 1. The process was analyzed for a population consisting of particles representing the following size groups:

- 0.1 [mm] = 100 [μm]
- 0.2 [mm] = 200 [μm]
- 0.3 [mm] = 300 [μm]
- 0.4 [mm] = 400 [μm]

For calculation purposes, the assumed mixing energy was $\varepsilon = 0.01$ [m^2 s^{-3}].

Table 1. Constants assumed for the modeling

Initial number of particles (N_0) [/m^3]	Agglomeration coefficient, α	Viscosity of fluid η [m^2s^{-1}]
5 000 000	1	$8.937 \cdot 10^{-7}$

The results of calculation for particular variants was presented graphically; the effect of agglomeration was analyzed for a substitute time t^*.

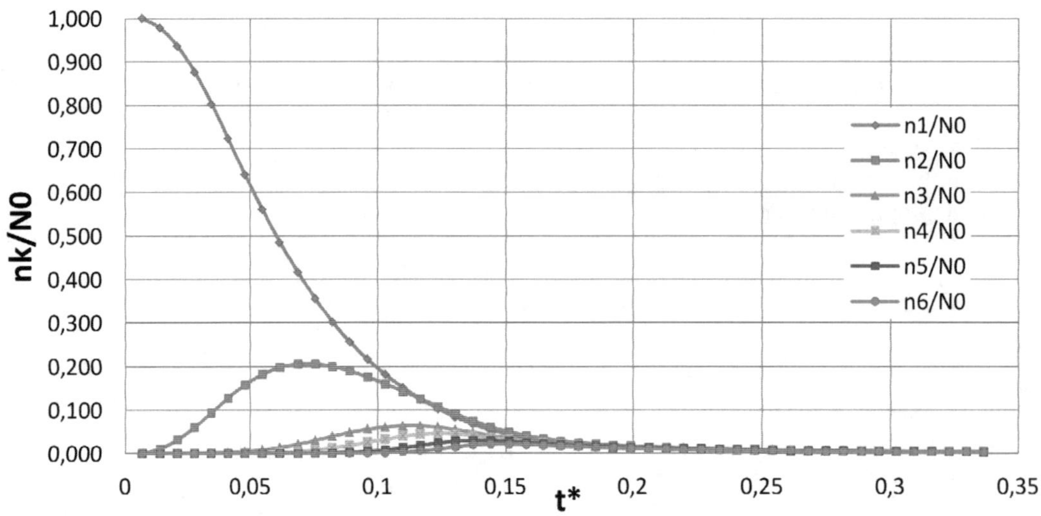

Figure 1. Results of calculations for a particle r = 100 [μm].

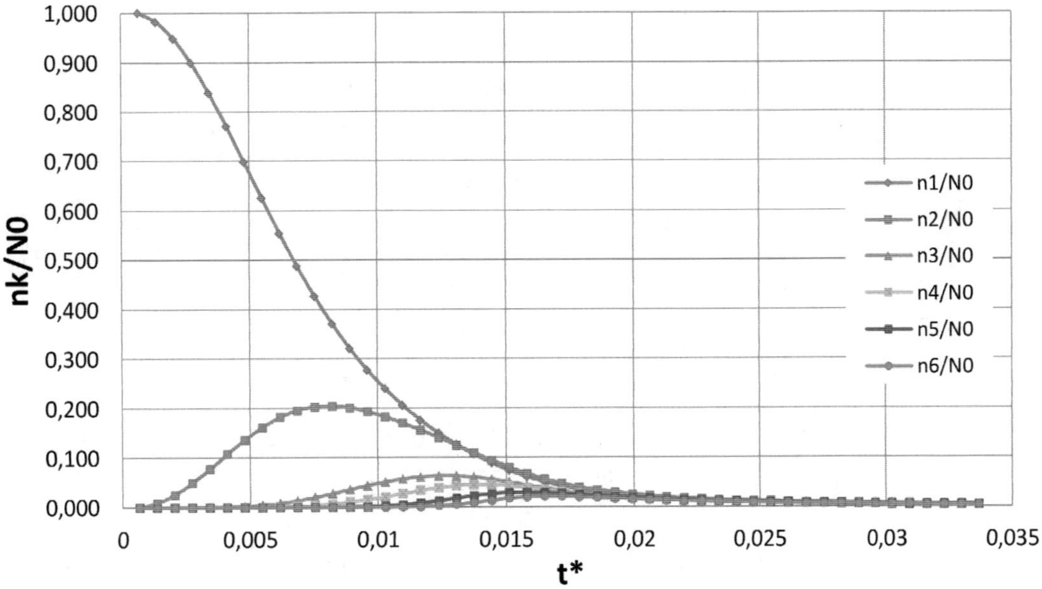

Figure 2. Results of calculations for a particle r = 200 [μm].

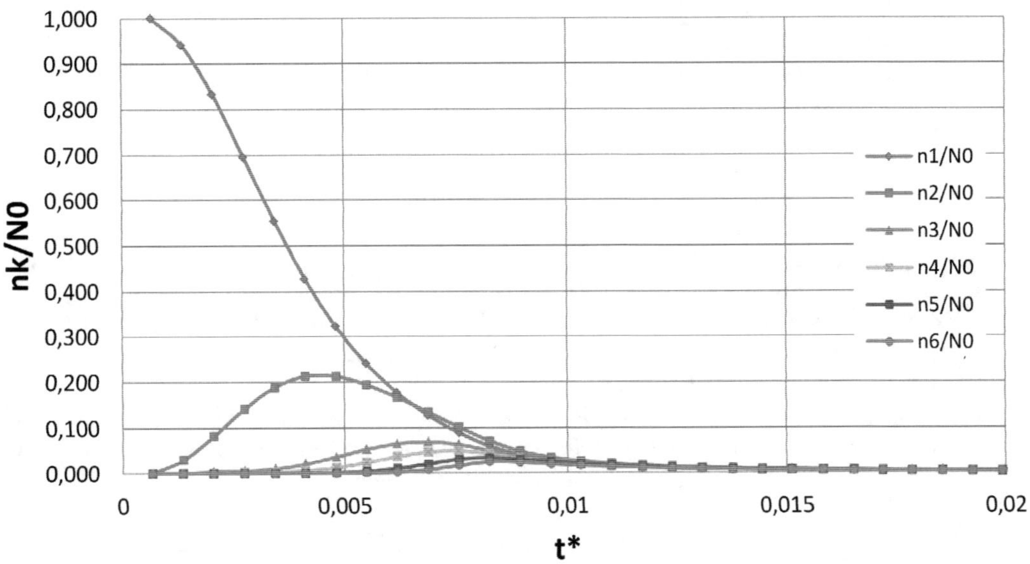

Figure 3. Results of calculations for a particle r = 300 [μm].

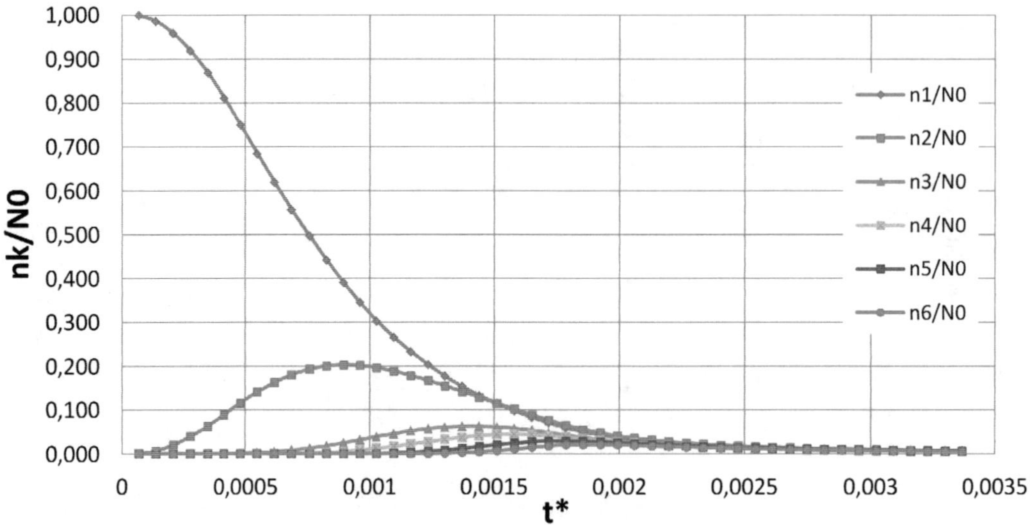

Figure 4. Results of calculations for a particle r = 400 [μm].

The analyzed agglomeration of carbon particles does not mean that flotation takes place. In the process of agglomeration bigger particles are formed as a result of colliding smaller particles, in the course of which bigger particles are formed, the size of which (if exceeding threshold values) is classified in a different size group. It was assumed in the calculations that in the initial stage of the process the particles have only a given radius, e.g. 100 μm (fig. 1). As a result of mixing, the particles collide and new particles are formed in particular, successive size groups. It should be noted that the collisions take place between particles belonging to the same group and between different size groups. This signifies that the initial assumed number of particles 5 000 000/ m^3 does not change and stays constant during the simulation. However various groupings take place as the process (time) proceeds.

The picture of changes of particles in particular groups presented in figures 1-4 illustrates the dynamics of carbon particles removal in the process of mixing a bath containing carbon particles. The process was observed to take place faster for bigger particles, e.g. 400 μm (fig. 4). In the analyzed case time t^8 required for the removal of particles belonging to a size group n1 is 2 orders lower as compared to particles 100 μm – group n1 (fig. 1). Characteristically, in all analyzed cases the biggest dynamics of the process was noted in the initial stage of the process, and were small in group 1 at the end of the process (fig. 1-4), which was caused by the decreasing number of particles in that size group. In this way the probability of occurrence of collision was also lower.

5. Conclusions

Coal flotation in view of mixing-induced agglomerates formation can be analyzed with the PSG method. The collisions cause the formation of bigger particles which are nor chemically bonded; their increase is solely a result of collisions. The assumed number of particles of a give volume remains unchanged over the agglomeration process, though this population is classified in particular size groups as the process proceeds. In the suggested solution only the dynamics of changes of particle size for the assumed mixing energy $\varepsilon = 0.01$ [m^2 s^{-3}] and given particle sizes in group n1 (100, 200, 300, 400 μm) are assumed. The process is definitely fastest in the case of bigger particles.

References

[1] Brożek M, Młynarczykowska A. Application of the stochastic model for analysis of flotation kinetics with coal as an example. *Physicochemical Problems of Mineral Processing* . 2006, 40, 31-44
[2] Brożek M, Młynarczykowska A. Analysis of kinetics models of batch flotation. *Physicochemical Problems of Mineral Processing*. 2007, 41, 51-65
[3] Brożek M, Młynarczykowska A. An analysis of effect of particle size on batch flotation of coal. *Physicochemical Problems of Mineral Processing*. 2013, 49, 341-356
[4] Kalisz D., Żak P L. PSG Method for Simulating of Al_2O_3 inclusions in liquid steel, *Acta Physica Polonica* A, 2016, 130.
[5] Kuglin K, Kalisz D. Effect of Energy Mix on the Phenomenon of Agglomeration of Non – Metallic Inclusion Particles in Liquid Steel, *Transactions of Foundry Research Institute*, 2017, 1
[6] Nakaoka T, Taniguchi S T, Matsumoto K, Johansen S T. Paricle – Size – Grouping Method of inclusion agglomeration and its application to water model experiments, *ISIJ Int.*, 2001, 41
[7] Higashinati K, Yamauchi K, Matsuno Y, Hosokawa G. Turbulent coagulation of particles dispersed in viscous fluid, *Journal of Chemical Engineering of Japan*, 1983, 16, 4
[8] Kalisz D, Żak P L, Kuglin K. Analysis of agglomeration of Al_2O_3 particles in liquid steel, *Archives of Metallurgy and Materials* 2016, 61, 4

New high definition X-ray sorting system based on X-MINE detection technology

J Kolacz

Comex Polska Sp. z o.o., 30-644 Krakow, Poland

jacek.kolacz@comex-group.com

Abstract. The new sorting system has been developed to achieve efficient separation at low mineral content levels. The system employs high sensitivity X-ray sensors providing multi-energy analysis, thus giving maximal information about processed materials. It makes it possible to analyse the internal structure of the particles and directly detect intrusions of minerals and metals like copper or gold. The paper describes sorting application examples for copper ore with metal content under 0.5% Cu. The sorting system still allows high efficiency analysis, quantification and removal of rock particles representing waste fraction with no metal or a negligible amount, being uneconomic to process. This brings a huge advantage, where almost no losses of valuable minerals in the waste fraction are achieved. The presented sorting system has been developed by Comex and X-MINE EU Project Consortium.

1. Current technology and potential new solutions

Processing of metal ores including copper and gold, is mainly based on complex mineral separation. It often includes several processing stages including crushing, grinding, flotation, leaching etc. The processing equipment provides an efficient grinding and separation, however, the operating cost is very high. The main reason is related to very low metal concentration, so the main material steam from the processing plant consists of fine ground waste particles and a very small amount of the metal concentrate fraction. The input material has to be ground to fine sizes to liberate different minerals, separated in complicated flotations circuits, and often treated by complex leaching. The water involved in the process must be recycled. The waste materials often contain toxic elements and compounds, which are problematic for simple landfilling. All these factors generate a very high cost of processing, which in addition indicates increasing tendency due to more and more restrictive environmental regulations.

Pre-concentration of such ore types by sorting, has a huge potential in reducing the processing cost and gaining important environmental benefits. Application of the sensor based sorting is very attractive when compared to other separation technologies. It provides the following advantages, when compared to the traditional systems:

- Possibility to apply in small capacity production lines
- Small space requirement
- No use of water (it is completely dry technology)
- No complicated additional equipment like, pumps, mixers, conditioners, recuperation devices, instrumentation, etc.

IOP Conf. Series: Materials Science and Engineering **641** (2019) 012028 doi:10.1088/1757-899X/641/1/012028

- No requirement of high density powder (ferrosilicon in DMS systems)
- Lower investment cost (about 50%)
- Very low operating cost (about 10 time lower)

Sorting process is very neutral for the environment, does not require water and reduces the cost by about 10-20 times when compared to the traditional mineral processing operations [2],[6]. Ideal pre-concentration means separation of particles containing 0% of ore and providing this with high stability through the severe mining conditions. However, there is always a certain loss of ore particles in such processes, which makes this sorting technology less attractive. Therefore, the sorting process must be carried out with the best possible precision to reduce these losses in the waste fraction. It is only possible by applying technology, which allows detecting the fine ore particles disseminated in the rock material. Currently used XRT sorting technology is often based on dual energy analysis (XRT-DE), which has a resolution of 0.4-0.8 mm. It means, potential ore particles, which have sizes under 400 μm, are not detected at all or they are detected with much lower accuracy, providing significant ore losses in the waste fraction. New technology described in this paper, gives a possibility to detect particles under 50 μm, which provides a significant breakthrough in sorting. An example of copper ore pre-concentration shows the efficient separation of waste particles, practically without any losses.

2. X-ray sorting technology

Application of the sensor based sorting systems, without any doubt, brings a lot of possible advantages in many mineral operations. The main advantage of the new system is related to its universality and at the same time very sophisticated image processing functions, which can be carried out in the same processing unit [1]. Figure 1 shows the CXR system from Comex, in the configuration where many different analysed parameters can be used to provide particle separation. The image analysis system includes a camera installed either over the transport belt conveyor or at its discharge end. The system includes the X-ray attenuation analysis realized by the XRT system in the central part of the conveyor belt. The sorting system can be used with both optical and XRT analysis or separately depending on an application.

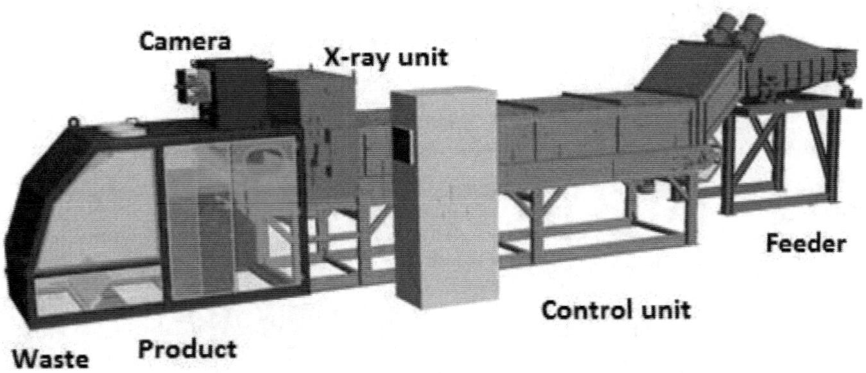

Figure 1. Comex CXR sorting system – configuration with the X-ray and the optical analysis.

Particle recognition used to separate different materials is based on a complex shape and colour analysis where the particles can also be identified by over 20 parameters used for shape description. Some of them are: diameter in different orientations, perimeter, centre of mass, moment of inertia, particle elongation factor, edge sharpness, etc. Additional combinations of these parameters can also be used for distinguishing particles of interest. The surface of particles where different colours or contours vary in intensity and frequency can be analysed by FFT filtration (Fast Fourier Transformation) to recognize differences in texture and structure of the processed particles. This analysis brings much more complex information about the analysed particles rather than colour recognition alone. Finally, the XRT picture is integrated into the optical analysis, which provides a lot more information about the particle surface properties and its internal structure. All these sophisticated analysing functions require a lot of computation power and they have to be optimized to allow high capacity sorting. This is done by special program architecture and algorithm solutions allowing efficient management of the calculation routines and sorting priorities. This allows achieving still high separation capacity and extremely high efficiency (Kolacz, 2014), where the product purity can reach even 99.9 %. Such results can be achieved in different production scale depending on the process requirements [3]. Current sensor based sorting systems with standard sensors are already successfully tested and applied in the metal ore processing like iron ore [1] including Zn/Pb ore [5] and coal [2].

3. New generation sensors

The new sorting system has been jointly developed by Comex, Advacam [4] and X-MINE partners in relation to the X-MINE EU project. The X-ray unit, as shown in Figure 1, sometimes called X-ray gate, contains the complete system for analysis like: X-ray source, detectors, air conditioning, communication devices, etc. It is therefore possible to install different sensors in different configurations inside the unit. The new sensors, developed in X-MINE project, include the highly sophisticated technologies involving high resolution XRT, collimated XRF and 3 D imaging, as shown in Figure 2.

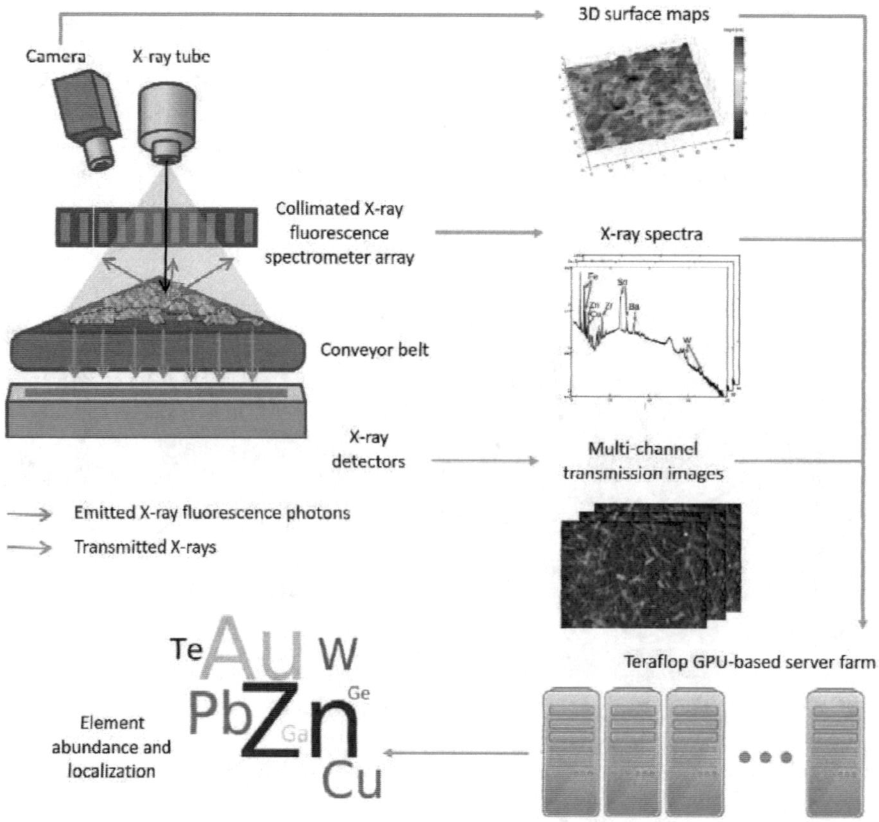

Figure 2. New complex sensor system – configuration with the XRT, XRF and 3D optical analysis.

The XRF detector (Figure 3) provides multi-energy analysis of the transmitted photons with about 50 μm resolution. The XRF sensor provides the collimated analysis of strictly defined areas allowing spectral analysis. Finally, the 3D camera provides the information about the topographic particle structure. The signals from the sensors have a very complex form and contain huge amount of information about each analysed pixel. This requires teraflop GPU based computing systems to analyse the images and provide the digital separation of product and waste particles. It is necessary that this computation sequence is finalised within very limited short time period, typically 5-10 ms. This short computation time is necessary to obtain a reasonable sorting capacity in industrial applications.

Figure 3. New XRT sensor with high resolution.

Applying the new XRT system alone, without XRF and 3D imaging, already allows a very sophisticated analysis, as shown in Figure 4. The high density intrusions having very small sizes, would never be registered by the traditional detectors. The new sensor is able to make the quantification and material differentiation in the micrometre range. Figure 4 shows the spectral response from the sensor indicating different X-ray attenuation characteristics. It allows direct identification of disseminated ore types like gold, copper, zinc, lead, tungsten, chrome, iron, etc.

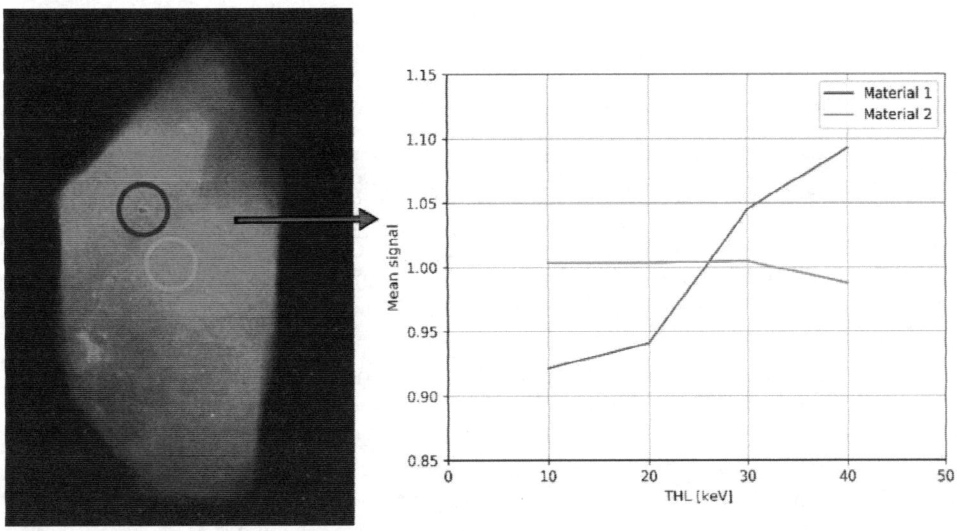

Figure 4. New sensor response indicating high density intrusions in the low density rock material.

Figure 5 shows even more sophisticated analysis. In this case, the high density particles (red colour) like gold or mercury ore, can be identified from medium density particle (yellow) like iron or copper ore, and both types of materials can be differentiated from the regular low density rock (blue). Spectral analysis shown for both materials indicates the differences in X-ray attenuation for both high and medium density particles.

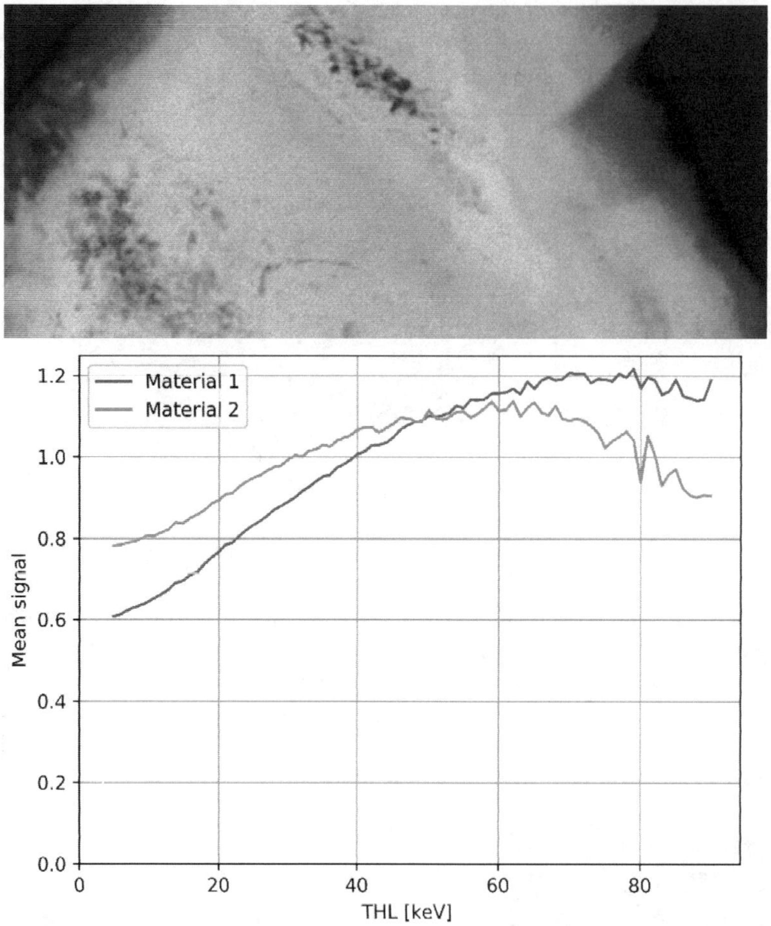

Figure 5. New sensor response indicating medium (yellow) and high (red) density intrusions in the low density rock material (blue).

4. Sorting results

The CXR-1000 X-ray sorting unit with 1 m belt width and the new XRT sensors, has been used for testing of the copper ore. In this case the other sensors as XRF and optical 3D cameras, were not applied. The feed material was fed with the low quality copper ore, where the average metal content varied from 0 to about 2 %. Such ore was completely impossible to sort by using the standard XRT-DE detectors. However, using the new XRT sensors, the low copper content areas in the rock material, could be detected as shown in Figure 6 (right side).

The separated particles were further analysed in terms of chemical composition. Table 1 shows the result from this separation test. The particles containing copper, were identified with very high variations of metal content from 0.01 to 8.96%. This is not unexpected since the copper ore is highly disseminated and very differently concentrated in the rock structure. However, the waste particles were identified with almost no copper content, which is the extremely important factor. This allows much more efficient application of sorting for metal ores, where the metal content is low or very low, and where very low losses in metal recovery can be achieved in the overall process.

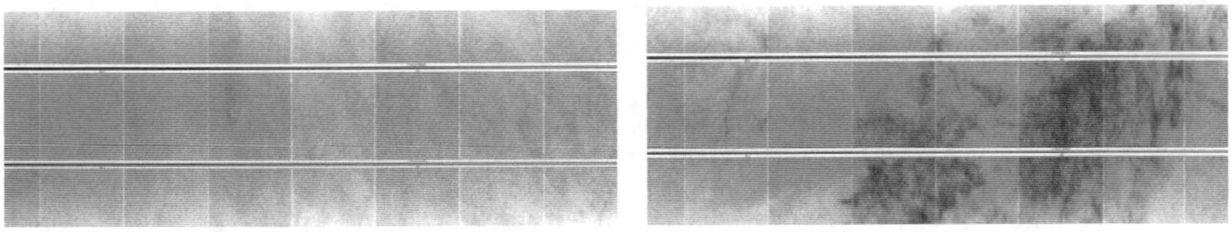

Figure 6. New sensor response indicating waste fraction (left) and disseminated copper ore (right).

Table 1. Sorting results for copper ore.

Batch no.	Unit	Product	Waste
B1	%	2.67	0.01
B2	%	0.14	0.01
B3	%	0.02	0.01
B4	%	1.82	0.02
B5	%	8.96	0.02
B6	%	0.30	0.01
B7	%	0.02	0.01
AVR Cu content	%	1.99	0.011
Yield	%	68	32
Cu recovery	%	99.7	0.3

The same new equipment with new XRT detectors has been tried for gold ore sorting. The sorting results indicate the similar advantage of identifying the ore particles even at the level of 1 ppm, by direct detection of the gold ore. This research work is still not finalized and current results are confidential, thus they cannot be published in this paper.

5. Conclusions

The new XRT sorting detectors can provide a very efficient pre-concentration of most of the metal ores like: Zn-Pb, Cu, Au, W, or other types, before further processing. The detection system allows identification of high density particles being smaller in size than 50 μm. This brings an enormous advantage over the current sorting equipment, where the recovery losses in processing of disseminated ores are limited to the absolute minimum.

Detection of particles smaller than 10-20 μm is not possible in the new detection system, however, this may even help to eliminate particles being uneconomic for further processing. Currently applied mineral processing systems for e.g. coper ore, are not able to separate so fine particles (mainly by flotation). Therefore, the mentioned sorting system can pre-concentrate the particles of metal ores being in the optimal size range for further processing. This brings another advantage to reduce the processing cost and gain the important environmental benefits of pre-concentration. Further development work is carried out in the X-MINE Project Consortium and further new technologies like collimated XRF sensors and 3D imaging, will be possible to combine with the described XRT system. This will bring even more possibilities for further material identification and more efficient sorting of complex minerals or materials. This can make many current mining operations more economic or bring new possibilities for new potential mines, where the current economic or environmental restrictions hinder their start or planning.

6. References

[1] Kolacz J 2014 Sensor based sorting with signal pattern recognition: the new powerful tool in mineral processing *XXVII International Mineral Processing Congress* Santiago-Chile p106-115 2014

[2] Kolacz J 2015 Dry coal beneficiation by sensor based sorting *Mineral Engineering Conference* 14-17 September 2015 Szczawnica Poland

[3] Kolacz J 2016 Efficient scale up of sensor based sorting systems *XXVIII International Mineral Processing Congress* 11-15 September Quebec Canada

[4] Polansky S, Doubravova D, Jakubek J, Jakubek M, Soukup P, Turecek D High-sensitivity on-line imaging analysis of mining ore extraction by X-ray multichannel transmission radiography *IEEE Nuclear Science Symposium and Medical Imaging Conference* Sydney Australia

[5] Wieniewski A, Szczerba E, Nad A, Luczak R, Kolacz J, Szewczuk A Evaluation of the application possibilities of modern separation techniques for pre-concentration of the Zn-Pb ore *XI International Non-Ferrous Metals Conference ICNOP* 27-29 May Trzebieszowice Poland

[6] Wills B A 2006 An Introduction to the Practical Aspects of Ore Treatment and Mineral Recovery *Wills' Mineral Processing Technology:* Seventh Edition, Chapter 11: Dense Medium Separation.

Mineralogical characterisation of Matsitama banded iron ore

C Ramakgala, G Danha

Department of Chemical, Materials and Metallurgical Engineering, College of Engineering and Technology, Botswana International University of Science and Technology, Plot 10071 Boseja Ward, Private Bag 16 Palapye, Botswana

comfort.ramakgala@studentmail.biust.ac.bw

Abstract. A recently discovered Banded Iron Formation (BIF) deposit on the outskirts of a village called Matsitama in the Central part of Botswana, remains unexploited due to inadequate knowledge of its mineralogy and economic value. Currently, Botswana relies on imports in order to satisfy all its iron and steel needs. Exploitation of the Matsitama iron deposit is of critical importance from a socio-economic point of view. To assess the viability and sustainability of potential economic exploitation of the deposit, characterization studies must be conducted on the ore. In this study, chemical and mineralogical examinations were carried out. Mineralogical examination was performed using X-ray Diffraction (XRD), X-ray Fluorescence (XRF) and specific gravity by pycnometer techniques were employed in this investigation. QEMSCAN technology was used to assess bulk mineralogy (BMA) and provide Particle Map Analysis (PMA) of the ore. Major minerals analysis by XRD showed that the ore mainly comprise 54.40% hematite, 44.00% quartz, 1.10% magnetite and 0.50% goethite minerals. XRF analysis established that the ore contains 55.9% Fe2O3 and 44.2% SiO2, with minor amounts of Al2O3, Cr2O3, P2O5 and TiO2 elements. QEMSCAN analysis indicated that 75% of the hematite is fully liberated and 25% associated with quartz. Characterization results showed Matsitama ore to have a moderate hematite grade, silica but low concentration of deleterious elements (<1%) which conform to generally acceptable limits for commercially traded iron ores.

1. Introduction

In recent years Botswana has experienced substantial growth in developments particularly in the construction industry which is a major consumer of iron and steel products. Despite this position, the country relies on imports in order to meet all its demand for iron and steel, with no local production. The Banded Iron Formation (BIF) deposit discovered in Matsitama is of significant importance to the socio-economic development of the nation and presents an opportunity to put Botswana on the world map as an iron ore producing country. Located near Matsitama village in the Central District of Botswana, about 100km west of the city of Francistown (figure 1), this deposit lies unexploited and has not been studied comprehensively.

Figure 1: Location map of Matsitama deposit (marked in red)

From a geological context, iron occupies about 5% of the earth's crust, making it one of the most abundant mineral resources (1). BIFs are the largest sedimentary type of iron ore deposits which occur through precipitation from mineral solutions and date back to the Precambrian period (2). They characteristically consist of alternating layers of iron oxide and silica and they are the major resource of iron ore for the world's current production. (3,4). The increasing global demand for iron ore fuelled by massive consumption of steel worldwide is challenged by the depletion of high grade ores and stringent environmental regulations imposed on the iron and steel industry (5,6).
Chemical and mineralogical characterisation of Matsitama iron deposit will allow for the preliminary evaluation of its economic viability and guide the design of suitable processing routes as well as optimisation of downstream processes. In this study, the quality of Matsitama ore is compared to other hematite BIF ores in South Africa.

2. Materials and methodology

Samples of the Matsitama deposit were collected from surface outcrop as rocks. About 20 chunks of ore samples were collected from the same location and lithology as there were no potentially different ore types identified at the time of sampling. Representative samples were taken to SGS South Africa for chemical and mineralogical analysis using the following technologies:

- X-ray Fluorescence (XRF) - major element analysis
- Pycnometer - specific gravity testing
- X-ray diffraction (XRD) – Quantitative mineral phases
- QEMSCAN Bulk Modal Analysis (BMA) and Particle Map Analysis (PMA) – quantitative mineral analysis, iron deportment, mineral liberations and associations, grain size distributions

2.1. Sample preparation

Three Fe ore rocks (blocks) being analysed were cut in half. A half from each block was combined to make two composite samples as shown in figure 2. One of the composites was stage crushed to 100% passing 1mm. The crushed ore was split into two representative aliquots. A representative sample (10 – 15 g) was split out from one of the crushed aliquots to prepare two polished samples for QEMSCAN analysis. About 50g of the other representative portion was pulverized for XRD, XRF and Specific gravity testing analyses.

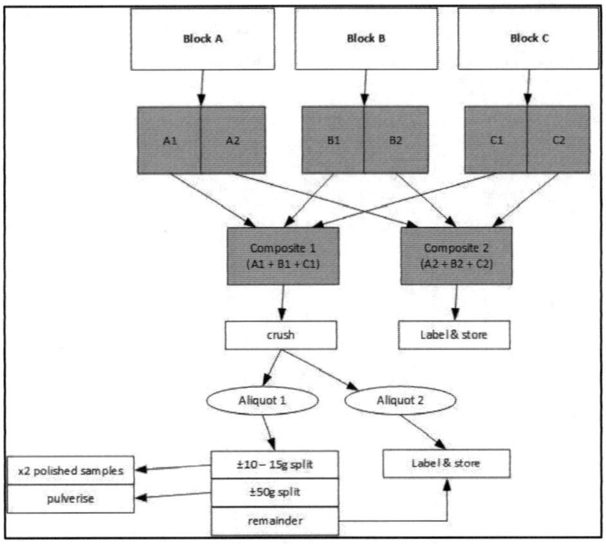

Figure 2: Sample preparation steps

2.2. Quantitative X-ray diffraction

In this investigation the constituents of the samples were studied using X-ray diffraction data obtained from a PANalytic X'Pert PRO diffractometer with a Cu tube X-ray source. The radiation used was a Cu K-α with a wavelength of 1.540598 Å within the values of 2θ between 5 and 90 degrees at steps of 0.029 degrees with a time of 0.45sec/step.

2.3. QEMSCAN

QEMSCAN technology is an automated electron beam technique that functions on a Scanning Electron Microscopy (SEM) platform with four light-element Energy Dispersive X-ray Spectrometers (EDS) (Ayling et al., 2012). In this study, a QEMSCAN 650 instrument was used for analysis. Polished sample blocks were analysed using Bulk Modal Analysis (BMA) to confirm the bulk mineralogy as previously determined by XRD. Particle Map Analysis (PMA) was used to determine iron elemental deportment, iron mineral liberations and associations as well as grain size distributions. The PMA mode is suitable for detailed characterization of mineral particles up to 1mm in size (7).

2.4. X-ray fluorescence

Borate fusion XRF was used for identification of major minerals occurring in the ore sample.

2.5. Pycnometer

Specific gravity of the ore was determined by pycnometer method

3. Results and discussions

3.1. X-ray fluorescence

The results of the XRF analysis in table 1 show that the ore sample contained 55.9% and 44.2% of Fe_2O_3 and SiO_2 respectively. The ore contains 0.028% phosphorus which is low and acceptable as compared to the upper limit of 0.11% imposed by the steel industry. Phosphorus is regarded as an impurity due to its detrimental impacts in steelmaking (8). In addition, the ore contains a considerably negligible amount of alumina (0.14%). Exploitation of Matsitama ore would require significant size reduction to liberate Fe oxides and the ore would therefore be marketed as iron ore concentrate for pellet feed or fines for sinter feed. Alumina is beneficial for forming the SFCA bonding phases (9) which are the most desirable bonding phases in iron ore sinter (10).

Table 1. XRF results for iron ore sample.

Elements	Detection limits %	Assay %
Al_2O_3	0.05 - 100	0.14
CaO	0.01 - 100	<0.01
Cr_2O_3	0.01 - 100	0.06
Fe_2O_3	0.01 - 100	55.9
K_2O	0.01 - 100	<0.01
MgO	0.05 - 100	<0.05
MnO	0.01 - 100	<0.01
Na_2O	0.05 - 100	<0.05
P_2O_5	0.01 - 100	0.028
SiO_2	0.05 - 100	44.2
TiO_2	0.01 - 100	0.02
V_2O_5	0.01 - 100	<0.01
LOI	(-)50 - 100	0.21
SG	0.01 – 13	3.66 (no units)

Matsitama ore contains 54.4% hematite, corresponding to a medium grade ore. It is also evident that the ore is significantly contaminated with quartz which is the silica-bearing mineral. The silica content is very high (44.00 % SiO2) compared to the generally accepted level of 6% for commercial ores.

3.2. Specific gravity by pycnometer

The specific gravity of the ore sample was found to be 3.66. Quartz has a specific gravity of 2.7 while that of hematite is about 5.3. The concentration criterion for this ore was found to be 2.53 which indicates that gravity separation should be relatively easy. The concentration criterion is a density quotient which gives an idea of the type of separation possible for an ore; when the value is greater than 2.5 then gravity separation is relatively easy (11).

3.3. X-ray diffraction

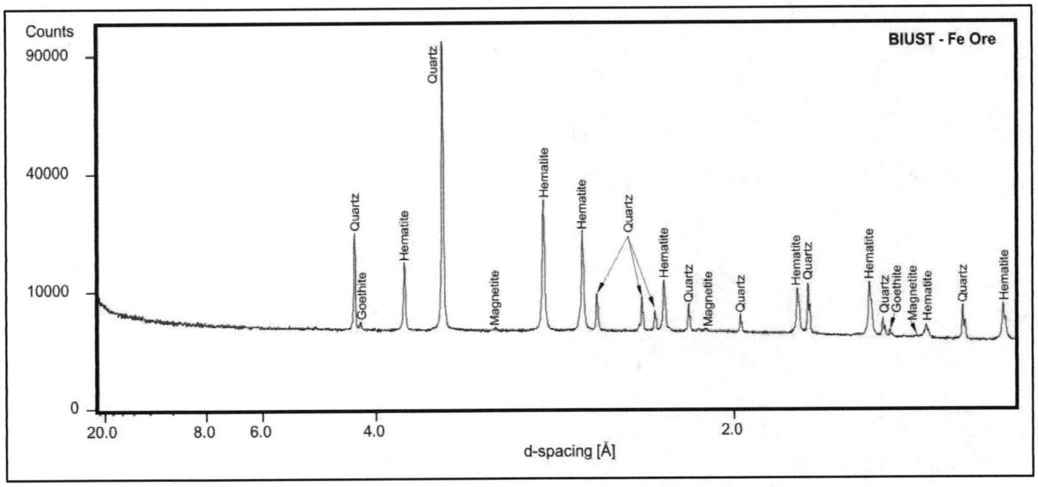

Figure 3: XRD diffractogram of ore sample.

The results obtained from quantitative analysis by XRD shown in table 2 indicate that Matsitama ore comprised ~54 % hematite, ~44 % magnetite, ~0.5% goethite and ~44% quartz. The diffractogram in figure 3 shows that these were the only detected mineral phases in the sample. Hematite was the most abundant iron containing mineral phase present in the sample making up ~97% of the Fe oxide/hydroxide group.

Table 2. Crystalline mineral phases and their abundances (values normalized to 100% of the crystalline proportion of the sample) as determined by XRD

Mineral	Approximate formula	Approximate abundance %
Hematite	Fe_2O_3	54.40
Quartz	SiO_2	44.00
Magnetite	Fe_3O_4	1.10
Goethite	α- FeO•OH	0.50
	Total	100.00

3.4. QEMSCAN

The bulk mineralogy of the iron ore as determined by QEMSCAN BMA analysis is presented in table 3. The investigation established that the iron oxide/hydroxide group constituted 56% of the sample. Quartz was identified as the major gangue mineral with other minerals occurring as traces.

Table 3. QEMSCAN bulk modal analysis results.

Mineral	Approximate abundance
Fe Oxides/Hydroxides	56.25
Quartz	43.70
Pyroxene/Amphibole	0.04
Other	0.01
Total	100.00

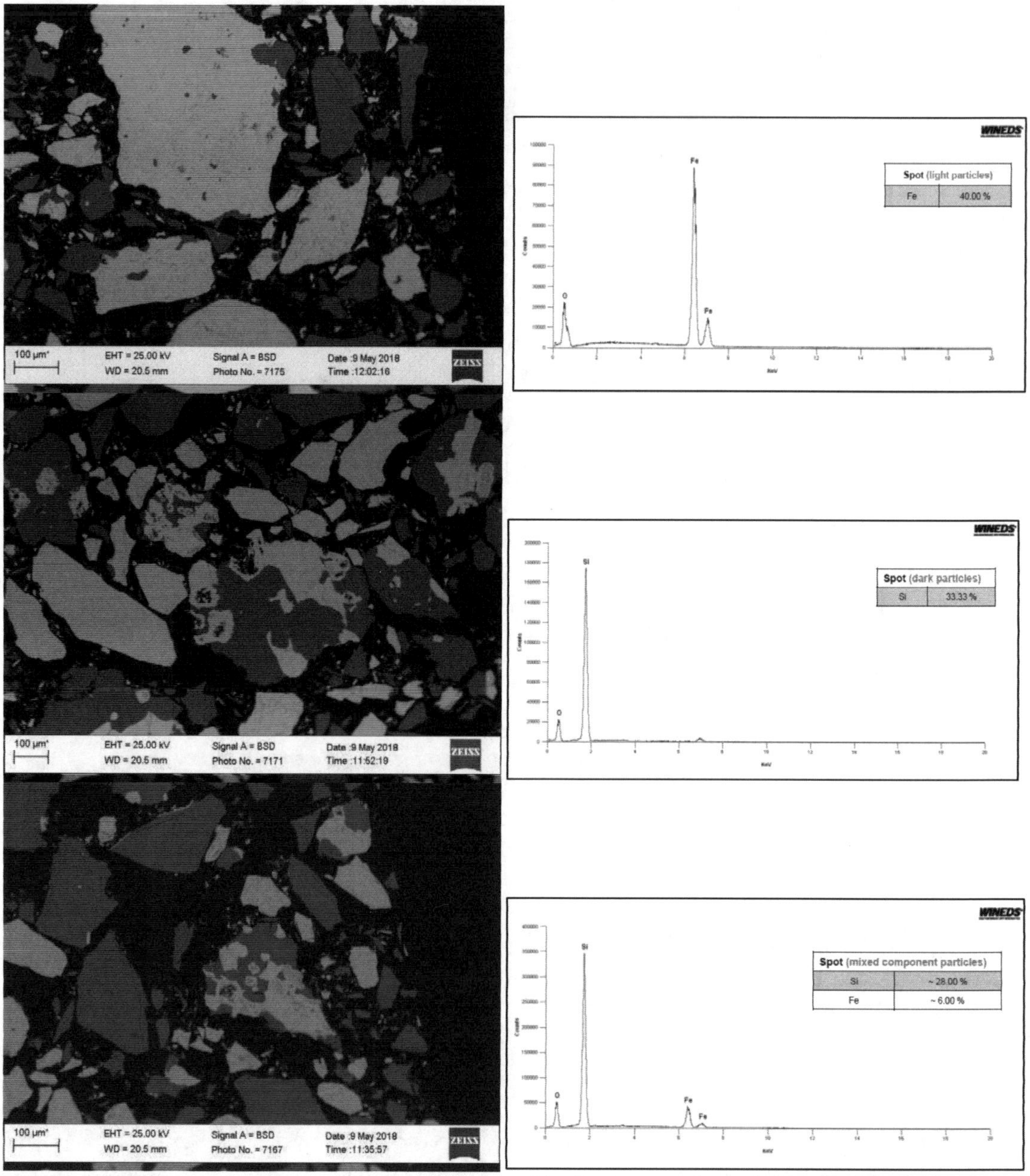

Figure 4: SEM images showing the minerals detected in the ore sample and quantified by BMA

Figure 4 shows SEM images of minerals detected in the ore sample and their quantities. The light particles are Fe_2O_3 and the dark particles are SiO_2. Particles with 'in between' shades are also depicted.

Figure 5 shows that 74.97% of Fe oxide/hydroxide was fully liberated, 20.51% was present in the middlings while 4.52% was associated with quartz. The grain size distributions curve of the two major components making up the sample (Fe oxides/hydroxides and quartz) is presented in figure 6. Approximately 70% of the Fe oxide/hydroxide is greater than 45µm grain size range. It can be deduced that there is an almost even distribution of Fe grains in different size fractions.

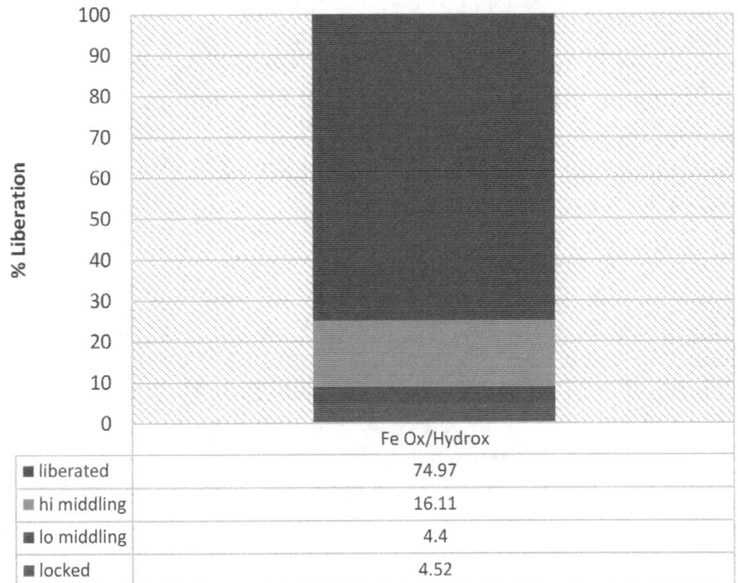

Figure 5: Percentage mass liberation of Fe oxide/hydroxide

In assessing the liberation characteristics, four classes were considered:

- Liberated – more than 80 % area of the particle is the mineral of interest
- High (Hi) middlings – between 50 and 80 % area of the particle is the mineral of interest
- Low (Lo) middlings – between 30 and 50 % area of the particle is the mineral of interest
- Locked – less than 30 % area of the particle is the mineral of interest.

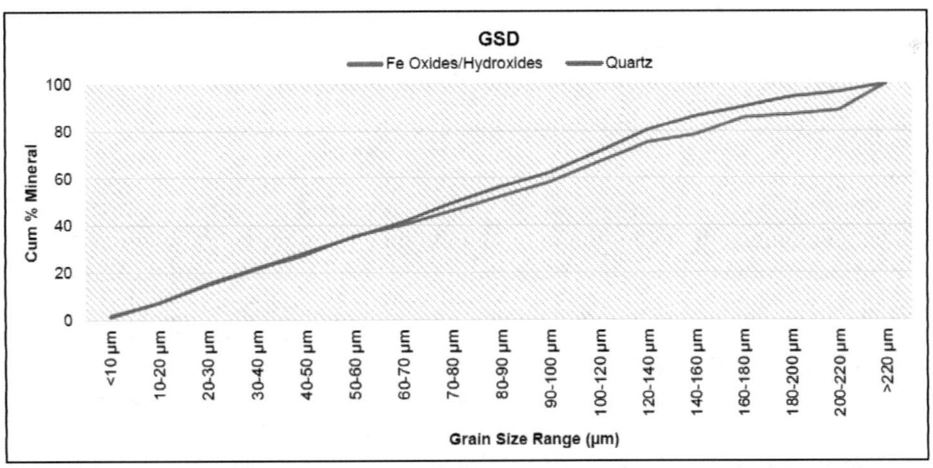

Figure 6: GSD of mineral grains of the two major components in the sample

4. Conclusions

From mineralogical and elemental analysis, it can be concluded that:

- Matsitama iron ore constitutes of hematite, magnetite, goethite and quartz minerals.
- The ore has a relatively low iron content (about 56% Fe), a high level of silica gangue (about 44%), with a low concentration of deleterious elements.

- From our literature reviews, Matsitama ore deposit can be considered economically recoverable based on its grade, however, the size of the deposit and processing requirements must be determined as they significantly affect feasibility of ore exploitation.
- Further work is necessary to estimate the size of the deposit and also to assess the sustainability of resource exploitation.
- Concentration criterion for the ore was determined to be 2.53, indicating that gravity separation can be easily achieved.
- If processed, the ore will be milled significantly, meaning it would be marketed as iron ore fines for sinter feed or iron concentrate for pellet feed.

South Africa has massive iron ore deposits with varying iron content. The Sishen and Thabazimbi deposits are reported (12) to have Fe content of 64.8% and 61% respectively. These are high grade shipping ores which in most cases do not require beneficiation. These high grade hematite ores are reported (13) to have benefited from supergene enrichment over years. Literature review revealed the presence of ore types containing 57.6% hematite associated with 37.5% silica (14). These ores are similar with Matsitama ore in hematite grade, but they have undesirable associations.

5. Recommendation for beneficiation

Characterization of Matsitama ore showed that the ore was moderate grade hematite and requires proper beneficiation before metal extraction. Liberation studies show that the two major constituent minerals (hematite and quartz) are liberated at around 45 microns therefore the ore can benefit from stage grinding at about 90% passing 50µm. The concentration criterion for this ore is more than 2.5 therefore concentration by gravity separation is encouraged. Spirals may be sufficient to enrich the ore to a grade that is acceptable for metal extraction. The middlings can be further milled to a finer size to liberate the hematite from quartz and spiralled again. Further purification may be obtained by using wet high intensity magnetic separation to achieve a required grade.

Acknowledgements

Special thanks to SGS South Africa (Pty) Ltd for supporting the experimental work in this investigation. Sincere gratitude to the co-author Dr. G. Danha for his invaluable input and guidance in this paper. Funding: This work was supported by the Office of Research and Development, Botswana International University of Science and Technology.

References

[1] Clout JMF, Manuel JR 2015 *Mineralogical, Chemical, and Physical Characteristics of Iron Ore. Iron Ore: Mineralogy, Processing and Environmental Sustainability* (Amsterdam: Elsevier)
[2] US Environmental Protection Agency 1994 *Extraction and Beneficiation of Ores and Minerals - Iron*. Washington DC p1–10
[3] Tonžetić I 2015 *Quantitative analysis of iron ore using SEM-based technologies. In: Iron Ore: Mineralogy, Processing and Environmental Sustainability* (Amsterdam; Elsevier)
[4] Ghosh R, Baidya TK 2017 Mesoarchean BIF and Iron Ores of the Badampahar Greenstone Belt, Iron Ore Group, East Indian Shield *J Asian Earth Sci* **150** p25–44
[5] Krishna SJG, Patil MR, Rudrappa C, Kumar SP, Ravi BP 2013 Characterisation and Processing of Some Iron Ores of India *J Inst Eng Ser D* **94** p113–20.
[6] Dwari RK, Rao DS, Reddy PSR 2014 Mineralogical and Beneficiation Studies of a Low Grade Iron Ore Sample *J Inst Eng Ser D* **95** p115–23.
[7] Gottlieb P, Wilkie G, Sutherland D, Suthers S, Perera K, Jenkins B, et al 2000 Microscopy for Process Mineralogy Applications *J Miner Met Mater Soc* **52** p24–5
[8] Matsubae K, Yamasue E, Inazumi T, Webeck E, Miki T, Nagasaka T 2016 Innovations in Steelmaking Technology and Hidden Phosphorus Flows *Sci Total Environ* **542** p1162–8
[9] Lu L, Ishiyama O 2015 *Iron Ore Sintering. Iron Ore: Mineralogy, Processing and*

Environmental Sustainability (Amsterdam; Elsevier)

[10] Webster NAS, Pownceby MI, Madsen IC and Kimpton JA 2012 Silico-ferrite of Calcium and Aluminum (SFCA) Iron Ore Sinter Bonding Phases: New insights into their formation during heating and cooling *Metall Mater Trans B Process Metall Mater Process Sci* **43** p1344–57

[11] Wills BA, Napier-Munn T 2006 *Wills Mineral Processing Technology: An Introduction to the Practical Aspects of Ore Treatment and Mineral Recovery* (Amsterdam; Elsevier)

[12] Hagemann SG, Angerer T, Duuring P, Rosière CA, Figueiredo e Silva RC, Lobato L, et al 2016 BIF-hosted iron mineral system: A review *Ore Geol Rev* **76** p317–59

[13] Lascelles DF 2012 Banded iron formation to high-grade iron ore: A critical review of supergene enrichment models. *Aust J Earth Sci* **59** p1105–25

[14] Mhonde NP, Wiese JG, McFadzean B 2017 Comparison of collector performance for a South African and a Brazilian iron ore considering mineralogical characteristics. *Miner Eng* **113** p55–67

FGX air-vibrating separators for cleaning steam coal – functional and economical parameters

W Blaschke and I Baic
Łukasiewicz Research Network – Institute of Mechanised Construction and Rock Mining, Racjonalizacji 6/8 Street, 02-673 Warsaw
Branch Office in Katowice, Poland

E-mail: wsblaschke@gmail.com, i.baic@imbigs.pl

Abstract. FGX Dry Separators are a construction developed at the turn of the 20th century. It was created in China as a combination of a vertical jet air classifier and a vibration screen with a tapered channel. This structure has been modified (Figure 1). These separators proved to be very effective in deshaling of excavated coal. They are designed to remove as many grains of stone as possible. For this reason, separation is carried out in the thickness range above 2.0 g/cm^3. The article describes the structure of dry separator as well as the principle of its operation. The factors influencing the enrichment efficiency and the separation accuracy of feed parameters have also been listed here. Moreover, the technical parameters of the separator which are subject to regulation and influence the course of the separation process have been discussed. Synthetic information on economic efficiency has been provided. The possibilities of application of FGX separators in the systems of existing enrichment plants or as independent processing plants have been presented. There are currently three FGX separators working in Poland. In the Institute of Mechanised Construction and Rock Mining in the Katowice Branch, the bituminous coal of some mines is tested on an installation with a capacity of up to 10 Mg/h. The results of the research confirm the possibility of implementing FGX separators in the bituminous coal mining in Poland. Two separators, with a capacity of about 30 Mg/h, improve the parameters of imported coal intended for individual customers; they are owned by private companies. More than 2000 FGX separators in more than a dozen countries are in operation in the world. They are effective and are referred to as '21st century technology'.

1. Introduction

Dry blowing is one of the oldest methods of steam coal enrichment. In the 1920s, there were SKB or Buray-Soulary air concentration tables working in reciprocating motion. Pneumatic jiggers called Raw or Humbolt air separation plants were also used. There were also gravitational vertical air jet classifiers separating the materials of different denseness. These devices were withdrawn in the 1950 because of low accuracy of separation and replaced with water jigs [8].

At the break of the 20th and the 21st century, Chinese company Tangshan Shenzhou Manufacturing Ltd. constructed dry separators which are sometimes erroneously referred to as air concentration tables. Their construction combines a vertical jet air classifier and a vibration screen.

Vibration screens were used in UK and USA in the 1940s and 1950s. They were used to dry blow the excavated coal. An example of a vibrating screen type FMC is shown in Figure 1.

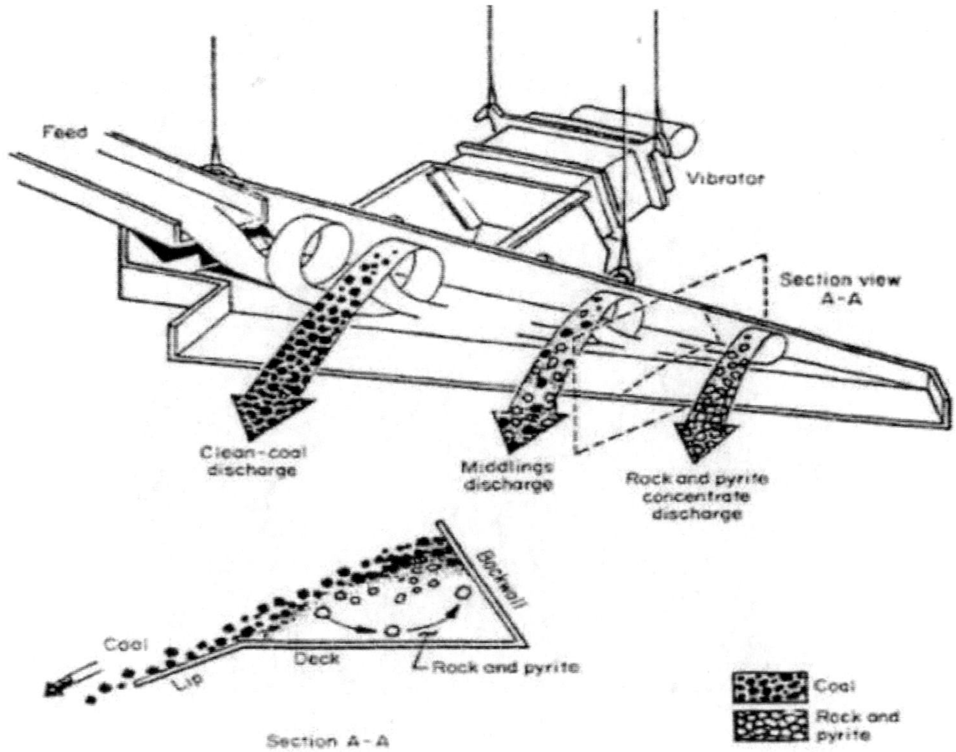

Figure 1. FMC – Vibrating air separator [8].

It consisted of a tapered channel, whose back wall was connected to a vibrator. The material moving within the channel was rotating. Thus it divided into lighter (coal) layer, which was fed to the separator. The heavier layers were fed into further parts of the working channel. In order to improve the separation accuracy, the channel was tapered. These separators were not highly accurate, therefore they were gradually removed from facilities and replaced with jiggers.

In the Chinese construction, the plate is perforated and air is fed through the holes just like in gravitational vertical air jet classifiers. Additionally, there are several slats placed at an angle in relation to the plate. Just like in the vibration screens, the back wall is attached to a vibrator which makes the coal grain rotate. The slats facilitate lifting of the grain and the air jets allow for formation of the suspension layer. How the separator works is described in more detail further in this article.

Air-Vibrating separators like this are marked FGX. It is an acronym of the Chinese name **F**uhe **G**anfa **X**uan mei. According to the producer's information [14,16,17], FGX separators are commonly used in China (more than 1800). The producer manufactures eleven types of those separators with the capacities of 10 through 1000 Mg/h. In Poland, there is an experimental installation in the Katowice branch of IMBiGS (Institute of Mechanised Construction and Rock Mining) and two industrial installations – FGX3 in Gdańsk and Toruń [2].

2. Construction of the air-vibrating separators

FGX air-vibrating separators are devices for dry enrichment of coal. Because they work in the thickness range from 2.0–2.2 g/cm^3, they are commonly called *devices for dry deshaling of excavated coal*. FGX devices consist of two modules: enrichment and dust removal modules [7,15].

ENRICHMENT MODULE – it consists of: conveyor feeding the material to the chute; vibrating conveyor feeding the material to the plate, equipped with a scale; perforated slatted plate mounted on slings; mechanism for changing the position of the plate and vibration frequency; air jet blowing a stream of air with regulation system under the plate; collector collecting the separated products with quantity regulation. The module is additionally equipped with: conveyor belt for collection of coal product, conveyor belt for collection of intermediate products; conveyor belt for collection of waste products. All conveyors are equipped with scales. Thus, each of the dry separation materials is an individual product. The module has a control panel and can be additionally equipped with mobile laboratory module for examining the quality parameters of the raw and processed materials (Figure 2).

Figure 2. Enrichment module [photo IMBiGS].

DUST REMOVAL MODULE - its task is catching the dust from the air circulation within FGX, and thus protecting the natural environment against contamination. The module consists of: rubber sealing screen (hood) over the working plate; collector transporting the contaminated air from the area above the plate to the dust extraction cyclone; the vertical vacuum cyclone extracts the grains of dust, which are discharged from the cyclone through a screw conveyor; a collector discharging the contaminated air from the remaining space above the working plate to a series of bag filters; the series of bag filters is closed with a container for the collected dust with a vibrating device – periodically run vibrating mechanism empties dust grains from filtration bags; the series of filters include an independent (auxiliary) exhaust fan used to create vacuum in the end part of the space above the working plate and to create a draught in the direction allowing to transport the air to the filtration process; the main exhaust fan used to create vacuum in the first part of the space covered by the rubber screen over the working plate and in the cyclone. According to the manufacturer's data, about 75% of the air is circulating in the system, i.e. it is driven by the exhaust fan to the cyclone dust extractor and is reused. The remaining part, about 25% of the air, is cleaned by a bag dust remover and is released to the atmosphere. The efficiency of the applied dust removal process is about 99.5%. The dust grains discharged from the dust extraction system are an individual product of the dry separation process (Figure 3)

Figure 3. Dust removal module [photo IMBiGS].

3. Separator operation

Excavated coal is transported by the feeder to a perforated and slatted separator working plate, which is made to vibrate by a vibrator. Under the plate, there are several air chambers fuelled by a centrifugal fan. The air passes through holes in the plate and creates air jets. Under the combined forces of vibration and air jets, the excavated material is lifted. Owing to the vibration and proper slating of the working plate, the material is rotating, which allows the grains to pass into separate containers and forces the grains to pass between separate slates (Figure 4).

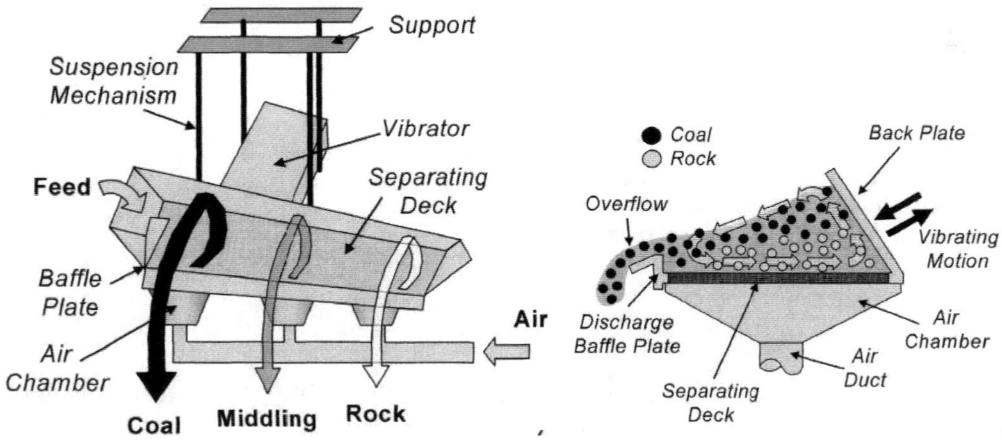

Figure 4. - FGX Air-Vibrating Separator [3].

Depending on the thickness of grains, the materials are divided. Lighter material goes to the surface of the suspension layer, and fractions of grains with higher densities are in the lower parts. Fine material and air is an autogenic medium. A suspension of air and solids is formed, sometimes referred to as fluidized bed. There are condition for restricted movement within the bed, depending on their size and thickness. Fluidization effect is used which occurs as effect of the density of fine grains forming the suspension and the bigger grains, which causes improvement of separation of thick grained fractions. Deshaling process is similar to the enrichment process in heavy fluid suspension. Because the working plate is slanting transversely, material with low density goes to the surface of the fluidized bed and has the tendency to move along that surface. Then, under gravity force, it falls through a partition located at the edge of the plate (dumping of enriched coal). Higher density material is concentrated in the bottom part of the fluidized bed and moves towards the waste material discharge outlet and falls through a driving plate to the waste chute. Depending on the type of raw materials and the settings of the device, more dumpings can be installed. Thus, more types of products can be obtained fulfilling the user requirements.

4. Factors affecting deshaling efficiency [5,14,10]

Process of deshaling separation on FGX dry separators depends on many factors. The most important factors are:

- pre-processing of raw materials including the grain sedimentation (small heavy grains will fall with the same speed as large light grains),
- grain size (grain composition),
- grain thickness (density composition),
- quantity of fed air,
- altitude, number and manner of slat mounting,
- slanting angles (transverse and longitudinal) of the working plate,
- working plate vibration frequency,
- load (efficiency) of the separator.

These factors are determined on the basis of enrichment capacity of raw coal, including the required quality of separation products. On this basis, technological regime of the enrichment is selected. Experiments prove that strict observance of set technological regime is necessary to obtain the assumed quality parameters of separation products.

Foreign experiments show that the separation efficiency also depends on technological parameters of the raw materials. It was noticed that separation accuracy are affected by the following raw materials parameters:

- total humidity,
- size of biggest grains,
- range of grain class,
- relation of quantity of stone to quantity of coal,
- ash content,
- pyrite sulphur content,
- quantity of intermediate material (excess).

Manufacturer of the FGX dry separators, on the basis of his own tests and industrial experience of the operating processing facilities (using the dry deshaling technology) developed general recommendation regarding performance of the separation process. In these recommendations, the manufacturer emphasizes the possibility of regulating the following technical parameters of the separator:

- altitude of dumping bars in the collection zones: of low-density product (coal), intermediate product and high-density product (waste materials),
- longitudinal angle of the working plate within the range of 0° through -2°,
- transverse angle of the working plate within the range of 0° through -10°,
- quantity of air fed under the individual separation zones,
- settings of flaps regulating directing the separated materials to specified and defined separation products.

Regulation of individual named technical parameters must be executed during preliminary testing in order to obtain the best possible raw material separation into individual products.

5. Auxiliary equipment in the dry separation installation

Dry shaling (enrichment) installations operating as independent processing facilities or research installations can be equipped with additional modules [7,16]. They can be classification, crushing or feeder modules. Their aim is to prepare the raw material (obtainment of proper grain class and elimination of excessively large grains of excavated coal) for separation in accordance with the accepted process regime.

CLASSIFICATION MODULE – Classification module includes: two-deck vibrating screen and conveyor collecting the lower classification product. Raw material has various granulometric composition, which has considerable impact on the dry separation process results. Two-deck vibrating screen optimizes the grain content in the material from the feeder module. It allows for limiting the upper limit of grains to, e.g. >50 mm, by sifting them from the upper deck and setting of the lower limit of grains to, e.g. <25 mm or <6 mm or others, specified experimentally, by sifting them with the lower deck. Lower class grains, <25 mm or <6 mm, are then removed from the installation with use of the conveyor belt (Figure 5).

CRUSHING MODULE – Crushing module includes: vibrating conveyor; jaw crusher; conveyor belt (reverse) to collect the crushed material and transport it to the feeder module. Sifted large material, e.g. >50 mm, unacceptable in the shaling procedure, from the upper deck of the vibrating screen is transported by vibrating conveyor (chute) to the jaw crusher. Properly regulated range of the crusher outlet allows for crushing of excessively large grains. Crushed material is then transported from the jaw crusher by a conveyor to the feeder module. Crushing module in such device configuration allows for crushing of the grains and thus obtaining grain size acceptable for the dry blowing in the dry separator (Figure 5).

Figure 5. Crusher & classification unit [photo IMBiGS].

FEEDER MODULE – Feeder module includes: intake container; belt dozer with inverter; raw material conveyor belt and integrated scale. The intake container stores a portion of the excavated coal. From the container, it is transported by belt dozer with regulated feeding speed, which allows for, if necessary, various loads on the deshaling installation. The feeder conveyor in the feeder module is used to transport the quantity of material specified by the deshaling regime to further installation modules. The integrated scale on the conveyor belt is used to register and monitor the quantity of material from the feeder module transported to the further installation modules (Figure 6).

Figure 6. Feeder unit [photo IMBiGS].

CONTROL MODULE – Control module is a control panel allowing for consecutive running of devices in individual modules of dry coal separation installation. Control panel, in case of a complex installation, allows for setting the order of operation of chosen individual modules. It also constitutes an important element of safety conditions during startup and shutdown of the devices.

6. Uses of dry enrichment process in FGX devices

Installations of dry coal separators can be individual facilities for enrichment of excavated coal. This is the case for several hundred such installations in China and individual installation in several other countries [17]. The enriched grain classes have the maximum grain size of 100, 80, 75, 50, 25 mm. Minimum grain size is most often 25, 12, 6 or close to 0 mm. Width of grain classes will be specified according to experience or result the granulation of raw materials.

FGX separators may replace the process of water-based enrichment in jiggers in a technological system of a processing facility. Replacement of jiggers or even cyclones with heavy liquids to dry separators was researched in USA and South Africa [5]. Considerable economic effects were found. Summary of that information is in the next section.

Dry shaling installations can also be a bypass in the enrichment sections of the existing processing plants. Such solutions are applied in China [17] in coking coal processing facilities. They are used to reduce the quantity of gangue before feeding of partially enriched raw materials to the water-based enrichment processes. FGX separators operating with separation density of at least 2.0 g/cm^3 guarantee obtainment of low ash contents in the concentrate for easily enrichable coals, which is required by the coking industry. In case of hard-enrichable coals, dry separation should be supplemented by water-based enrichment.

FGX separators, owing to the dust removal modules, allow for removal of the finest grains of the raw materials, which will not be introduced into the water system. Owing to this, coal sludge management is much less problematic. Dry dust can be a trading product and can be added to a concentrate.

Dry separators can be used to adjust the raw material if it has varying levels of gangue. This happens in case of mining several layers and lack of selective feeding of the raw material to the processing facility [9].

7. Economic efficiency

Economic efficiency analysis of dry coal separation technology was a subject of many reports developed in USA and Republic of South Africa. The simplified results of the economic analysis obtained for a single dry separation installation operating in the USA are shown in Table 1.

Table 1. Approximate investment outlays and operating costs – USA [11,12].

Type of process	Investment expenditures	Operating costs
	$/Mg/hour	$/Mg
Dry separation (FGX air-vibrating separator)	6.200,00	0.50
Wet enrichment methods	13.000,00	1.95

The summary presented in Table 1 shows that investment outlays of dry coal separation technology account for 48% of investment outlays of wet enrichment methods (2 times lower). Whereas operating costs of dry coal separation technology account for 25% of operating costs of wet enrichment methods (4 times lower) [11,12]. However, it should be emphasized here that the data presented in Table 1 reflect legal and environmental conditions as well as the location of coal mining plants and coal enrichment, quality parameters of coal, technological infrastructure as well as requirements set by the power sector in USA.

While the report developed in Republic of South Africa [13] presents, among others, approximate investment outlays and operating costs of dry separation technology in comparison to wet enrichment methods using cyclones with heavy liquid - Table 2.

Table 2. Approximate investment expenditures and operating costs – Republic of South Africa [13].

Type of process	Investment expenditures	Operating costs
	$	$/year
Dry separation (FGX air-vibrating separator)	1.250.000,00	825.000,00
Wet enrichment methods (Cyclones with heavy liquid)	5.000.000,00	2.480.500,00

The summary in Table 2 shows that the investment outlays of dry separation technology account for 25% of investment outlays of wet enrichment methods (4 times lower). While operating costs of dry separation technology account for 32% of operating costs of wet enrichment methods (3 times lower). The economic efficiency measures – PP (Payback Period) and ROI (Return on Investment) as well as NPV (Net Present Value) of the aforementioned technology were also compared – Table 3 and Table 4.

Table 3. Approximate values [PP] and [ROI] [13].

Type of process	Payback Period	Return on Investment
	years	%
Dry separation (FGX air-vibrating separator)	0.72	39
Wet enrichment methods (Cyclones with heavy liquid)	0.92	9

Table 4. Net Present Value [NPV] versus time [13].

Years	Dry separation (FGX air-vibrating separator)	Wet enrichment methods (Cyclones with heavy liquid)
	$	$
1	563.377,00	- 182.269,00
2	3.139.096,00	5.075.908,00
5	9.325.539,00	17.705.164,00
10	15.934.341,00	31.196.642,00
15	19.684.353,00	38.852.068,00
20	21.812.210,00	43.195.963,00

The results presented in Table 3 show that dry separation systems using air-vibrating separators of the FGX type have a shorter payback period [PP] than those using for separation the cyclones with dense liquid. Moreover, they have a higher return on investment ratio [ROI].

Low investment outlays and operating costs of installations with FGX separators allow to obtain a positive NPV value already at the end of the 1st year of operation, whereas for installations using cyclones with dense liquid the NPV value at the end of the 1st year of operation is negative. After the second year of operation, the value of NPV index for installations using cyclones with dense liquid takes a higher value than NPV value for systems with FGX separators. As can be seen from the data presented in Table 4, the value of the NPV index also increases in the following years, whereas the increase of NPV for installations using cyclones with dense liquid is faster than increase of NPV for installations with FGX separators, due to the higher value of annual outlays.

The analysis shows that dry coal separation installations could be a good solution for short-term or low-capacity investments in South Africa. In case of long-term or high-capacity investments, installations based on wet separation technologies could be more economical, despite higher investment outlays and operating costs.

The author of the report [13] emphasizes that the selection of a given technology, apart from investment outlays and operating costs, is above all influenced by many other factors such as: availability of water for enrichment processes, location of enrichment plant and recipients of commercial products, characteristics of raw coal dispersibility, quality requirements of the clients and the availability of the necessary infrastructure.

Application of the dry separation process allows for [1,4,6]:

- lowering of investment costs of coal processing facilities by full or partial elimination of water-based enrichment methods,
- reduction of operational costs connected with the production of traded coal products and increasing of market competitiveness,
- reduction of exploitation costs of the water-based enrichment process with the use of by-passes thanks to limitation of the water and sludge use and reduction of water and energy consumption,
- limitation of number of installations and devices, and prolonging their life by constructing individual dry separation facilities replacing the traditional processing facilities,
- application of a technological solution auxiliary to the existing technological installations for energy industry coals enrichment using the water methods, reducing the load on jigs, which allows for increasing the quantity of enriched material,
- effective deshaling (removing gangue), improvement of calorific value of the concentrate, desulphurization (removing pyrite sulphur and mercury),
- secondary enrichment of the trade product for high quality ecological production of qualified fuels,
- effective use of fuel products from this technological solution, used as substitutes for natural crushed stone in road and engineering works and as materials for filling the post-mining voids,

- recovery of coal substances from excavated materials distributed in the environment and crushed stone production.

8. Conclusion

In USA and South Africa (and many other countries), enrichment is not executed in cyclones with heavy liquids. The reason is relatively low accuracy if separation causing losses in coal substances placed among the waste materials and intermediate materials. Research performed in Australia, South Africa, USA and by ITG KOMAG (presented during KOMEKO conferences) confirm the above opinion. According to the reference materials, separation accuracy rate (probable dispersion) in cyclones with heavy liquids falls within the range of 0.04-0.12, in jiggers: 0.14–0.2, and for FGX separators it reaches the level of 0.2. However, often in the industrial conditions, the separation accuracy rate for jiggers can reach the level of 0.31 as result of their improper functioning [9]. High probable dispersion of jiggers caused their replacement in USA, South Africa, Australia and many other countries, and replacing them with heavy liquid cyclones. Deshaling in FGX installations occurs in the fraction zone with the density above 2.0 g/cm^3. Thus, lower accuracy of separation does not matter that much, because under the separation conditions the coal substance (with regulated device operation) is not removed with the waste. Therefore, dry deshaling of excavated coal in FGX separators can replace jiggers in coal enrichment facilities and in designed new enrichment sections of middle and fine class. This also allows for considerable economic benefits. It is worth mentioning that the partially deshaled coal product fulfils the quality requirements (guarantee parameters of the boilers) of the domestic recipients from power plants and heat and power plants. FGX dry separators are perfect for improving the quality of traded energy industry coal products for individual recipients. This is confirmed by the fact that two FGX3 installations are currently active in Poland.

The advantages of dry separation technology fully justify the opinion of the American authors presented at the World Coal Processing Congress [10] that the enrichment process in FGX installations is the „21st century technology".

References

[1] Baic I and Blaschke W 2018 Preliminary study on the reduction of mercury content in steam coal by using a pneumatic vibrating concentrating *table Inżynieria Mineralna – Journal of the Polish Mineral Engineering Society* **1(41)** pp 141-149 DOI: 10.29227/IM-2018-01-24

[2] Baic I and Blaschke W 2017 Coal preparation in Poland – development trends for increasing production efficiency *Inżynieria Mineralna – Journal of the Polish Mineral Engineering Society* **2(40)** pp 7-14 DOI: 10.29227/IM-2017-02-01

[3] Baic I, Blaschke W, Szafarczyk J 2014 Dry coal clearing technology *Inżynieria Mineralna – Journal of the Polish Mineral Engineering Society* **2(34)** pp 257-262

[4] Baic I and Blaschke W 2013 Analysis of the Possibility of Using Air Concentrating Tables in Order to Obtain Clean Coal Fuels and Substitute Natural Aggregates *Polityka Energetyczna* **16** issue pp 247-60

[5] Baic I, Blaschke W, Góralczyk S, Szafarczyk J and Buchalik G 2015 A New Method for Removing Organic Contaminants of Gangue from the Coal Output *Annual Set The Environment Protection* **17** Wyd. Środkowo-Pomorskie Towarzystwo Naukowe Ochrony Środowiska Koszalin pp 1274–85

[6] Baic I, Blaschke W, Sobko W and Fraś A 2015 Application of Air Cocentrating Table for Improvement in the Quality Parameters of the Commercial Product Jaret *Inżynieria Mineralna – Journal of the Polish Mineral Engineering Society* issue **1/35** Annual vol XVI pp 221-26

[7] Baic I, Blaschke W, Sobko W and Szafarczyk J 2016 Implementation of Innovative Technology of Hard Coal Purification Using the Dry Method of Enrichment (FGX) by Lowering the Costs of Production of Commercial Products in the Domestic Mining Industry *Czasopismo Techniczne* KTT No. 166 pp 8-18

[8] Blaschke W 1976 Air Enrichment *Poradnik Górnika* **V** Wyd. Śląsk pp. 556-563
[9] Blaschke W and Baic I 2018 Improvement of the Parameters of Coal Separation in Jigs by the Initial Averaging of the Feed Using the Dry Deshaling Method *Zeszyty Naukowe Instytutu GSMiE PAN* Kraków **104** pp 163-72
[10] Ghost T, Path D, Parekh B.K and Honaker R.Q 2013 Uprading Low Rank Coal Using a Dry Density Based Separator Technology *Proceedings of the XVII ICPC* Istambul pp 295-308
[11] Honaker R.Q and Luttrel G.H 2009 *Final technical report: Development of an advanced deshaling technology to improve the energy efficiency of coal handling, processing and utilization operations* U.S Department of Energy Industrial Technologies Program, Mining of the future USA
[12] Honaker R.Q 2007 *Coarse dry coal cleaning* Workshop on coal beneficiation and utilization of rejects: Initiatives, Polices and Best Practices" Ranchi India
[13] de Korte G.J 2014 *Dry Processing of Coal Status Update.* Report Csir/Nre/Mnr/Er/20140040B Coaltech South Africa
[14] Gongamin Li 2006 Coal Compound Dry Cleaning Technique – Study and Practice *Proceedings of XV ICPC* Pekin China **2** pp 439-47
[15] Mijał W, Blaschke W and Baic I 2018 Dry Coal Beneficiation Method in Poland *Przegląd Górniczy* issue **11** pp 9-18
[16] Mijał W and Tora B 2018 Development of Dry Coal Gravity Separation Techniques Mineral Engineering Conference. IOP Publishing Conf. Series: Materials Science and Engineering 427
[17] Tangshan Shenzhou Machinery Co Ltd 2012, *Company prospectus of Tangshan Shenzhou Machinery Co Ltd.* China

IOP Conf. Series: Materials Science and Engineering **641** (2019) 012031 doi:10.1088/1757-899X/641/1/012031

Bioreduction in the development of new mineral technology

A Pawlowska[1] **and Z Sadowski**[1]
[1]Wroclaw University of Science and Technology
Department of Chemical Engineering
Wybrzeze Wyspianskiego 27, 50-370 Wroclaw, Poland
E-mail: agnieszka.pawlowska@pwr.edu.pl, zygmunt.sadowski@pwr.edu.pl

Abstract. Reductive dissolution is like "biomining in reverse gear". Selected sulfur reducing bacteria (SRB) can be used under anaerobic conditions – as in bioleaching – for metal recovery from oxide minerals and laterite. General assumptions of the BioSulphide® and Ferredox processes for nickel recovery from laterite ores and copper from acid mine drainage or waste water were presented.

1. Introduction

It is natural for bacteria to interact with minerals. This biogeochemical cycle of bioweathering gradually destroys rocks [1]. The intensive interaction of chemolithotrophic bacteria with sulfide minerals results in acid mine drainage The Tinto River (Spain) is an excellent example of this phenomenon [2]. Acid mine drainage (AMD) can be the major source of various heavy metals. Ferric hydroxide precipitation enables selective separation of other metals present in the solution [3, 4]. Such opportunities offer an industry implemented BioSulphide® process [5].

The use of microorganisms for mineral degradation and metal extraction is known as "biomining" [6]. Biological oxidation of sulfide minerals is applied on the industrial scale in biomining. Bioleaching is mainly carried out either as a heap or tank leaching. In the case of the former, low grade sulfide ores are collected in a pile irrigated by acidic liquor containing bacteria which while percolating through the heap come into contact with sulfide grains. As a result, metal ions are extracted. The pregnant leach solution is collected in a special pond and then directed to the top of the heap. Heap bioleaching is used to extract copper from low grade ores [7].

The stirred-tank bioleaching has mainly been applied for gold refractory ores [8]. BIOX®, designed for gold refractory ore treatment, is one of such processes. It consists of the biotreatment of flotation concentrate with a solid content of 20% (w/w). Its duration in the tank is 4 to 6 days. Biopretreatment opens the structure of sulfide minerals for the extraction of gold with the use of cyanide. The biomodification of the mineral surface changes its properties in such a manner that the mineral can be used in selective flotation and flocculation [9].

Bacteria acting on minerals do not only limit bioxidation but under anaerobic conditions can also participate in bioreduction. The main reaction within reductive leaching has been described as "bioleaching in reverse gear" [10].

Below, we attempt to describe and determine the main mechanism of reductive dissolution of oxide minerals in laterite ores and present the applications of biogenesis of hydrogen sulfide with the metal obtained from acid mine drainage.

2. Sulfate reducing bacteria

Under anaerobic conditions, many bacteria are able to reduce sulfate, thiosulfate, and elemental sulfur to produce hydrogen sulfide in a process which is defined as biosulfidogenesis [11-13].

SRB is a special group of bacteria which use sulfate as the terminal electron acceptor and reduce sulfates to sulfides. The source of electrons is organic substances accompanying sulfates. Natural SRB can be classified into three main categories:

i. mesophilic proteobacteria – *Desulfovibro, Desulfobacterium, Desulfobacter, and Desulfobulbus;*
ii. thermophilic gram-negative bacteria – *Thermodesulfovibrio;*
iii. gram-positive bacteria – *Desulfotomaculum.*

SRB convert sulfate into hydrogen sulfide (H_2S) at the presence of organic matter. The resultant H_2S reacts with some metal cations and forms insoluble metal sulfide precipitates. This process enables metal ions to recovery from waste solutions (BioSulphide® process).

Typical chemolithotrophic bacteria can be used for the anaerobic dissolution of minerals. *Acidithibacillus ferrooxidans* growing under anaerobic conditions have been shown to reduce ferric iron in the presence of sulfur [14]. The anaerobic growth of acidophilic bacteria such as mesophiles (*Acidithibacillus thiooxidans*, *Acidithiobacillus ferrooxidans*) moderate thermophiles (*Acidithibacillus caldus, Sulfobacillus acidophiles*) and thermophiles (*Acidianus* and *Metallosphaera*) was induced through the addition of 5 g/dm^3 of sulfur and 50 mM of ferric iron, with a pH of 2. The obtained bacterial suspensions were used for metal extraction from mineral material taken from the mound of the Talviaara Mine (Finland). Microbiological reduction of iron under anaerobic conditions takes place in a temperature range of 30-70°C. Iron removal was much greater at 70°C with thermophiles [14].

3. Reductive dissolution of metals

Oxidative dissolution can be carried out by chemoautotrophic bacteria applied to sulfide minerals. Since many metals occur in ore bodies as oxides and silicates, the alternative treatment appears to be reductive dissolution [6]. The presence of goethite is also a positive factor. Biodissolution of goethite was achieved with the transfer of electrons from elemental sulfur to ferric iron present in the mineral. Anaerobic reductive dissolution of iron oxide minerals is referred to as Ferredox [15]. *Acidithiobacillus ferrooxidans* can grow at anaerobic conditions using ferrous iron as an electron donor. The flowsheet of the Ferredox process enabling the reductive dissolution of limonitic minerals is presented in figure 1.

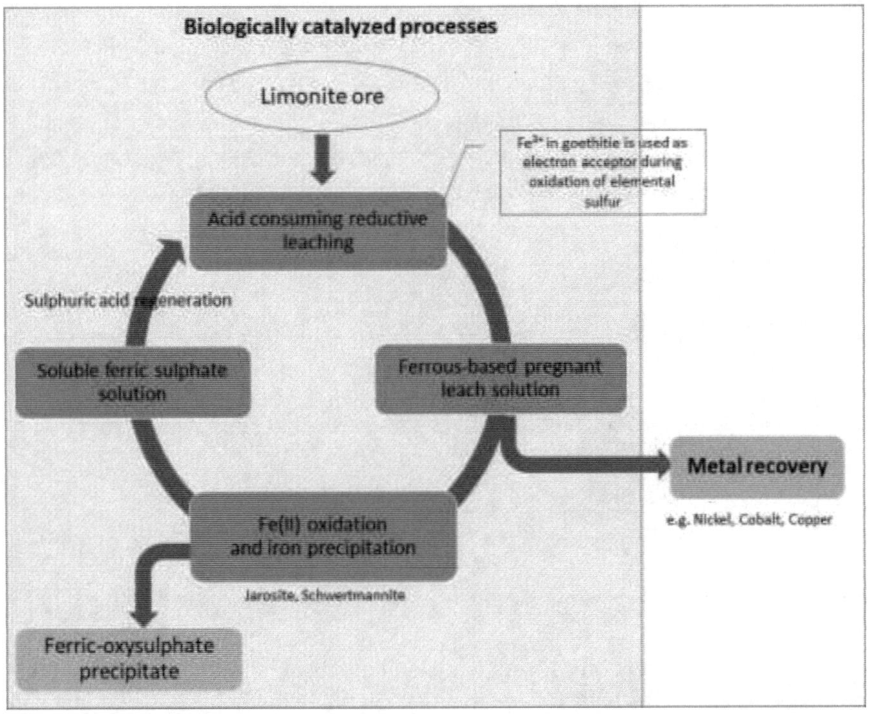

Figure 1. Flowsheet of the Ferredox process. Own elaboration based on [15].

Acidithiobacillus ferrooxidans were used for the reductive dissolution of limonite. Limonite, an iron ore, is a mixture of a hydrated iron oxide such as goethite, akageneite, schwertmannite, and jarosite.

Iron reducing bacteria utilized ferric iron (Fe^{3+}) as an electron acceptor. At the same time, electrons were needed for reduction. Sulfur, hydrogen, or some organic compounds can be electron donors.

The extraction of nickel, cobalt, and manganese from laterite ore was induced by acidophilic *Acidithiobacillus ferrooxidans, Sulfobacillus beneficiens, Acidicaldus organivorans,* and *Acidophilium* sp., with the source of Fe^{3+} being the goethite contained in laterite ore. Reductive dissolution of laterite allows for extracting 70-80% of nickel from laterite ore [16].

The reductive dissolution of goethite was connected with the elemental sulfur oxidation. The comparison of aerobic bioleaching with anaerobic reductive dissolution showed greater effectiveness of the latter [16]. Iron reducing bacteria use ferric iron as an electron acceptor. Sulfur, hydrogen or organic compounds are used as an electron donor. The selection of the right electron donor depends on the type of raw material and the used bacteria. Figure 2 shows the characteristics of the substances most often used as electron donors.

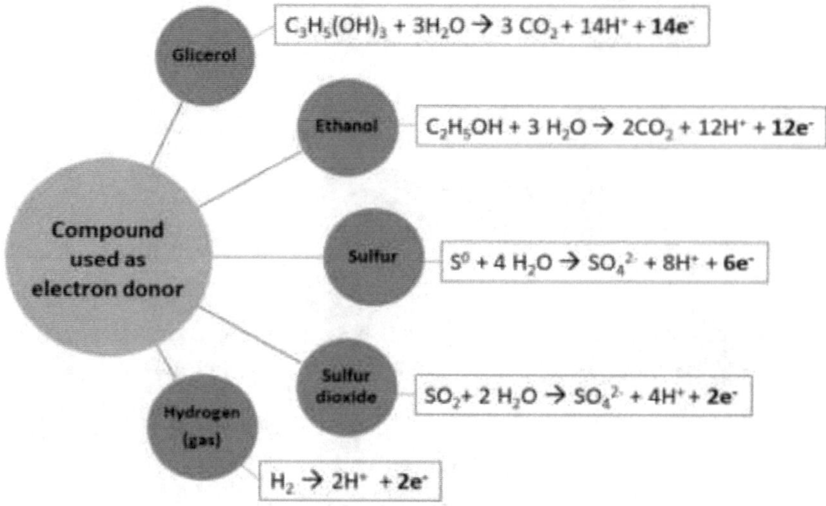

Figure 2. Compounds used as electron donors. Own elaboration based on [15].

The copper laterite ore containing 15.5% of goethite underwent reductive dissolution with the presence of sulfur [17]. The process allows for the recovery of 78% of copper. It turned out that the relatively slow acid dissolution of goethite occurs at the beginning, and can be described as follows:

$$2S^0 + 12FeOOH + 21\ H^+ = HSO_4^- + SO_4^{2-} + 12Fe^{2+} + 16H_2O$$

More than 60% of the world's nickel reserves are estimated to occur in the form of laterites. Chemical leaching with the use of organic acids does not yield expected results due to the strong adsorption of nickel ions by the biomass of fungi used for the production of organic acids [18], which has called for studies on the chemolithotrophic bacterial adaptation for laterite ore leaching [19, 20].

Nickel can be leached from limonite ore in the anaerobic bioreactor with adapting chemolithotrophic bacteria. *Acidithibacillus ferrooxidans* were first grown aerobically with excess sulfur (50g). When the number of cells reached the level of up to $5 \cdot 10^8$ cell/ml, the limonite ore was added to the bioreactor. Bioleaching's Within the course of 30 days This bioleaching yielded an over 75% nickel extraction from limonite ore [21].

The oxidative dissolution of UO_2 entails a serious risk to the environment and people. Microorganisms living within the sulfidogenic environment are capable of reducing U(VI). *Desulfovibrio desulfuricans* may be included in this group. The enzymatic U(VI) reduction by *D. desulfuricans* bacteria was carried out at the presence of lactate as electron donors [22].
Three cobalt-bearing oxidized ores were bioleached under the anaerobic condition, at a pH of 1.8 by means of reductive dissolution. Two ores were obtained from Shevchenko, Kazakhstan, and one from the Acoje Mine in the Philippines. The ores contained mainly iron (goethite), manganese, nickel, zinc, and cobalt. The extraction of cobalt from these three ores was far more efficient, with the recovery being close to 90% [23].

Bioreductive treatment of U(VI) species reduces uranium ions mobility. Iron nanoparticles in the form of FeS play a special role during uranium immobilization. With FeS present, the dissolution rate of UO_2 is over 1 order of magnitude lower than without nanoparticles [24].

Manganese nodules available from the ocean floor can be an alternative source of metals. Polymetallic manganese nodules are a natural source of Cu, Co, Ni, and, Mn [25]. Bioleaching was carried out at 30°C. The bacterial consortium was developed with the bacteria isolated from manganese ore mine. The reduction of MnO_2 phase dissolved Co and about 30% of Mn.

4. BioSulphide® process

Sulfate reducing bacteria used for the recovery of metals from minerals have several applications in the mining industry. The development of BioSulphide® technology depends on the thorough understanding of the mechanism of biological sulfate reduction.

The BioSulphide® process consists of (i) the biological conversion of sulfate to hydrogen sulfide and (ii) chemical precipitation of sulfides. This process enables metal ions selective removal from acid mine drainage solutions or wastewater. The same procedure was used for the precipitation of copper ions from industry wastewater [26] where most of the metal occurred as CuS (covellite).

Also, Johnson and Hallberg [27] proposed the recovery of metal from the main wastes containing a variety of soluble metal ions under anaerobic conditions.

The BioSulphide process (figure 3) has been successfully commercialized at the Copper Queen Mine in Bisbee, Arizona, US, which was closed in 1970 after nearly 100 years of exploitation, leaving a large amount of mining waste [28].

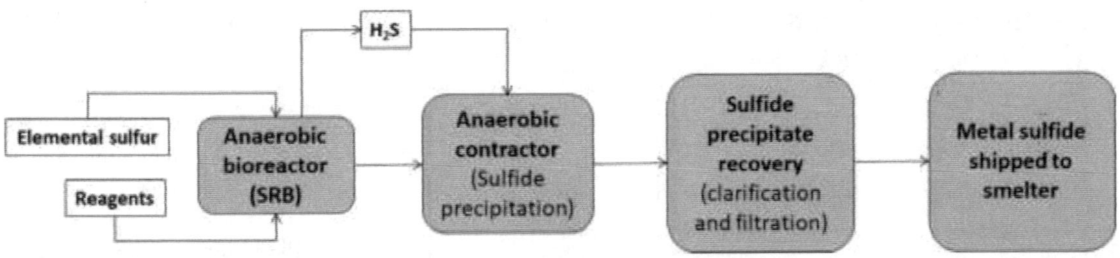

Figure 3. Technological scheme of the BioSulphide® process. Own elaboration based on [29].

5. Summary

Sulfidogenesis and bioreduction induced by sulfur reducing bacteria and *Acidithiobacillus ferrooxidans* enable extraction of valuable metals from oxide minerals, mainly laterite ores. The use of typical iron-oxidizing bacteria like *Acidithibacillus ferrooxidans* for these processes creates new application possibilities. An example of practical use of the biological synthesis of H_2S and application is the BioSulphide® process allows the copper recovery from acid mine drainage and wastewater.

References

[1] Gadd GM 2013 Microbial roles in mineral transformations and metal cycling in the Earth's critical zone, in Xu J and Sparks DL (eds.) Molecular Environmental Soil Science, *Progr. Soil Sci.* Springer, Dordrecht, pp 115-165

[2] Gonzalez-Toril E, Aguilera A, Rodriguez N, Fernandez-Remolar D, Gomez F, Diaz E, Garcia-Moyano A, Sanz JL, Amils R 2010 Microbial ecology of Rio Tinto, a natural extreme acidic environment of biohydrometallurgical interest *Hydrometallurgy* **104(3-4)** pp 329-333

[3] Hallberg KB 2010 New perspectives in acid mine drainage microbiology *Hydrometallurgy* **104(3-4)** pp 448-453

[4] Panda S, Eslher J, Bhotra T, Pradhan N, Sukla BL, Mishra KB, Akcil A 2015 Sequential bioreduction-bioleaching and bioreduction-chemical leaching hybrid tests for enhanced copper recovery from a concentrator ball mill reject sample *Hydrometallurgy* **157** pp 171-177

[5] Nancharaiah YV, Venkata Mohan S, Lens PNL 2016 Biological and bioelectrochemical recovery of critical and scarce metals *Trends Biotechnol.* **34(2)** pp 137-155

[6] Johnson DB 2013 Development and application of biotechnologies in the metal mining industry *Environ. Sci. Pollut. R.* **20(11)** pp 7768-7776

[7] Gentina JC, Acevedo F 2013 Application of bioleaching to copper mining in Chile, *Electron. J. Biotechn.* **16(3)** pp 1-14

[8] Kaksonen AH, Boxall NJ, Gumulya Y, Khaleque HN, Morris C, Bohu T, Cheng KY, Usher KM, Lakaniemi AM 2018 Recent progress in biohydrometallurgy and microbial characterization *Hydrometallurgy* **180** pp 7-25

[9] Hanumantha Rao K, Vilinska A, Chernyshova IV 2010 Minerals bioprocessing: R & D need in mineral biobeneficiation *Hydrometallurgy* **104(3-4)** pp 465-470

[10] Johnson DB, du Plessis CA 2015 Biomining in reverse gear: Using bacteria to extract metals from oxidized ores *Miner. Eng.* **75** pp 2-5

[11] Hallberg BK 2006 Sulfidogenesis in low pH (3.8 – 4,2) media by a mixed population of acidophilic bacteria *Biodegradation* **17(2)** pp 159-167

[12] Jameson E, Rowe OF, Hallberg KB, Johnson DB 2010 Sulfidogenesis and selective precipitation of metals at low pH mediated by *Acidithiobacillus* spp. and acidophilic sulfate-reducing bacteria *Hydrometallurgy* **104** pp 488-493

[13] Hussain A, Hasan A, Javid A, Quazi JI 2016 Exploited application of sulfate-reducing bacteria for concomitant treatment of metallic and non-metallic wastes: a mini review, *3 Biotech.* **6(2)** pp 119-129

[14] Norris PR, Gould OJP, Ogden TJ 2015 Iron solubilization during anaerobic growth of acidophilic microorganisms with a polymetallic sulphide ore *Miner. Eng.* **75** pp 77-84

[15] du Plessis CA, Slabbert W, Hallberg KB, Johnson DB 2011 Ferredox: A biohydrometallurgical processing concept for limonitic nickel laterites *Hydrometallurgy* **109(3-4)** pp 221-229

[16] Hallberg KB, Grail BM, du Plessis CA, Johnson DB 2011 Reductive dissolution of ferric iron minerals: A new approach for bio-processing nickel laterites *Miner. Eng.* **24(7)** pp 620-624

[17] Nancucheo I, Grail BM, Hilario F, du Plessis CA, Johnson DB 2014 Extraction of copper from an oxidized (lateritic) ore using bacterially catalysed reductive dissolution *Appl. Microbiol. Biot.* **98(14)** pp 6297-6305

[18] Valix M, Usai F, Malik R 2001 Fungal bio-leaching of low grade laterite ores *Miner Eng* **14(2)** 197-203

[19] Marrero J, Coto O, Goldmann S, Graupner T, Schippers A 2015 Recovery of nickel and cobalt from laterite tailings by reductive dissolution under aerobic conditions using *Acidithiobacillus* species *Environ. Sci. Technol.* **49(11)** pp 6674-6682

[20] Marrero J, Coto O, Schippers A 2017 Anaerobic and aerobic reductive dissolution of iron-rich nickel laterite overburden by *Acidithiobacillus Hydrometallurgy* **168** pp 49-55

[21] Johnson DB 2012 Reductive dissolution of minerals and selective recovery of metals using acidophilic iron- and sulfate-reducing acidophiles *Hydrometallurgy* **127-128** pp 172-177

[22] Lovely DR, Phillips EJP 1992 Reduction of uranium by *Desulfovibrio desulfuricans Appl. Environ. Microb.* **58(3)** pp 850-856

[23] Smith SL, Grail BM, Johnson DB 2017 Reductive bioprocessing of cobalt-bearing limonitic laterites *Miner. Eng.* **106** pp 86-90

[24] Bi Y, Hayes KF 2014 Nano-FeS inhibits UO_2 reoxidation under varied oxic conditions *Environ. Sci. Technol.* **48(1)** pp 632-640

[25] Aishvarya V, Mishra G, Pradhan N, Ghosh MK 2016 Bioleaching of Indian Ocean nodules with in situ iron precipitation by anaerobic Mn reducing consortia *Hydrometallurgy* **166** pp 130-135

[26] Sheng YX, Cao HB, Li YP, Zhang Y 2010 Effect of bacterially produced precipitates on the metabolism of sulfate reducing bacteria during the bio-treatment process of copper-containing wastewater *Sci. China Chem.* **53(12)** pp 2608-2615

[27] Johnson DB, Hallberg KB 2005 Acid mine drainage remediation option: a review *Sci. Total Environ.* **338(1-2)** pp 3-14

[28] Ashe NL, McLean I, Nodwell M 2008 Review of operations of the biosulphide® process plant at the Copper Queen Mine, Bisbee, Arizona *Hydrometallurgy: Proceedings of the Sixth International Symposium*, Young CA, Taylor PR, Anderson CG, Choi Y(eds.) pp 98-107

[29] Lawrence R, Philippe R, Fleming CA 2007 Sulphide and ion exchange technologies for metal recovery and water treatment in the copper mining industry *HydroCopper Conference in Santiago, Chile, May 14-16*

Acknowledgment

This study has received funding from the European Institute of Innovation and Technology (EIT), a body of the European Union, under the Horizon 2020, the EU Framework Programme for Research and Innovation (Project BioLeach: Innovative Bio-treatment of RM).

Energy Policy of Poland – current status, opportunities, challenges, threats

D Polek, T Niedoba and W Mijał

Department of Environmental Engineering, Faculty of Mining and Geoengineering, AGH University of Science and Technology, Al. Mickiewicza 30, PL-30059 Cracow, Poland

E-mail: polek@agh.edu.pl

Abstract. Energy security is currently one of the most important and widely discussed topics in the country. Over the years, Poland has not developed a coherent energy policy, and the consequences of it are currently being felt. New requirements of the European Union, ending of hard coal resources and its growing imports, weak ratio of energy from RES, no new opencast brown coal mines - this are only few problems of the contemporary energy policy of the country. The article presents the current situation of the power industry, reviewed the applicable laws - domestic and European, and also identified the greatest threats to the country's energy security.

1. Energy situation – current status

Poland is a country, in which almost 80 percent. the share of energy still comes from coal: hard coal (about 49%) and brown coal (about 30%) [3]. In 2017 and 2018, the share of hard and brown coal in electricity production remained at a similar level (78.2% and 78.4% respectively) [5,6].

One of the main problem is the shrinking hard coal resources that are enough for several hundred years and decreasing mining. In 2018, Polish mines extracted 63.4 million tons of hard coal - the least since 1947. In December 2018 occurred the smallest production since the Second World War. Coal mining has decreased from 65.5 million tonnes in 2017 to 63.4 million tonnes in 2018 [8].

A serious problem is also the increase in coal imports, which is currently record-high, and over 78% of the volume comes from Russia. Other import destinations are Colombia, USA and Kazakhstan.

On the other hand, the export of energy coal from Poland is the lowest for 15 years. As a result, foreign suppliers cover about 25% of domestic demand. For many years, coal was a sign of energy security for Poland, and now we are becoming more and more dependent on supplies of this raw material from Russia [6,7].

Table 1. The volume and the value of hard coal imported from Russia [7]

	2016	2017	2018
The volume of hard coal imported from Russia by Poland [PLN bn]	5,2	7,6	13,3
The value of hard coal imported from Russia by Poland [PLN bn]	1,1	1,9	3,4

The situation is also unstable when it comes to brown coal. The deposits currently in operation ensure a stable level of production in the range of 60 million Mg annually by 2020. After this period until 2030, currently working mines can guarantee a level of about 50 million Mg per year. In the following years, due to the progressing depletion of these deposits, there will be a sharp drop in output and thus a reduction in electricity production based on this fuel until the liquidation of opencast mining at the beginning of 2040. Without the construction of new complexes, in the years 2040-2045 there will be a total disappearance of generation capacity based on brown coal in Poland [4].

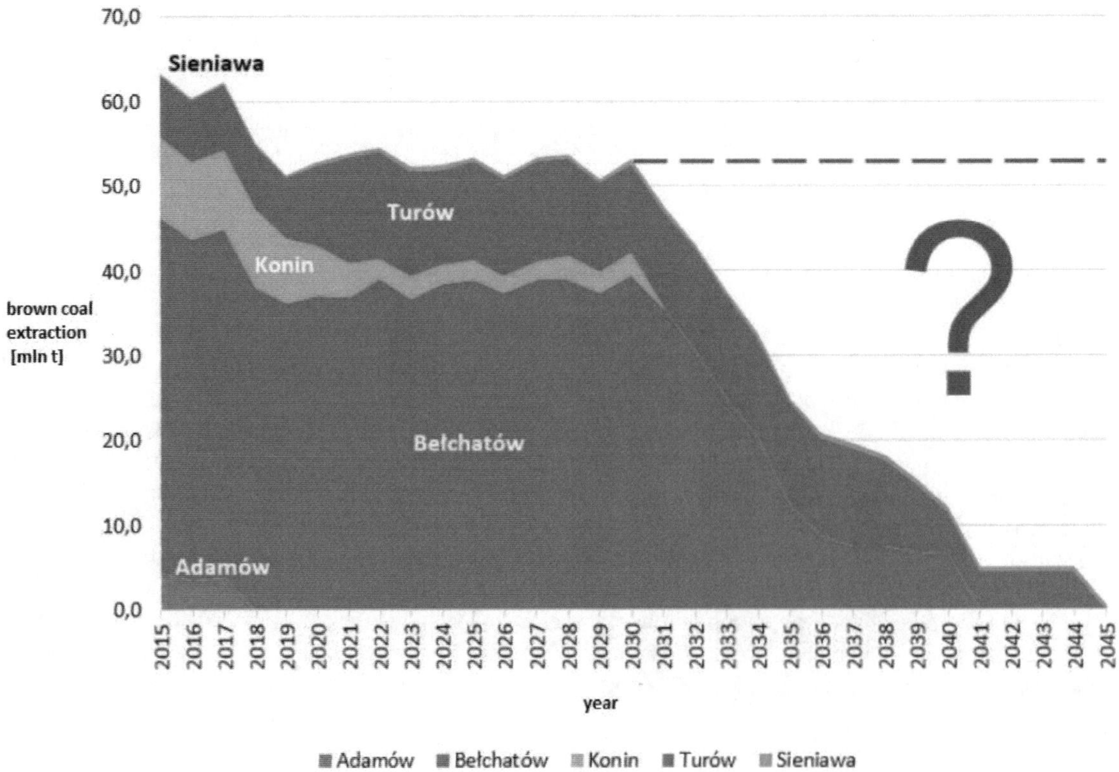

Figure 1. Forecast of resources sufficiency in brown coal open mining complexes [4].

In addition to hard coal and brown coal, oil and natural gas are used to produce energy in Poland.

Unfortunately, these raw materials are imported in large quantities from abroad, mainly from Russia. The domestic economy is dependent on these supplies. Oil production in the country does not satisfy even 3% of demand, while natural gas production accounts for about 30% of total demand. Shale gas deposits that are likely to be found in Northern and Eastern Poland have great potential. However, its extraction may be difficult due to its location and unprofitability.

Reports from the events "Energy transformation in Poland" from 2018 and 2019 prepared by the Energy Forum, do not differ in conclusions and observations about the state of energy in the country. A constant problem is the fact that Poland still has the least diversified mix of sources of electricity generation in the European Union. However, a slight decrease in the share of coal in favor of gas and renewable sources can be observed. To a small extent, this was associated with a decrease in greenhouse gas emissions.

The problem is also the continuous increase in the demand for electricity (from 2007 to 2017 by 12%, or 18.5 TWh).

In 2014, Poland became a net importer of electricity, although in 2005 we exported 11 TWh. Of the 17 importing countries in the EU, we import in Poland the smallest percentage, only 1.2% of the demand for electricity.

Electricity imports are also growing because its prices in Poland are high compared to other countries [5,6].

Just like the increase in coal imports, the stagnation of renewable energy sources is also worrying, making it impossible to diversify the energy risk of the country.

In 2017, the share of energy from renewable sources in the final gross energy consumption was 11.0%, ie it decreased by 0.32 percentage points. in relation to 2016, [1,2, 20]

2. National and European law

One of the key documents related to the energy of the country is the Energy and Climate Package, also known as the climate package, the "3x20" or "20-20-20" package, and a set of binding laws aimed at ensuring the implementation of the European Union's objectives on combating climate change. The package sets three key objectives:

- a 20% reduction of greenhouse gas emissions (compared to 1990 levels);
- 20% share of energy from renewable sources in total energy consumption in the EU;
- increase by 20% energy efficiency.

The package was accepted by the European Parliament in December 2008. The documents included in the package focus on three key objectives: reducing greenhouse gas emissions, promoting the use of energy from renewable sources and increasing the energy efficiency of the European Union. On October 25, 2012, the European Union accepted the Directive of the European Parliament and of the Council 2012/27 / EU on energy efficiency. This directive, by establishing a common framework to reduce 20% of primary energy consumption in the EU, was an important factor in the success of the implementation of the EU energy strategy for 2020. This document indicated measures to improve energy efficiency also after this date. The document also defined the principles on which the energy market should operate in order to eliminate, among others, any irregularities limiting the efficiency of supply. The legal act also provides for the establishment of national energy efficiency targets for 2020 [9].

The act that caused not a little confusion was the Act of 20 May 2016 on energy efficiency (Journal of Laws of 2016, item 831), which imposed on large enterprises the obligation to conduct energy audits of the enterprise. The audit should have been carried out at the latest within 12 months from the date of entry into force of the act, that is to October 1, 2017, and provide a report to the Energy Regulatory Office [19].

The main objective of the audit was to identify the potential for energy savings in the enterprise and to make a list of priority pro-efficiency actions.

However, the Act did not specify the required competences of entities performing audits. There was only a record that these entities should have appropriate knowledge, experience and technical and organizational measures to carry out such task in a manner consistent with the provisions of the Act [11, 14, 15, 16, 17, 18]. Therefore, the competence of auditing companies turned out to be a problem. Due to the inaccuracy of the records, the services were often performed by people without proper substantive preparation and without equipment back-up (measuring equipment). Therefore, having regard to the manner of conducting audits, its objective has been achieved to a small extent.

On 24 December 2018, Directive of the European Parliament and of the Council (EU) 2018/2002 of 11 December 2018 amending Directive 2012/27 / EU on energy efficiency referred to in this article came into effect. The revised directive as an objective demonstrates an increase of at least 32.5% energy efficiency in 2030 [10].

One of article of the directives indicated that Member States must achieve total savings in final energy consumption in each year from 1 January 2014 to 31 December 2020 at least 1.5% of the value of the volume of energy sold to end users. In addition, from January 1, 2021 to December 31, 2030, they must achieve new savings of 0.8% of annual final energy consumption each year (averaged for 2016-2018). After 2030, Member States still have to implement new annual savings for the next 10 years, unless the EC's review in 2027 shows that it is not necessary [15].

National laws and regulations need to be adapted to the revised directive within 18 months, by 25 June 2020. On 1 January 2021, further amendments to the directive will come into force, which were introduced by Regulation (EU) 2018/1999, from 10 January 2019 in force directly in all EU Member States.

The December directive sets a new target for the 2030 horizon, namely to further increase energy efficiency by at least 32.5% by 2030, and to create the conditions for further improvement of energy efficiency beyond these dates. The national target for improving energy efficiency by 2030 is 23% for primary energy consumption according to the primes 2007 forecast.

Both the new directive and the state document "National plan for energy and climate for 2021-2030" put a strong emphasis on the energy efficiency of the country. The content of the documents clearly suggests maintaining the existing support systems and obligations set out in the Act of May 20, 2016 [12].

The topics discussed in the directive are reflected in the "National Plan for Energy and Climate 2021-2030. These include, among others: the closed cycle economy, the question of energy poverty or raising the awareness of final consumers of energy.

3. Summary

The general problem of the country is the lack of a coherent development plan for maintaining energy security. A mistake that can cost a lot is the lack of diversification of risk in the area of energy sources (80% of energy from coal).

The Polish economy faces huge challenges related to electricity prices, emission reductions, hard-to-reach hard coal deposits and maladjustment of transmission networks to work with renewable energy sources

Most experts, including specialists from „Polish Power Grids", predict a further increase in the demand for electricity.

EU and state regulations clearly indicate that the improvement of energy efficiency will be a trend occurring in the following decades. Therefore, Poland will have to face the search for new solutions to improve efficiency, because the identified activities carrying the potential for improving energy efficiency are most often presently discounted payback periods of 10 years and more.

Energy efficiency will play an even greater role in the coming years, which is confirmed by the amendment to Directive 2012/27 / EU, as well as the draft "National Plan for Energy and Climate for 2021-2030". Improvement of efficiency will be increasingly difficult, which is why there is a need to review existing tools and develop new ones. The future in this respect will be inextricably linked with the full awareness of the potential for energy savings at the enterprise level, which ultimately should translate into the level of the national economy [15].

References

[1] Naczelna Izba Kontroli, 2018. *Rozwój sektora odnawialnych źródeł energii – Informacja o wynikach kontroli,* <https://www.nik.gov.pl/plik/id,18357,vp,20955.pdf> [dostęp: 30.07.2019]

[2] Główny Urząd Statystyczny, 2018. *Energia ze źródeł odnawialnych w 2017 r.,* <https://stat.gov.pl/download/gfx/portalinformacyjny/pl/defaultaktualnosci/5485/10/1/1/energia_ze_zrodel_odnawialnych_w_2017.pdf> [access: 30.07.2019]

[3] Główny Urząd Statystyczny, 2018, *Energia 2018,* <https://stat.gov.pl/files/gfx/portalinformacyjny/pl/defaultaktualnosci/5485/1/6/1/energia_2018.pdf> [access: 30.07.2019]

[4] Kasztelewicz Z., Ptak M. and Sikora M., 2018. *Węgiel brunatny optymalnym surowcem energetycznym dla Polski*, Zeszyty Naukowe – Instytut Gospodarku Surowcami Mineralnymi i Energią Polskiej Akademii Nauk, vol. 106, p. 61-84

[5] Macuk R., Maćkowiak-Pandera J. and Rubczyński A., 2018, *Transformacja energetyczna w Polsce,* Forum Energii, <https://forum-energii.eu/public/upload/articles/files/Polska%20transformacja%20energetyczna%202017%20final%20(2).pdf> [dostęp: 30.07.2019]

[6] Macuk R., Maćkowiak-Pandera J. and Rubczyński A., 2019, *Transformacja energetyczna w Polsce,* Forum Energii, <https://forum-energii.eu/public/upload/articles/files/Transformacja%20energetyczna%20w%20Polsce%202019%20-%20wersja%20ost.pdf> [access: 30.07.2019]

[7] Zasuń R., 2019, *Rachunek za importowany węgiel wyniósł w 2018 ok. 7 mld zł,* < https://wysokienapiecie.pl/18638-rachunek-za-importowany-wegiel-wyniosl-w-2018-ok-7-mld-zl/> [dostęp: 30.07.2019]

[8] Derski B., 2019, *Wydobycie węgla w Polsce w 2018 w dół, zatrudnienie w górę,* < https://wysokienapiecie.pl/18649-wydobycie-wegla-w-polsce-mln-ton-zatrudnienie/> [online: 30.07.2019]

[9] Dyrektywa Parlamentu Europejskiego i Rady (UE) 2018/2002 z dnia 11 grudnia 2018 r. zmieniająca dyrektywę 2012/27/UE w sprawie efektywności energetycznej, Dz.Urz.UE L 328/210.

[10] Dyrektywa Parlamentu Europejskiego i Rady (UE) 2012/27 z dnia 25 października 2012 r. w sprawie efektywności energetycznej, zmiany dyrektyw 2009/125/WE i 2010 /30/UE oraz uchylenia dyrektyw 2004/8/WE i 2006/32/WE Dz.Urz.UE L 315/1

[11] Ustawa z dnia 20 maja 2016 r. o efektywności energetycznej, Dz.U. 2016 poz. 831 ze zm.

[12] Krajowy plan na rzecz energii i klimatu na lata 2021-2030, Ministerstwo Energii, https://www.gov.pl/documents/33372/436746/Projekt_KPEiK_na_lata_2021-2030.pdf/aaefd8b3-0dff-3cdd-f016-b9c478b96ce1 [dostęp: 30.07.2019].

[13] Słupik T., 2019. *Nowe rozdanie*, „Energetyka Cieplna i Zawodowa"

[14] PN-EN 16247-1:2012 Audity energetyczne - Część 1: Wymagania ogólne;

[15] PN-EN 16247-2:2014-06 Audity energetyczne - Część 2: Budynki;

[16] PN-EN 16247-3:2014-06 Audity energetyczne - Część 3: Procesy;

[17] PN-EN 16247-4:2014-06 Audity energetyczne - Część 4: Transport;

[18] PN-EN 16247-5:2015-06 Audity energetyczne - Część 5: Kompetencje auditorów energetycznych;

[19] Urząd Regulacji Energetyki, *W związku z obowiązkiem sporządzania audytu energetycznego przedsiębiorstwa, wynikającym z ustawy z dnia 20 maja 2016 r. o efektywności energetycznej*

(Dz. U. z 2016 r. poz. 831) - zwanej dalej: „ustawą", nałożonym na określoną kategorię przedsiębiorców oraz mając na uwadze zgłaszane przez przedsiębiorców wątpliwości interpretacyjne, poniżej przedstawiono wyjaśnienia odnośnie sporządzania tych audytów <https://www.ure.gov.pl/pl/efektywnosc-kogenerac/efektywnosc-energetyczn/audyt-energetyczny-prze/7127,W-zwiazku-z-obowiazkiem-sporzadzania-audytu-energetycznego-przedsiebiorstwa-wyni.html > [dostęp: 30.07.2019].

[20] Naczelna Izba Kontroli, 2018, *Raport „Rozwój sektora odnawialnych źródeł energii"*

IOP Conf. Series: Materials Science and Engineering **641** (2019) 012033 doi:10.1088/1757-899X/641/1/012033

Extraction, Production and Consumption of Gravel and Sand Aggregates in Poland
An Attempt to Assess National and Regional Balances

W Kozioł and I Baic
Łukasiewicz Research Network – Institute of Mechanised Construction and Rock Mining, Racjonalizacji 6/8 Street, 02-673 Warsaw
Branch Office in Katowice, Poland

E-mail: w.koziol@imbigs.pl, i.baic@imbigs.pl

Abstract. Natural aggregates are the basic group of extracted minerals. In Poland, their share in the extraction of solid minerals over 30 years (1989–2018) increased from about 24% to 54%. Current aggregate production is about 300 million Mg and in 2019 it will probably exceed the record volume of 2011 – over 330 million Mg. In the extraction and production of aggregates in Poland, there is a decisive preponderance of gravel and sand aggregates – their share in the total production of natural aggregates amounts to 70–75%. The remaining part consists of crushed-stone aggregates produced from compact and moderately compact rocks of magma origin (basalts, granites, gabbro and diabases, melaphyres, porphyry, syenites, etc.), sedimentary rocks (dolomites, limestones, sandstones, etc.), and metamorphic rocks (amphibolites, migamatites, gneisses, serpentinites, etc.). A gradual deterioration in the quality of the raw material base of gravel and sands as well as a simultaneous increase in the demand of the construction industry for the best quality thick aggregate fractions (5/8mm, 8/11, etc.) has a significant impact on the rise in the amount of hard to sell and unsalable (waste) fractions of aggregates produced in Poland. This applies especially to gravel and sand aggregates in whose deposit the share of fine fractions (below 2 mm) is systematically increasing, while the demand for them in the construction sector is limited and they are often treated as useless (waste) material. Since it is practically unknown what is the production and consumption of these aggregates, an attempt was made to assess the amount of extracted and produced sand and gravel fractions of natural aggregates in Poland.
The deficit of natural aggregates in many countries and regions as well as the limited aggregate resources in Poland and increasing difficulties in obtaining licenses for their extraction indicate the need for selective storage of sand aggregate assortments instead of "melting" them in post-mining excavation pits. The presented research results should contribute to the development of more accurate market forecasts regarding the demand for and production of natural aggregates in Poland and in individual regions, especially when it comes to gravel and sand aggregates, including also fine fractions.

1. Introduction

Natural aggregates are the basic group of extracted minerals. In Poland, their share in the extraction of solid minerals over the period of 30 years (1989–2018) increased from about 24% to 54%. Aggregate production amounts to approximately 300 million Mg and in 2019 it will probably exceed the record volume of 2011, i.e. over 330 million Mg. In the extraction and production of aggregates in Poland, there is a decisive preponderance of gravel and sand aggregates – their share in the total production of natural aggregates amounts to 70–75% [7]. The remaining part consists of crushed-stone aggregates produced from compact and moderately compact rocks of magma origin (basalts, granites, gabbro and diabases, melaphyres, porphyry, syenites, etc.), sedimentary rocks (dolomites, limestones, sandstones, etc.), and metamorphic rocks (amphibolites, migamatites, gneisses, serpentinites, etc.). In the European Union and other European countries, crushed-stone aggregates produced from magma and sedimentary rocks prevail (their share in the production amounts to about 55%), but there are countries in which, similarly to Poland, gravel and sand aggregates predominate (Holland, Latvia, Iceland, Switzerland, Israel). It is dependent on the geological structure of the countries and documented, extractable particular types of rocks. In Poland, a gradual deterioration in the quality of the raw material base of gravel and sands as well as a simultaneous increase in the demand of the construction industry for the best quality thick aggregate fractions (5/8mm, 8/11, etc.) [2,6,7] has a significant impact on the rise in the amount of hard to sell and unsalable (waste) fractions of aggregates produced in Poland. This applies especially to gravel and sand aggregates in whose deposit the share of fine fractions (below 2 mm) is systematically increasing, while the demand for them in the construction sector is limited and they are often treated as useless (waste) material. Since it is practically unknown what is the production and consumption of these aggregates, an attempt was made to assess the amount of extracted and produced sand and gravel fractions of natural aggregates in Poland on a national and regional scale (voivodeships, regional zones).

2. National resource base for gravel and sands as well as trends in changes

2.1. Gravel and sand resources

In this article, due to the availability, consistency and repeatability, the primary source of data was *Bilans Zasobów Złóż Kopalin i Wód w Polsce* (*The Balance of Mineral Resources and Waters in Poland*) [2], published annually by the Polish Geological Institute – National Research Institute in Warsaw. The analysis took into account data from 2007–2017. The number of documented gravel and sand deposits in Poland is steadily growing and over the analysed years, it increased from 6029 in 2007 to 10117 in 2017, including the number of developed deposits which increased from 2278 to 4004. It seems that the main reason for the increase in the number of deposits results from the division of the documented deposits into smaller and often very small ones (up to 2 ha of land, which makes it possible to apply for the so-called *koncesje starościańskie*, i.e. *Starost Concessions*). In the years 2007–2015, starosts issued 3283 concessions [1], which accounted for about 2/3 of the total number of open-pit mining concessions in Poland, including concessions for the extraction of gravel and sand aggregates, which accounted for about 94%. As the number of deposits increases, so do the resources. In the years 2007–2017, the balance resources of gravel and sands increased by about 28% (to 19.3 billion Mg), and the industrial resources by as much as 80% (to 3.96 billion Mg). The increase in industrial resources contributed to an increase in the sufficiency rate of industrial resources from a low level of around 12 to 18 years. An alarming threat to the aggregate production is the deteriorating quality of gravel and sand deposits, which has an impact on the production volume of the gravel products sought and the increase in their costs. In the geological documentation of gravel and sand deposits and in the balance sheets of resources [2], three basic groups of gravel and sand aggregate are distinguished (Table 1), namely: sands, sands with gravel, and gravel. What constitutes the division criterion is the proportion of fine grains up to 2 mm in diameter. There is also a fourth group of resources, i.e. dusty clay sand, but these resources were excluded from the analysis due to a very small share (about 0.4%) and lack of economic significance. The analysis of changes in the size of deposits in the period of 10 years (2007–2016) [7] shows that we have quite a large increase in deposits despite exploitation, but it is disadvantageous that it is mainly the deposits of sand (SP>75) that are growing. The industrial resources of sand deposits have almost doubled (by 190%), while the resources of sand and gravel deposits have increased by about 50% and the resources of gravel deposits have decreased by almost 60%.

The change in the structure of deposits affects the share of particular subgroups of gravel and sand deposits in the total balance and industrial resources, as shown in Table 2.

Table 1. Division of sand and gravel aggregate resources [7].

Type of mineral		Sand point[a] [%]	Basic grain fraction [mm]	Dust content (<0,063 mm) [%][a]
Sands	sand	> 90	0.05-2.0	up to 10 (up to 5 in quartz ones)
	sand with gravel additions	75-90		up to 10
Sands with gravel (all-in aggregate)	sand and gravel mix	50-75	0.05-63	up to 15
	gravel and sand mix	30-50		
Gravel		< 30	2.0-63	
Boulders			over 63	

[a] according to balance criteria

Table 2. Percentage contribution of individual subgroups of deposits in the total resources of gravel and sands in 2007 and 2016 [7].

Type of deposit	Balance resources		Industrial resources	
	2007	2016	2007	2016
Sand	27.8	37	25.7	42.5
Gravel and sand	65.5	58.1	65.5	55.4
Gravel	6.7	4.9	8.8	2.1
Total	100	100	100	100

The share of sands in industrial resources increases particularly fast from 25.7 to 42.5% (in 2017, there was a further increase to 46%) while the share of gravel and gravel-sand resources decreases.

2.2. Trends in the share of sand fractions in gravel and sand resources

The assessment of the number of fine fractions in the resources of gravel and sand aggregates can be approximated based on the calculation of medium sand points (fraction content below 2 mm) in the analysed deposits. Assuming the division of documented gravel and sand resources into three basic groups: sands, sands with gravel and gravel, and determining for each of these groups the medium sand points (SP), i.e. sands – 85%, sands with gravel – 60%, gravel – 25%, the medium sand points were then calculated in the balance and industrial resources and in the extracted mineral (resources) in the annual balance of minerals [7]. Sample calculations for individual voivodeships, zones and the whole country are presented in Table 3 (balance resources) and Figures 1–4 (balance, industrial and extracted resources). The analysis was conducted for the years 2007–2016, which allowed to determine the trend of changes in the content of fine fractions in resources and extracted mineral over a 10-year period. Table 3 and Figure 1 show that in 2016 the medium sand point **in the country in terms of balance resources** was 67.5% and over 10 years it increased by 4.5%.

Table 3. Medium sand points in balance reserves of gravel and sand aggregate in the years 2007–2016 [2,7].

Description	Medium SP in balance resources in years, %									
	2007	2008	2009	2010	2011	2012	2013	2014	2015	2016
Poland	64.6	64.7	65.2	65.8	66.1	66.5	66.7	66.9	67.4	67.5
northern zone	62.3	62.6	63.4	63.9	64.3	65.1	65.2	65.5	66.0	66.4
central zone	78.4	78.0	78.4	79.0	79.1	79.4	79.5	79.7	79.8	80.0
southern zone	58.6	58.8	59.1	59.6	59.9	59.9	60.1	60.2	60.7	60.5
Voivodeships										
dolnośląskie	60.4	60.2	60.5	61.3	61.5	61.6	61.8	62.2	63.9	62.8
kujawsko-pomorskie	74.4	75.3	77.7	78.5	79.5	79.5	79.8	80.3	80.7	81.3
lubelskie	83.9	83.7	83.7	83.7	83.8	83.9	84.0	84.0	84.1	84.1

lubuskie	62.4	62.7	64.0	64.4	65.3	65.5	65.4	65.7	66.0	66.1
łódzkie	72.8	73.7	75.0	77.8	78.1	77.7	77.8	77.9	77.7	77.8
małopolskie	48.3	50.0	50.7	50.8	50.8	50.6	50.6	50.5	50.5	50.5
mazowieckie	75.4	75.3	75.7	76.2	76.1	76.9	77.2	77.4	77.6	78.0
opolskie	58.5	58.5	58.8	58.9	59.1	59.2	59.4	59.3	59.3	59.5
podkarpackie	67.7	67.2	67.2	68.1	68.7	68.9	68.9	68.9	69.0	69.3
podlaskie	60.6	60.7	60.8	61.1	61.2	61.3	61.3	61.2	61.2	61.3
pomorskie	65.1	64.5	65.8	66.5	66.9	67.4	68.3	68.6	69.9	70.7
śląskie	63.5	63.7	64.2	64.2	64.0	63.7	63.9	64.0	64.0	64.1
świętokrzyskie	83.1	82.8	82.8	82.9	82.9	82.9	82.9	82.9	82.9	82.9
warmińsko-mazurskie	60.6	61.7	62.2	62.9	63.4	63.7	63.8	64.1	64.2	64.5
wielkopolskie	75.7	74.0	74.5	75.0	75.4	76.3	76.5	77.0	77.6	77.8
zachodniopomorskie	64.1	64.4	65.3	66.2	66.0	68.7	68.7	69.9	71.0	71.2

The resources in the southern zone have the lowest SP (60.5%), including the małopolskie (50.5%) and opolskie (59.5%) voivodeships. In the central zone, the medium SP is the highest and amounts to 80%, including 84.1% in the lubelskie voivodeship and 82.9% in the świętokrzyskie voivodeship. In the industrial resources (Figure 2) in 2016, the medium SP in the country was higher in comparison with the balance resources, i.e. 69.9%, and – **what is characteristic – within 10 years, it increased by as much as 10.4%, i.e. the medium annual growth of SP in industrial resources is over 1%.** What is also characteristic as well as alarming is the fact that the highest increase was recorded in the southern zone (by 16.4%), i.e. in the region with the best gravel and sand deposits in terms of quality (grain size composition), which denotes the fastest deterioration. Industrial resources have the lowest SP values in the following voivodeships: opolskie (50.8%), małopolskie (58.4%), podlaskie (61.4%); while the highest values in the following ones: świętokrzyskie (85%), lubelskie (83%), wielkopolskie (81.2%), and kujawsko-pomorskie (81.1%) [7]. Higher SP values in industrial resources compared with balance resources indicate that some gravel and sand deposits with relatively favourable graining (lower SP values) are not currently being developed, probably for environmental reasons. Especially large differences in SP value occur in the southern zone (in 2016, balance resources – 60.5%, industrial resources - 64%), including the following voivodeships: dolnośląskie (62.8/69.3%) and małopolskie (50.5/58.4%). However, in the opolskie voivodeship, the opposite situation is true, i.e. it seems that in 2016, SP in industrial resources (50.8%) was much lower than SP in balance resources (59.5%). Relatively large differences in SP value were also noted in three voivodeships: lubuskie (in 2016, balance resources – 66.1, industrial resources – 73.4%), łódzkie (77.8/80.2%) and wielkopolskie (77.8/81.2%) [7]. In 2017 (the data for 2018 are still not available), there was a further increase of SP in industrial resources up to the medium value of 70.6% [2]. From the perspective of exploitation, what matters significantly are **SP values in the extracted mineral (resources) of gravel and sands**. In 2016, the medium SP in extracted resources (Figure 3–4), similarly to industrial resources, amounted to 69.9% and within 10 years increased by 4.8% [7]. The lowest PP was in the southern zone (65.1% – increase by 8.7%) and the highest in the central zone (79.9%). On each individual voivodeship's scale (Figure 4), the lowest SPs were observed in the extracted resources in the following voivodeships: małopolskie (54.6% in 2016), opolskie (59.3% – increase over 10 years by 12.0%), podlaskie (62.5%) and podkarpackie (65.8%).In turn, the highest SPs in the extracted resources were recorded in the świętokrzyskie (85%), lubelskie (83.8%), wielkopolskie (81.2%) and łódzkie voivodeships (79.4%). These values are similar to SP values in industrial resources. The comparison of average SP values in extracted and industrial resources shows that on a national scale and in the three regional zones the values are the same (country, central zone) or very similar (northern and southern zones). Whereas on the regional scale, in 4 voivodeships the values are the same or very similar (lubelskie, łódzkie, świętokrzyskie, wielkopolskie), in 6 voivodeships they are higher (dolnośląskie, mazowieckie, opolskie, podlaskie, śląskie, warmińsko-mazurskie) and in 6 voivodships lower (voivodeships: kujawsko-pomorskie, lubuskie, małopolskie, podkarpackie, pomorskie, zachodniopomorskie). The analysis of trends of SP changes in the extracted resources in the years

2007–2016 shows that these changes (the SP growth) are slower compared to the changes of medium SP in industrial resources, but also in balance resources. This means that priority is given to exploitation of better quality resources with lower SP values, which is obvious from an economic point of view. Summarizing the SP analysis of the documented and utilized aggregate resources, it should be stated that the medium sand points in the gravel and sand resources range from approximately 50 to 85%. In 2016, the medium SP in extracted resources was as follows: the country – 69.9%, northern zone – 67.2%, central zone – 79.9%, southern zone - 65.1%. On the individual voivodeship's scale in extracted resources, the medium SP ranged from 54.6% in małopolskie voivodeship to 85% in świętokrzyskie voivodeship [2,7].

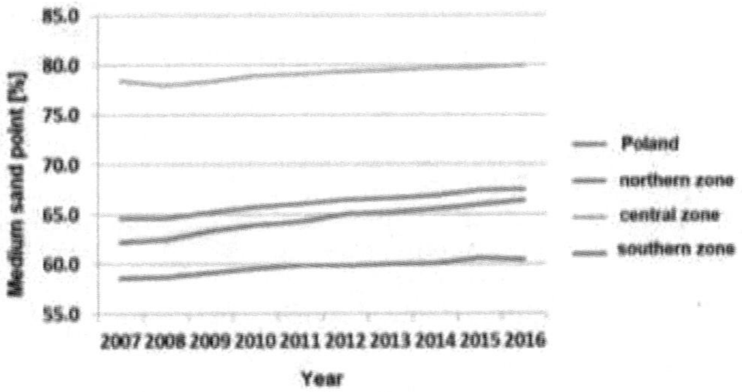

Figure 1. Trends in changes of medium sand points for balance reserves in the years 2007–2016.

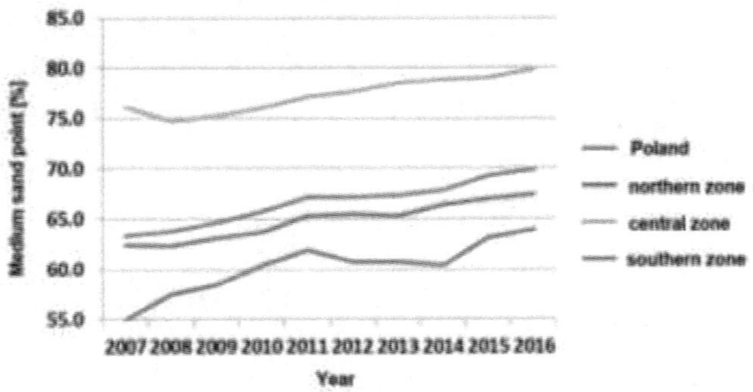

Figure 2. Trends in changes of medium sand points for developed reserves in the years 2007–2016.

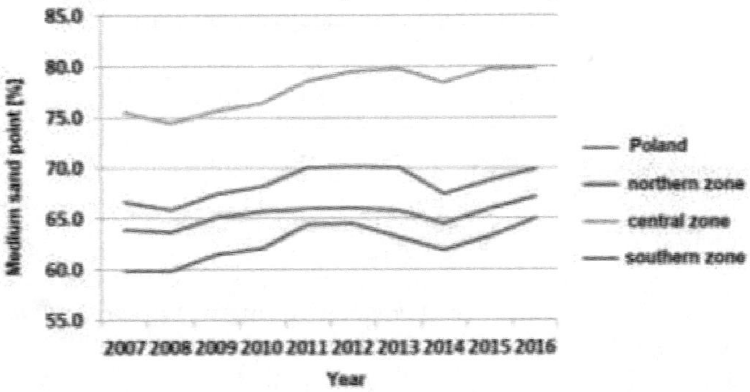

Figure 3. Trends in changes of medium SP for resources extracted in the years 2007–2016.

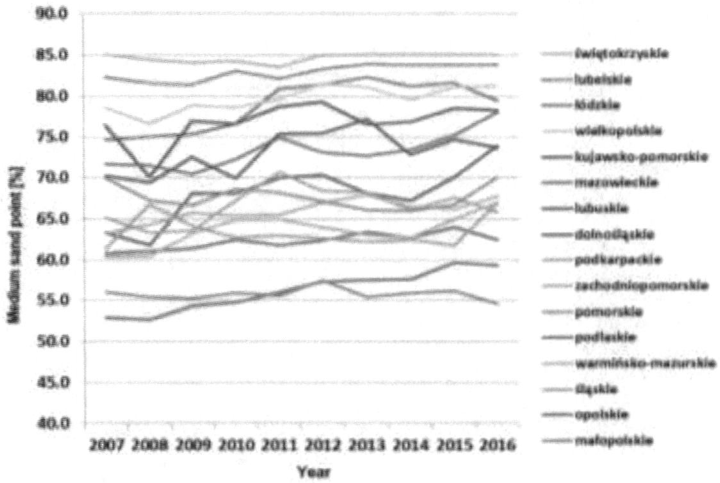

Figure 4. Trends in changes of medium SP for resources extracted in voivodeships in the years 2007–2016.

3. Production of sands (0-2 mm) from extracted mineral resources

3.1. Separation of minerals in the extraction process

Knowing the content of sand fraction (0–2 mm) in the extracted mineral it is possible to determine the amount of recovery (production) of this fraction in the extraction and treatment process. However, in some of the gravel and sand extraction technologies used, part of the fine fractions are already lost during the extraction process. This applies in particular to the exploitation under the water surface, which is predominantly used in Poland (over 75% of gravel and sand extraction). As an example, below one can find separations of extracted minerals by means of dredgers that are most commonly used in Poland to extract sands and gravel.

<u>A. Sand and gravel extraction with suction dredgers</u>

In Poland, suction dredgers (dredger cutters) (Figure 5) are currently used most frequently and are usually used to extract sand and gravel aggregate deposits with an SP point of more than 35%. The mineral separation process during the extraction of the minerals is as follows (Figure 6)

- oversized solids that may be in the deposit are not mined; the suction pipe of the dredger is secured with an appropriate strainer to prevent blocking with oversized grains;
- the spoil, which is extracted by the suction pipe of the dredger in the form of a hydromixture, is dewatered directly on the dredger or on land; separation of water from the mineral is carried out in a dehydrator or on a dewatering screen;
- what is also drained along with the water are dusty and clay particles as well as occasional grains of sand;
- the extracted spoil remaining after dehydration is usually fed by a system of belt conveyors to the processing plant.

<u>B. Sand and gravel extraction with single-bucket grapple, scoop or scraper dredges</u>

Out of single-bucket dredgers, the most common types of dredgers are those with a scoop (Figure 7). At present, they are mainly used for extracting deposits with relatively low sand points. The separation of dredging spoil on the dredger is carried out as follows:

- oversized solids (determined depending on the operating parameters of the processing plant and the type of technological transport used) are separated on the initial grate and discharged directly to the excavation pit;

Figure 5. Extraction of gravel and sand aggregates with a suction dredger.

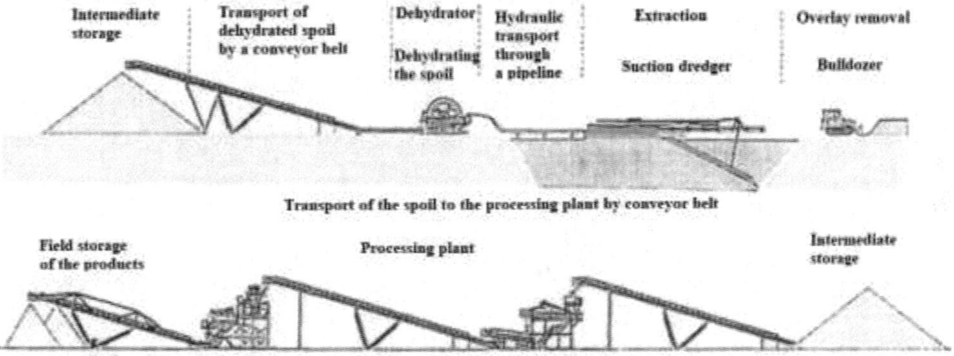

Figure 6. The production scheme of sand and gravel aggregates [12].

- from a 2 mm sifting screen placed on the dredger's deck, the fraction is directed onto the transport equipment and fed into the processing plant;
- the undersize grain from the sifting screen is discharged into the water tank below the dredger deck (useless fraction).

In the processing plant, silty (< 0.063), clay and sand grains as well as part of sand grains are discharged as processing waste to an excavation pit or a settler.

Figure 7. Extraction of gravel and sand aggregates with a grab dredger.

C. Sand and gravel extraction with bucket-ladder dredgers (Figure 8)

The distribution of minerals mined by a ladder (chain) dredger is generally as follows [12]:

- the oversized fraction (above 100 mm) is discharged from the dredger into an excavation tank;

- from a 2 mm sifting screen, the fraction is fed with belt conveyors or vessels to the processing plant;
- the fraction which is below 2 mm is usually discharged directly from the excavator to the excavation pit (useless fraction).

Further separation of the extracted material (feed) takes place in the processing plant with a division into commercial products and processing waste consisting mainly of the remaining silty (< 0.063) and clay fractions, which usually constitute about 10 % of the feed.

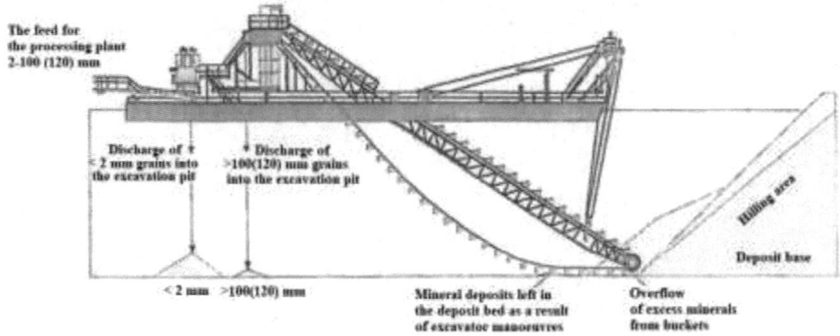

Figure 8. Example separation of sand and gravel aggregates with a multi-bucket chain dredger.

3.2 Production of aggregates of gravel and sand fractions - quantitative assessment

The analysis presented in section 3.1 shows that practically only the use of suction dredgers enables full recovery of fine sand fractions from the extracted mineral, whereas in the case of single- and multi-bucket dredgers, sand fractions are often directly melted in the post-extraction pit. The construction industry is mainly looking for coarse aggregates (both gravel and crushed-stone), while the demand for fine aggregates (sand) is changeable and largely depends on the demand for road construction. In the years 2013–2016, this demand was much lower than the volume of sand production and mines had great problems with their sale (aggregates that are difficult to sell and unsellable). The application of scrubbers and hydrocyclones to classify and enrich these fractions for most small plants is too expensive. Unsellable and hard to sell sand fractions of aggregates are often used in mines for reclamation of post-extraction pits. Recently, due to the implementation of the national road construction programme, their consumption has increased significantly.

In order to determine the estimated amounts of recovery (production) of small (sandy) fractions, the following assumptions have been made [7]:

- the basis for assessing the size of the recovered fraction of 0–2 mm is the value of SP in the extracted resources of sand and gravel (in the extracted mineral);
- approx. 75% of gravel and sand is extracted from underwater in Poland (with a growing tendency), including over 50% by means of suction dredgers with recovery of fine fractions; suction dredgers are used in mines with higher extraction volume (usually over 100 thousand Mg/year);
- small plants with the output of up to 40 thousand Mg (Starost Concessions for the extraction), predominant in terms of quantity (over 75% of the number of exploited gravel and sand mines), from which over 17% of domestic extraction is obtained [4,7], apply technologies of dry or underwater extraction with exploitation from the land and mainly use single-bucket excavators (bucket, grab, scraper) or rope scrapers, etc.;
- the onshore (dry) exploitation (approx. 25% of extraction) in larger mines equipped with processing and flushing installations also recovers fine sand.

The adopted assumptions show that in Poland, depending on the extraction technology, the demand (which is changeable) and the region, the recovery (production) of small fractions is in the range of 60 to 80% of the content of this fraction in the extracted mineral. For an illustrative determination of the production volume of fine sand assortments in 2016, the medium recovery rate of 70% was assumed

(Table 4). Based on the assumed assumptions, it follows that in 2016, when approx. 173.2 million Mg of gravel and sand were mined, it was practically possible to obtain approximately 51.8 million Mg of gravel aggregates and 84.6 million Mg of sand assortments (0–2 mm), i.e. the estimated total production of gravel and sand aggregates was probably approximately 136.4 million Mg, i.e. approximately 78.7% of the total annual production of gravel and sand [7]. The remaining part (21.3%) is made up of losses (useless fractions). The amount of fine fractions recovery is changeable because part of the extracted sand and gravel mineral is used in the form of mixes (sand and gravel mixture) and sand with admixture of gravel. The share of these fractions in the production and consumption of aggregates varies depending on the quality and volume of resources and the fluctuating demand of the construction industry. In some years and voivodeships, a higher share of the consumption of mixes and sands results mainly from the implementation of road construction engineering works (mainly for road foundation). An example of such a period are the years 2011–2012, when approximately 50% of gravel and sand extraction was consumed by road construction in the form of raw sands [8], also now (2017–2019) there has been an increase in demand for these aggregates due to the relatively large scale implementation of infrastructure investments. This favourable period is likely to continue over the next few years.

Table 4 presents the results of calculations of production (recovery) of small sand assortments (0–2 mm) in particular voivodeships and regional zones in 2016. The comparison shows that the highest volume of sand recovery was recorded in the following voivodeships: mazowieckie (9.1 million Mg), podlaskie (8.8 million Mg), dolnośląskie (8.7 million Mg), pomorskie (8.7 million Mg) and warmińsko-mazurskie (8.2 million Mg), while the lowest volume of sand was recorded in the świętokrzyskie (1.2 million Mg) and lubelskie (2.5 million Mg) voivodeships. In the regional zones, the estimated production of the 0–2 mm fraction sands was as follows:

- northern zone (region) – 33.9 million Mg,
- central zone (region) – 26.1 million Mg,
- southern zone (region) – 24.6 million Mg.

4. Assessment of the production and consumption balances of gravel and sand

Fine assortments of gravel, sand and crushed-stone aggregates are used both in the construction industry and in other various branches of the economy. Quantitatively, however, the basic demand concerns the construction industry, including primarily concrete and concrete products (prefabricated products, etc.). In the structure of production of concrete and concrete products, the dominating factor is concrete mix (ready-mixed concrete), used both by the volumetric construction (residential, industrial, services) and road infrastructure (transport) – about 50–60% of consumption [8]. The second position is occupied by concrete slabs and cubes for transport infrastructure engineering about 17–20%, further prefabricated structural elements about 8–10%, mortars and dry mixtures about 7–10%, wall elements, concrete pipes – about 3%, other consumption – about 5–8%. Until recently, the production of concrete and concrete products was traditionally based on mixtures and all-in aggregates (unclassified sands), but the need to manufacture increasingly high quality products results in a steadily developing use of gravel and complementary classified sands with little use of all-in aggregates, i.e. unclassified mixes, for these purposes. The production of concrete and concrete products on individual construction sites is currently used for a very small number of applications. The above shares concern medium values and fluctuate in particular years depending on the size and structure of the executed volumetric construction and infrastructure engineering [8].

Assuming typical proportions of the three main components of concrete products [7], i.e. cement approx. 18%, gravel-sand aggregates and crushed-stone aggregates (for higher classes of concrete) – approx. 61%, classified and unclassified sands – approx. 21%, the estimated consumption of classified and partially unclassified sands for concrete mix was determined on the example of 2016 (Table 4). On the national scale, it amounted to approx. 29.0 million Mg, and in particular zones (regions) it was the following:

- northern region – 6.5 million Mg,

- central region – 13.0 million Mg,
- southern region – 9.5 million Mg.

As for the voivodeships, the highest demand was specified for the following ones: mazowieckie along with the agglomeration of Warsaw (4.2 million Mg), wielkopolskie (3.1 million Mg), dolnośląskie (2.5 million Mg) and śląskie (2.5 million Mg), while the lowest for the following voivodeships: opolskie (0.4 million Mg), lubuskie (0.9 million Mg) and zachodniopomorskie (0.9 million Mg).

Sand consumption apart from concrete mix in 2016 was estimated at approx. 36.0 million Mg (increase in consumption in the road engineering). Since there are no data concerning both the national volume and the territorial distribution of this consumption, it was assumed that it is similar to the consumption of sand for concrete, and on that basis the consumption for individual voivodeships and regions was determined (Table 4).

The comparison of the territorial distribution of the predicted total sand consumption with the estimated potential (probable) amount of production (recovery) of fine aggregate fractions resulted in the territorial distribution of the production balance - sand consumption of the 0-2 mm fraction (Table 4). It shows that in 2016, the estimated production (recovery) of sands in Poland exceeded their consumption by 19.6 million Mg. The highest positive balance was determined for the northern voivodeships: podlaskie (5.7 million Mg), pomorskie (5.3 million Mg) and warmińsko-mazurskie (4.2 million Mg), while the deficit voivodeships were: śląskie, mazowieckie, świętokrzyskie (in this voivodeship crushed-stone aggregate sands are used as a substitute) and małopolskie. The zone division of extraction and production of gravel and sands shows that the positive balance of sand production is mainly in the northern region (+19.4 million Mg), while the southern region (+3.2 million Mg) is in balance with the deficit in the central region (-3.0 million Mg). The negative balance in the central region is affected by the high demand for gravel (4.2 million Mg) and sands (5.3 million Mg) in the Warsaw agglomeration. In the central zone in the years 2012–2013, the calculated production of sands amounted to approx. 35 million Mg, i.e. much more than in 2016.

Table 4. Balance of production and consumption of fine assortments of gravel and sand aggregates in 2016 [7].

Description	Extraction, thousand Mg	Fraction's share in the mineral, thousand Mg		Recovery of 0–2 mm fraction, million Mg	Predicted consumption for concrete	Other consumption	Balance (recovery - consumption)
		0 - 2 mm	>2 mm		million Mg	million Mg	million Mg
Poland	**173239**	**120764**	**51825**	**84.6**	**29.0**	**36.0**	**19.6**
northern zone	72039	48410	23629	33.9	6.5	8.0	19.4
central zone	46596	37230	9366	26.1	13.0	16.1	- 3.0
southern zone	53954	35124	18830	24.6	9.5	11.9	3.2
Voivodeships:							
dolnośląskie	16895	12485	4410	8.7	2.5	3.1	3.1
kujawsko-pomorskie	5124	4012	1112	2.8	1.2	1.5	0.1
lubelskie	4308	3610	698	2.5	1.3	1.6	-0.3
lubuskie	5954	4388	1566	3.1	0.9	1.1	1.1
łódzkie	6011	4773	1238	3.3	2.0	2.5	1.2
małopolskie	12084	6598	5486	4.6	2.2	2.7	-0.3
mazowieckie	16580	12932	3648	9.1	4.2	5.3	- 0.4
opolskie	7653	4561	3092	3.2	0.4	0.5	2.3
podkarpackie	6750	4442	2309	3.1	1.9	2.5	-0.3
podlaskie	20073	12546	7527	8.8	1.4	1.7	5.7
pomorskie	17791	12471	5320	8.7	1.5	1.9	5.3
śląskie	10572	7083	3489	5.0	2.5	3.1	-0.6
świętokrzyskie	2052	1744	308	1.2	1.1	1.4	-1.3
warmińsko-mazurskie	17588	11784	5804	8.2	1.8	2.2	4.2
wielkopolskie	12521	10167	2354	7.1	3.1	3.8	1.2
zachodniopomorskie	10633	7199	3434	5.0	0.9	1.1	3.0

In the estimated sand consumption reported herein, the use of fine sand fractions has not been specified as a separate group outside the construction industry. Compared to the values given above, however, this use is not significant, and in addition, the share in the consumption of sand from the production of crushed-stone aggregates and from the regulation of rivers and water reservoirs (extraction of aggregates not subject to mining activities) has not been taken into account. The share of sand from crushed-stone aggregates and from the regulation of rivers and water reservoirs certainly exceeds the volume of sand fractions use from gravel and sand deposits outside the construction industry.

The presented estimates of both production and consumption of fine sand fractions should be treated as approximations for several reasons. Firstly, there is no precise information on the contribution of various technologies to the extraction of gravel and sand, either underwater or on land. Moreover, not all mines using suction dredgers for extraction are equipped with appropriate classification nodes and dehydration products (dehydrators, hydrocyclones, presses, etc.) [10]. The consumption of fine sand is also approximated and varies depending on whether it is estimated on the national or local scale. However, it is a fact that fine sands are often not used industrially and are deposited in excavation voids, which entails their loss. Current and new directions and technologies of fine assortments application [7] justify the need for their selection and separate storage. These landfills, as so-called anthropogenic deposits, should in the future become the basis for the extraction of aggregates used in industrial applications.

5. Final conclusions

1. An analysis of the databases of gravel and sand deposits shows that with the growth of documented resources, the share of resources classified as sands increases. A particularly large increase in sand fractions is observed in the industrial resources in the years 2007–2017, i.e. from 25.7 to 45.3%.
2. What constitutes a measurable indicator of the deterioration in the quality of resources is the tendency towards change in the medium sand point (the percentage content of fine fraction of 0-2 mm) in the documented resources. In 2016, the average sand point in the balance resources was 67.5% and over 10 years (2007–2016) it increased by 4.5%. The resources in the southern region (zone) (60.5%), including the małopolskie (50.5%) and opolskie (59.5%) voivodeships, have the lowest SP. Whereas in the central region, the average SP reaches 80%, including 84.1% in the lubelskie voivodeship and 82.9% in the świętokrzyskie voivodeship.
3. In 2016, the medium SP in the industrial resources in Poland was higher compared with the balance resources, i.e. 69.9% and, what is characteristic, within the period of 10 years, it increased by as much as 10.4%, i.e. the average annual growth of SP in industrial resources is over 1%. The highest growth was recorded in the southern region (by 16.4%), i.e. the region with the best deposits in terms of quality (grain size); it is there that the fastest deterioration can be observed. The lowest SP values were observed in industrial resources in two voivodeships, i.e. opolskie (50.8%) and małopolskie (58.4%), while the highest values were noted in the following voivodeships: świętokrzyskie (85%), lubelskie (83%), wielkopolskie (81.2%) and kujawsko-pomorskie (81.1%). In 2017 (data for 2018 are not yet available), there was a further increase of SP in industrial resources to a medium value of over 70.0%.
4. The medium SP values in the extracted mineral are similar to those in the industrial resources (the national average is 69.9%), not big differences can be noticed for regional zones and voivodships [7].
5. After the sand point in the extracted mineral was estimated, an attempt was made to assess the amount of recovery (production) of this fraction in the extraction and treatment processes. Based on the adopted assumptions, it follows that in 2016, when approximately 173.2 million Mg of gravel and sand were mined, it was actually possible to obtain approximately 51.8 million Mg of gravel aggregates and 84.6 million Mg of sand assortments (0–2 mm); thus, the estimated total production of gravel and sand aggregates probably amounted to ca. 136.4 million Mg, i.e. about 78.7% of the annual production of gravel and sand according to PGI. The remaining part (21.3%) represents losses (useless fractions).
6. The volume of fine fractions recovery is changeable because part of the extracted sand and gravel mineral is used in the form of all-in aggregates (sand and gravel mixture) and sand with admixture of gravel. The share of these fractions in the production and consumption of aggregates differs depending

on the quality and size of resources and the alternating demand of the construction industry. A higher share in the consumption of all-in aggregates and sand in some years and voivodeships results mainly from the implementation of road infrastructure engineering works (mainly for road foundation). An example of such a period are the years 2011–2012, when approximately 50% of gravel and sand extraction in the form of raw sands was consumed by road construction, and there has also been an increase in demand for sands due to the good economic situation in road infrastructure and volumetric construction.

7. Deterioration of the quality of the raw material base and, at the same time, the increase in the building industry demand for thick aggregate fractions (5/8, 8/11, etc.) contribute to an increase in the extraction of gravel and sand aggregates with a simultaneous increase in the production of fine, hardly marketable assortments of aggregates.

8. Since it is practically unknown what is the production and consumption of fine (sand) fractions of aggregates, the present article constitutes an attempt to determine the balance of their production and consumption (demand), both at the national and regional level.

9. The estimated calculations show that, for example, in 2016 the production of sands was presumably about 20 million Mg higher than their consumption. For this reason, the sands from this period belonged to such categories of aggregates that were difficult to sell or unsellable. Large production surpluses (balances) were recorded in the northern region (three voivodeships: podlaskie, pomorskie, and warmińsko-mazurskie).

10. The deficit of natural aggregates in many countries and regions as well as the limited aggregate resources in Poland and increasing difficulties in obtaining licenses for their extraction indicate the need for selective storage of sand aggregate assortments instead of "melting" them in post-mining excavation pits.

11. In the future, the presented research results should contribute to the development of more accurate market forecasts regarding the demand for and production of natural aggregates in Poland and in individual regions, especially when it comes to gravel and sand aggregates, including also fine fractions.

References

[1] Baradziej M 2015 Fewer Concessions, More Liquidations *Surowce i Maszyny Budowlane* **2**, BMP Racibórz

[2] *Balances of Mineral and Groundwater Resources in Poland for the years 2007-2017* PIG–PIB Warszawa 2008-2018

[3] Kabzinski A 2018 Will There Be No Sand on Earth? *Surowce i Maszyny Budowlane* **4** BMP Racibórz pp 11–13

[4] Kozioł W and Baic I 2018 Natural Aggregates in Poland. Current Condition and Future Prospects *Przegląd Górniczy* SIiTG Katowice pp 1-8

[5] Kozioł W and Baic I 2018 Rock Mining in Poland. Opportunities and Threats *Inżynieria Mineralna* **2(42)** pp 65–72

[6] Kozioł W, Baic I and Ciepliński A 2018 Gravel and Sand Aggregates. Trends in Resource Quality *Kruszywa Mineralne Wydział Geoinzynierii, Górnictwa i Geologii Politechniki Wrocławskiej* **2** Wrocław pp 69–84

[7] Kozioł W, Baic I and Stankiewicz J 2018 Extraction and Production of Fine Fractions of Natural Aggregates and Technologies of Their Management *Monograph IMBiGS* Warszawa p 212

[8] Kozioł W and Galos K 2013 *Scenarios of Demand for Natural Aggregate in Poland and Its Regions* Wyd. Poltegor-Instytut Kraków–Wrocław p 206

[9] Ney R (ed.) 2007 *Mineral Resources of Poland. Raw Rock Materials - Mineral Aggregates* Instytut Gospodarki Surowcami Mineralnymi i Energią PAN Kraków

[10] Naziemiec Z 2013 Recovery and Application of Fine Sands *SiMB* **1** BMP Racibórz pp72–77

[11] Radwanek–Bąk B, Miśkiewicz W and Bąk B 2018 Each Sand Is Different *Kruszywa: produkcja – transport – zastosowanie* **1** pp 32–37

[12] Witt A (ed.), Schmidt T and Pomorski A 2013 *Underwater Exploitation of Domestic Sands and Gravel Deposits with Introduction of New Technological Solutions Poltegor – Instytut Wrocław*

AUTHOR INDEX